The
Cancer
Biopathy

The
Cancer
Biopathy

VOLUME II OF

THE DISCOVERY OF THE ORGONE

by Wilhelm Reich

*Translated by Andrew White with Mary Higgins
and Chester M. Raphael, M.D.*

FARRAR, STRAUS AND GIROUX

NEW YORK

Love, work and knowledge are the well-springs of our life. They should also govern it.

WILHELM REICH

Foreword

Reich's theory that cancer is not primarily a tumor that arises mysteriously in an otherwise healthy organism but a systemic disease due to chronic sexual starvation will startle the average person who tends to view a disturbance of sexuality as distressing but not pathogenic. It will also enrage many who, because of moral prejudice, find such a connection offensive and untenable. Wilhelm Reich, with unerring appreciation for the relatedness of *all* natural phenomena, disregarded this prejudice and included the orgasm as a subject for serious investigation. His studies eventually led to an inquiry into the exact nature of the energy expressed in the orgasm and to its demonstration not only in the living organism' but as the common functioning principle in nature.

The path Reich followed to the discovery of this ubiquitous energy, which he called orgone, is described in *The Function of the Orgasm*. Here, in *The Cancer Biopathy*, he details the actual discovery of orgone energy and reveals its practical importance to the problem of cancer. In so doing, he makes a contribution of enormous significance to an understanding of the gravest and most perplexing disease afflicting humanity today.

First published in 1948, *The Cancer Biopathy* is virtually unknown. It had an extremely limited distribution and was subsequently forced out of print by an injunction that caused Reich's books to be withheld or destroyed by an agency of the United States government. Fortunately, this new translation appears concurrent with a growing openness to innovative approaches to cancer.

At the basis of Reich's cancer theory is orgone energy, which can be utilized in the study of all natural phenomena and in the investigation, treatment, and prevention of disease. One would think that the actual proof of the existence of a cosmic energy, about which man has speculated during the entire course of his history, would be eagerly received. However, the incapacity of the average human being to experience or understand his own bodily sensations —which are manifestations of the movement of this energy—has made him reject the reality of a specific force that governs his organism. Consequently, he has viewed the discovery of orgone energy by Reich as a fantasy or a fraud.

A major obstacle to an understanding of Reich's cancer theory is the conventional, mechanistic way of comprehending disease. Until fairly recently, actually less than a hundred years ago, diseases were attributed to the effects of the interaction of many variables in the individual and his environment. However, beginning with the investigations of Pasteur and Koch, "the doctrine of specific etiology" emerged, according to which a disease is caused by a specific factor, e.g., a bacterium or a virus or a hormonal deficiency. Modern medicine is based on this mechanistic viewpoint and it is the one that is presently being supported with vast federal grants in the investigation of cancer. Enthusiasm for this approach derives from the knowledge that a single, isolated factor can be introduced to produce disease in an experimental animal or that a mechanical procedure or chemical substance, often serendipitously discovered, can be effective in the treatment of disease. There are prominent scientists who take issue with this approach and assert that the search for a specific causal factor is futile. Nevertheless, the search continues.

Several individual "causes" for cancer are being investigated at this time, among them the viral, psychosomatic, and biochemical theories. Thus, some investigators are convinced that cancer is an infectious disease of viral origin and believe that a vaccine is soon to be developed. Others have drawn attention to the possibility of an interactional psychosomatic etiology and have speculated about the relationship of psychic depression, lack of aggression, etc., to the development of malignant tumors. Still others suggest that psychological factors upset the hormonal balance of the organism or depress the mechanisms of immunity, thereby contributing to the etiology of cancer. Finally, in the biochemical area, the long-neglected finding by Otto Warburg that the normal oxidative proc-esses are irreversibly damaged in the cancer cell and replaced by anaerobic processes is being reconsidered today, in view of the observation that lack of oxygen appears to contribute to the develop-ment of cancer.

Despite the interest stimulated by these diverse theories, it is evident that many questions about etiology remain unanswered and that much is obscure and confused. For instance, if viruses are involved, where or how do they originate? If there is something more fundamental than viruses at work, something chemical, what is it? If the emotions are etiologically involved, how do they actually produce cancer? That there is a relationship between cancer and viruses, the emotions, the lack of oxygen, etc., appears certain, but what it is or how it brings about the malignant transformation in the tissues is unknown.

In the absence of known etiology, the treatment of cancer has been largely symptomatic and the results have been unpredictable and generally discouraging. In fact, the suffering of the cancer pa-tient is often due as much to the means that are employed to treat the symptoms as to the disease itself. Since the tumor is the most visible feature of the disease and is considered by most investigators to be the disease per se, treatment consists either in its excision or in an attempt to destroy it by radiation or chemicals. Controversy rages as to the value of these measures. For instance, there is constant disagreement about how much tissue need be removed in order to make certain that there are no cancer cells left that will invade and destroy the surrounding healthy tissue. George Crile, Jr., M.D., of the Cleveland Clinic, has found many surgical procedures to be excessive and has complained that "in our haste to stamp out cancer by indiscriminate use of surgery, we are forgetting the patient and even disseminating the disease." Yet, despite the limitations in treating the disease by removing or destroying the tumor, standard medical practice considers the tumor to be virtually the only target for therapeutic intervention because of the mechanistic premise that the tumor arises *de novo* in an otherwise healthy organism.

In *The Cancer Biopathy*, Reich presents a functional theory of cancer that explains the origin and development of the disease and offers possibilities for its treatment and, more importantly, its prevention. This is accomplished without excluding the prevalent speculations about the relationship of the disease to infection, emotional disorder, damage to cellular metabolism, the value of simple excision of large tumors, etc. The theoretical "cancer virus" is undoubtedly related to Reich's T-bacilli, which produced cancerous tumors in experimental animals, thus supporting the present infection theory. However, to accommodate Reich's views, the infection theory would have to include the fact that the T-bacillus originates endogenously from the bionous disintegration of living substance. (This, of course, discredits the metaphysical theory of "air germs" from which all bacteria are presumed to develop.) The psychic depression or lack of aggression, noted by the psychosomaticists, is Reich's "characterological resignation." But, for Reich, "resignation" is not just an interesting finding that is obscurely involved in the origin of the disease; it is the first phase of a shrinking process that results from a disturbance in the discharge of biosexual energy. The current theory of oxygen deficiency on the cellular level, originally noted by Warburg, is not an isolated, unexplained finding but, according to Reich, the internal biochemical expression of the impairment of external respiration. In other words, in Reich's theory of cancer these and other factors are not miscellaneous and unconnected; they are symptoms of a systemic disease that has its origin in the prolonged stagnation of the organism's biological energy. That is, these factors have a common origin and then become capable of functioning autonomously, thereby giving the impression of being of primary etiological significance.

Every feature of cancer is accounted for in Reich's theory, in contrast to the insufficiencies of all other explanations offered so far. He not only made the same observations that are now being individually investigated, but he demonstrated a functional relationship between them which mechanistic methodology has been unable to discover. The tragedy is that his findings were greeted with scorn, neglect, and, above all, indifference when they were disclosed over a quarter of a century ago, and that no attempt has ever been made to examine them impartially. Even the present interest in Reich's early writings, which continue to be appropriate and timely in our current social climate, does not extend to his later works, which relate to the discovery of orgone energy. Perhaps, however, this new interest will stimulate a more favorable reception for his orgone theory and make possible the utilization of orgone energy in the study and treatment of somatic diseases, such as cancer.

One hopes that *The Cancer Biopathy* will provoke neither mystical enthusiasm nor blind rejection. Reich anticipated the possibility of irrational reactions to this work and warned that his solution of the cancer problem does not imply that a cure has been found. Yet, in spite of his efforts to clarify misunderstandings and discourage excessive expectations, he was ridiculed and condemned for claims he not only did not make but predicted would be falsely attributed to him. The fact that he was mindful of the inevitability of the distortions and malevolent reactions is distinctly stated in his preface. It should be read carefully to avoid any misconceptions regarding what he actually did claim. In addition, to dispose of any lingering doubt in this respect, the attention of the reader is also directed to the last chapter, in which Reich emphatically states that the ultimate solution to the cancer problem lies in preventing the disease rather than in curing it. The means to this solution are to be found primarily in the social realm, for it is our repressive social order that creates the sexual misery and the resulting stagnation of biological energy from which cancer originates.

Chester M. Raphael, M.D.

Forest Hills, N.Y.
1973

Contents

Preface

This book is the second volume of *The Discovery of the Orgone* and is the direct continuation of the first volume, *The Function of the Orgasm*. It is composed of a series of articles concerning the discovery of cosmic orgone energy, first published between 1942 and 1945 in the *International Journal of Sex Economy and Orgone Research*. These essays are being offered in collected form so that orgone biophysics may be seen more clearly as a logical outcome of relevant observations, experiments, and work hypotheses. The unprejudiced reader will now be able to convince himself more easily than through the individual articles that the discoverer of orgone energy was much more a tool of scientific logic and consistency than a creator of "new theories." The wealth of facts and deductions recorded in this volume far exceeds the inventive capacities of the human mind. During the process of the discovery of cosmic orgone energy my task was not to construct theories but simply and solely to record my observations with care, integrity, and objectivity, to verify them by appropriate experiments, and to build the logical bridges of thought between one realm of functioning and another.

I have in part rearranged the previously published articles in order to avoid repetition and to present the contributions in chronological order. I have also added an account of the errors inherent in the "air-germ theory." Further, for the benefit of the specialist in cancer research, a discussion is included to establish the relation between classical and orgonomic cancer research. At the conclusion of the sections on orgone physics, there is a short note on the demonstration of atmospheric orgone energy by the use of the Geiger-Müller counter. Unfortunately, a comprehensive account of this phenomenon was impossible for reasons of time, since it was not discovered until the summer of 1947.

I hope and believe this volume will be accessible to the scientifically untrained reader who has familiarized himself with the principles of scientific research in general and orgonomy in particular. Sections that are too technical can be passed over by such readers without undermining their understanding of the whole.

The present volume comprises the results of work done over a period of seventeen years, between 1930 and 1947. I have concentrated on essentials, since any attempt to include all the details would have made the book unreadable. There will be opportunity enough in other contexts to provide any important information omitted here.

It is regrettable but understandable that this volume cannot provide a complete account. There are still many gaps in orgone research, as is always the case in objective natural science. It provides neither a "system of thought" nor a new "philosophy of nature," merely new facts and some new connections between known facts, insofar as they have hitherto been verified. Where uncertainties remain, I have made appropriate notations.

Present-day orgone research is much more advanced than this book. The orgonometric results of recent years must await later publication. Similarly, a systematic exposition of the technique of functional thinking, fundamental to all our observations, experiments, and conclusions, has to be postponed until a later date. The omission is unfortunate but cannot be avoided. Over the course of the last twelve years, it has become obvious that orgone research is either not understood or misunderstood by biologists and physicists, because they fail to see the new facts from the point of view of *energetic functionalism,* and instead try to comprehend them with the aid of traditional, mechanistic methods of thinking. This is impossible. The bacteriologist, for instance, sees the staphylococcus as a static formation, spherical or oval in shape, about 0.8 micron in size, reacting with a bluish coloration to Gram stain, and arranged in clusters. These characteristics are important for orgone biophysics, but are not the essentials. The name itself says nothing about the origin, function, and position of the blue coccus in nature. What the bacteriologist calls "staphylococcus" is, for orgone physics, a small *energy vesicle* in the process of degeneration. Orgone biophysics investigates the origin of the staphylococcus from other forms of life and follows its transformations. It examines the staphylococcus in connection with the processes of the total biological energy of the organism and produces it experimentally through degenerative processes in bions, cells, etc.

I give this example merely as an indication, and no more than an indication, of why the facts of orgonomy cannot be comprehended if one uses classical mechanistic and chemical methods, and why a systematic exposition of the thought techniques and methods of orgonomy is so important for an understanding of orgone energy. But I have to limit myself and can only hope that the facts and functions presented will speak for themselves, even if they should appear new and strange to bacteriologists, biologists, and medical specialists trained in the classical way.

The natural processes discussed here will not be easy to understand without knowledge of the *biophysical function of the orgasm*. Just as the student of animal species must have adequate knowledge of geology, the scientist who wishes to investigate cosmic orgone energy must have precise knowledge about the function of the orgasm. The other requirement of the observer working with orgone energy, namely that his organ sensations be relatively unimpeded, can only be stated here and not substantiated. But certainly it is clear that the emotional structure of the natural scientist will color his observations and thinking and that therefore organ sensation is a tool of his work. This is just as true for me as for anyone else working with orgonotic natural functions. Experiment of course has to be applied to confirm or refute observations and work hypotheses. But the manner of conceiving and executing experiments depends upon the researcher's organ sensations. Sensory perceptions and organ sensations are decisive factors here. It is a mistake to believe that experiments alone can provide enlightenment. It is always the living, feeling, thinking organism that explores, experiments, and draws its conclusions.

So much for the broad, difficult subject of the technique of functional thinking, an area of study only marginally touched upon in this book.

Our subject is a very serious one, with decisive implications for natural science in general. I have been fully conscious of this fact from the beginning. For that reason I have always allowed several years to pass before submitting a new observation or an unusual experiment to public scrutiny. I have made it a rule not to announce any new fact until it has been verified by additional findings. I ask the attentive reader to trust that I have not invested my private income since 1933, more than $100,000, in my research merely for the benefit of some "illusion," or a mere "idea," or just for fun. On the contrary, many people acknowledge that orgone research has overthrown several old and incorrect ideas about nature. Many people already understand that the rigid boundaries between the specialized sciences are broken down in orgonomy. Every person who works with cosmic orgone energy must possess adequate knowledge of medicine, biology, sociology, physics, and astronomy to understand the orgone functions in their various realms. Nature knows no boundaries between specialized functions. My own original starting point was biopsychiatry. The knowledge of human emotions plays a large part in orgone research, not only in understanding the basic functions of orgone energy but especially in understanding human reactions to the existence of a universal cosmic energy, which, in the living realm, functions as "biological energy," the energy of our emotions. This certainly has very serious implications.

Since my investigations into the essential biological functions of orgone energy have been carried out in connection with the cancer biopathy, this disease understandably is the hub of the orgonomic thesis as presented here. It may be considered a triumph for the field of biopsychiatry that it opened the way to an understanding of *biological cell energy*. In turn, that understanding led to the discovery of atmospheric orgone energy. This process will become apparent in a logical way in the accounts that follow. It is a further satisfaction that it was the *sex-economic* branch of biopsychiatry in particular that succeeded in solving the riddle of cancer and raised hopes for a possible method of cancer prevention. In making such statements, I carry a frightening responsibility. But I cannot shy away from it if I am to communicate to the reader my sense of the gravity of this book's subject matter, which in itself demands a thoughtful and critical evaluation of my facts and claims. To offer a brief summary:

Cancer, the essential mechanism of which consists in a gradual shrinking of the autonomic system, is easily understood as soon as one overcomes his resistance to comprehending the following facts as a unified whole:

1. The air-germ theory must be abandoned and "endogenous infection" recognized.
2. The role of the emotions in organic diseases must be given full consideration.
3. The development of a living, spontaneously moving substance from other living or even non-living substances, indeed from mass-free orgone energy, must be acknowledged. In other words, in dealing with cancer we are directly confronted with the problem of *biogenesis.*
4. It is imperative, in our work on cancer, that we place *sexual pathology,* which is generally hated and avoided, at the center of our medical efforts.
5. If cancer is to be understood in a simple way, we must finally acknowledge the existence of a basically new, ubiquitous, *cosmic* energy that obeys functional rather than mechanistic laws. I have called this energy *orgone.*

Any one of these five points is enough to initially arouse skepticism in the serious natural scientist. I assure the reader, however, that I waited many years before I dared reveal to others the wealth of newly discovered facts and their application. Dr. Walter Hoppe once wrote to me, quite rightly, that the biggest difficulty about my work was that *too much* had been discovered.

In serious scientific research there is the obligation to recognize facts even if it means risking one's neck. It was neither possible nor proper for me to evade this obligation if I was to do justice to the discovered facts. In time, the enormous significance of these facts began to seem less terrifying. I believe that the open-minded reader will also become less frightened of my discoveries when he considers the following:

1. Work in medicine and basic research is greatly facilitated by overcoming the sharply drawn boundaries between specialties in the natural sciences. In spite of its infinite variety, nature is basically a unified whole. The unity and simplicity underlying nature is revealed when we work with orgone functions. It is my belief that orgone energy is far less frightening and complex than other forms of energy which make possible the annihilation of entire cities.

2. The more familiar one becomes with the orgone functions, the more "at home" one feels with them. For example, the understanding provided by this work relieves the constant pressure felt when working with cancer patients without a knowledge of biological energy. After a few years of habitually using this knowledge, one cannot conceive how it once was possible to get along without it. Choreatic movements and epileptic seizures lose their mystery. These processes become simple and clear.

3. One gradually learns how to deal with human irrationality more easily, how to better understand what is going on inside people who fall victim to mysticism or the emotional plague.

4. Furthermore, it is a great relief, which is not to be underestimated, to be·able to have a deeper and fuller understanding of the religious person because one knows that, present everywhere, there is an all-pervading cosmic energy (Newton's "ether," the "God" of all ages and peoples) that can be experienced, seen, and also measured by means of the thermometer, the electroscope, and the Geiger-Müller counter.

5. Finally, it is a relief to be able to give the medical term "disposition" a concrete meaning. It is a relief to understand why one person is constantly suffering from colds and another never; why only certain individuals succumb to an epidemic and others do not; why one person dies from cancer or vascular hypertension and another does not; and what biologically distinguishes a lively child from a sluggish child.

In short, the enlightenment derived from knowledge of orgone energy more than compensates for the fear experienced when the great mysteries of nature reveal themselves.

I would like to conclude with a few comments addressed to those colleagues who have made the research and practical application of cosmic orgone energy their life's work.

The revolutionary character of our work necessitates certain new attitudes toward the world around us and the relinquishing of a few of the usual techniques of dealing with it, if we are to fulfill our responsibility as orgone researchers. It is not personal interest but rather interest in achieving recognition of cosmic orgone energy for the common good that compels me to make the following remarks:

In our relations with professional colleagues and with laymen, we encounter sharp hostility, even dangerous attacks on our personal and professional integrity. As psychiatrists, we understand the irrational nature of the hostility and the attacks and recognize their true sources. They have nothing to do with the personal character of this or that orgone researcher or orgone therapist, and consequently they are dealt with in a prescribed manner by me and by others living and working far from my laboratory. In public, we cannot apply our knowledge of the motives of irrational behavior in any personal way, nor can we tell a physicist who neurotically dismisses the functions of orgone eneregy what is really motivating him to make his judgments. We can point out these motives only in general; we can never make personal judgments about specific individuals. The only thing we can do in good conscience is ask ourselves whether a certain attack is rational or irrational. Irrational attacks should never be responded to. Our retaliation takes the form of revealing the irrationalism in human behavior. For the most part, these attacks will pass with time, even if they occasionally appear to be dangerous. We are perfectly aware that the average person today fears nothing so much as the knowledge of his biological nature; at the same time his greatest longing is for the fulfillment of his biological nature. Both the fear of knowledge and the longing for fulfillment confront us simultaneously. We must therefore always try to find the rational in the irrational and attempt to understand and reveal it without hatred or indignation. In time, the rational will prevail. Unfortunately, however, I am unable to offer any advice as to how one can protect oneself from the kind of irrationalism that is a threat to life. Neither lawsuits nor name-calling are any use here.

However, there is one proven way to force both laymen and professionals to respond to us rationally: *Delegate no authority in matters of orgone research if the critic cannot prove that he has thoroughly familiarized himself with our publications and findings over a long period of time.* Our science can be judged only from the standpoint of its own premises, methods, and thought techniques, and from no other. This is a strict rule in scientific intercourse, upheld wherever scientific research is conducted. We expect and welcome criticism, but only immanent criticism.

Therefore if a sexually abstinent court psychiatrist, or a "bogged-down" cancer specialist, or even a "free-lance writer" presumes to damn our work because he either does not understand it or takes it personally, or because it shatters his world view or threatens his political party, we respond with silence. We refuse to involve ourselves in any irrational discussion or brawl. I would like to stress this rule; it has proved very useful.

It is customary when one has made a discovery to try to have it endorsed by certain "authorities," to humble oneself and to make use of all kinds of stratagems and underhanded tactics to secure its recognition. Usually an attempt is also made to gain publicity in the newspapers as soon as possible. Such activities are not proper for those of us whose work is extremely serious. If we work honestly and conscientiously, sticking to the facts and not yielding to the temptation to make compromises in essential issues like the orgasm function, then, sooner or later, we will win public confidence. There is little the world needs more urgently than knowledge of the orgone functions, inside and outside of the organism.

We cannot concede authority in questions concerning orgone energy, where no proven authority exists. And yet we have to delegate responsibility. A hospital that treats people suffering from cancer has, without question, the responsibility to work with orgone energy. It is the responsibility of every individual physician who has seen the therapeutic effects of orgone energy to advocate these facts professionally and not ignore them or wait for the opinion of "authorities." It is the responsibility of every individual who has enjoyed the therapeutic effects of orgone energy to help his fellow-man wherever it is possible. It is the indisputable responsibility of a writer not to hinder the use of the life-saving effects of orgone energy with scandalous, sensational newspaper articles. He must be made to realize that indirectly he kills people when he agitates against us. Finally, it is the responsibility of the government of this or that country to decide whether, and how quickly, cosmic orgone energy is made available to the general public. We do our duty in every way and as well as we are able. We work hard, for decades. We sacrifice money and leisure. We try as hard as possible to be decent and honest. We make known our results in a responsible manner. There is nothing more we can do. The rest is up to the public. A public that tolerates the publication of defamations, untruths, and distortions is hurting itself and not one or another orgone therapist. I wish I did not have to say these things, but it is my duty not to be silent about them.

At the same time, we have to understand that the world of serious natural science needs much time to orient itself in our field, which contains so much that is new. Human welfare is undermined by the fact that the ignorant and incompetent can so quickly and easily find an outlet for the articles they write; our political process makes the publication of an inflammatory article much easier than the publication of vitally important facts. It is true, of course, that significant facts develop more effectively and sharply when in conflict with irrational human reactions. But it is an unfortunate fact that, in the social sphere, it takes time for the rational to achieve full acceptance—a great deal of time!

I should like to thank all those friends who helped me through the difficult years to build the framework that this book describes. I could list many important names, but those who have shared in our work will understand why I do not name them here. A few of my close friends and colleagues themselves advised me to depart from custom in this regard.

It should be obvious from many of my publications that I am well aware of how much I owe to the great pioneers in natural science, without whose careful efforts the discovery of cosmic orgone energy would not have been possible. I have repeatedly stressed the continuity and interdependence of all branches of vitally important scientific work. Furthermore, I must emphasize that the wealth of material gathered together by the painstaking efforts of mechanistic cancer research was indispensable for my new understanding of the cancer biopathy, despite the fact that the orgonomic theory of cancer differs greatly from the classical theory and even contradicts it in many details. Many cancer specialists are already aware that the problem of cancer is solved, and that its solution required the discovery of orgone energy and the elucidation of biogenesis.

On the other hand, some unjustified claims of priority put forward in the field of psychosomatic medicine after the publication of *The Function of the Orgasm* (1942) must be rejected. As the basis for the understanding of psychosomatic disturbances, the orgasm theory is much older (1923) than any of the other concepts derived from psychoanalysis. If the function of the orgasm, the central problem of psychosomatic processes, is ignored so completely in those concepts, they merit little consideration. We can only be amazed at the consistency with which the most important factor is avoided. Those who suffer most are only, again, the many sick.

I do not publish this book without serious concern, mainly that many readers of our literature will now assume that a cure for cancer has been found. This is not at all the case. It is true that the riddle of cancer has become fully accessible through the discovery of orgone energy. But it is incorrect to believe that every cancer victim can now be saved. A great deal of hard work and cooperation will be needed before we will know how much orgone energy can help in specific cases of cancer. But a beginning has certainly been made.

ORGONON
September, 1947

WILHELM REICH

The
Cancer
Biopathy

CHAPTER I

The Function of Tension
and Charge

1. THE FUNCTION OF THE ORGASM

Those familiar with Volume I of *The Discovery of the Orgone* know of the important event in 1933 that marked the turning point in the development of our research: *the discovery of the biological function of tension and charge.* I would like to describe in brief the substance of this discovery.

From clinical investigation we have learned that the function of the orgasm is the key to the problem of the source of energy in neurosis. Neuroses result from a stasis of sexual energy. The cause of this stasis is a disturbance in the discharge of high sexual excitation in the organism, regardless of whether or not this disturbance is perceived by the ego. It makes no difference whether the psychic apparatus does or does not misinterpret the process neurotically; nor does it matter that the person may develop false notions about the disharmony in his energy system and glorify it with ideologies. Experience in everyday clinical practice leaves no doubt: *The elimination of the sexual stasis by the orgastic discharge of the biological excitation removes every kind of neurotic manifestation.* The difficulty that must be overcome is largely of a social nature. Attention must be drawn to these simple basic facts again and again.

It has long been a known fact in sex-economy that the orgasm is a fundamental biological phenomenon; "fundamental" because the orgastic discharge of energy occurs at the very root of biological functioning. This discharge appears in the form of an involuntary convulsion of the entire plasma system. Like respiration, it is a basic function of every animal system. Biophysically it is not possible to make a distinction between the total contraction of an amoeba and the orgastic contraction of a multicellular organism. The most salient characteristics are *intense biological excitation, repeated expansion and contraction, ejaculation of body fluids,* and *rapid subsidence of the biological excitation.* To understand these characteristics as biological functions, we had to free ourselves from the lascivious emotional reactions that every consideration of sexual functions—in fact, of autonomic functions in general—arouses in man. These emotional reactions are themselves neurotic expressions which constitute a problem in our psychiatric work.

More precise observation shows that these four functions are not paired but occur rather as a specific, lawful, four-beat pattern. The increasing tension that occurs in biological excitation appears as sexual excitement and produces a charging of the organism's periphery. This phenomenon was demonstrated unequivocally by measurements of the potentials at the erogenous zones during pleasurable excitation. Once the tension and the bio-energetic charge have reached a certain intensity, they are followed by convulsions, i.e., contractions of the entire biological system. The high-energy tension at the periphery of the organism is released. This is revealed objectively as a sudden drop of the bio-electric skin potential and is felt subjectively as a rapid decrease of excitation. The sudden shift from high charge to discharge is called the "acme." Following the discharge of biological energy, a mechanical relaxation of the tissues occurs as a result of the flowing back of body fluids. That the discharge of energy occurs is demonstrated by the evidence that the organism is not capable of renewed sexual excitation immediately thereafter. In the language of psychology, this state is called "gratification." The need for gratification, or in biophysical terms, *for the discharge of excess energy by merging with another organism,* occurs at more or less regular intervals, varying with the individual as well as the species. The intervals generally become shorter in the spring. In animals, there is the phenomenon of heat or rut in which a concentration of this biologi-cal need occurs at certain times of the year, predominantly in spring. This fact reveals a close connection between the function of the orgasm and an energy function of a cosmic nature. Along with the well-known effects of the sun on the living organism, the orgasm function is one of the phenomena that cause us to regard the living organism as a special, functioning part of non-living nature.

The function of the orgasm thus reveals itself as a four-beat rhythm: *mechanical tension → bio-energetic charge → bio-energetic discharge → mechanical relaxation*. We shall call it the function of tension and charge or, in brief, the TC-function.

Earlier investigations have demonstrated that the TC-function not only is characteristic of the orgasm but also applies to all func-tions of the autonomic life system. The heart, the intestines, the urinary bladder, the lungs all function according to this rhythm. Even the division of cells follows this four-beat pattern. The same is true of the movement of protozoa and metazoa of all kinds. Worms and snakes, in the movements of their individual parts as well as of their total organism, clearly display the rhythmic functioning desig-nated by the TC-formula. There seems to exist *one* basic law that governs the total organism, in addition to governing its autonomic organs. With our basic biological formula, we encompass the very essence of living functions. *The orgasm formula thus emerges as the life formula itself*. This corresponds exactly to our earlier formula-tion that *the sexual process is the productive biological process per se*, in procreation, work, joyful living, intellectual productivity, etc. The acceptance or refutation of orgone biophysics depends upon the acknowledgment or rejection of this formulation.

The mechanical tension of organs through tumescence may be easily understood: the tissues take up body fluids, and the indi-vidual particles in the biological colloid separate. Conversely, mechanical relaxation occurs through detumescence: the fluids are forced out of the tissues and, thereupon, a mutual coming together of the particles occurs. The question of the nature of charge and discharge is more difficult. The fact that we can measure electrical potentials gives rise to the temptation to dispose of a gigantic problem by labeling the process merely a matter of "electrical charge" and "electrical discharge." After all, the quantities of electrical energy produced in contracting muscles and by electric eels, for instance, have been measured. And have we not progressed to the point where the electrical waves of the brain are measurable? In the accounts of my bio-electrical experiments (1934–1936), I recorded the changes in potential occurring in pleasure and anxiety in terms of millivolts.

2. THE POSTULATE OF A SPECIFIC BIOLOGICAL ENERGY

Is the specific biological energy identical with electricity? The problem is not as simple as it may seem. It would certainly be convenient if we were able to describe the functioning of the organism in terms of familiar physical concepts. The organism would then appear as nothing more than "a particularly complicated electrical machine." It would be convenient, and very easy, to explain away the reaction of rheumatic persons to changes in the weather by asserting that their "body electricity" is influenced by the "electrical" charges in the air. The attempt has also been made to apply the laws of iron magnetism to the living organism. We speak of a beloved person as having a "magnetic" attraction, or we feel "electrified" with excitement. We shall soon find, however, that such analogies are erroneous. In previous publications, I have spoken of "bio-electricity," using the customary terminology. The organism undoubtedly contains electricity in the form of electrically charged colloid particles and ions. All of colloid chemistry as well as neuromuscular physiology depends upon this. Muscular contractions can be induced by the application of an electric current. Combing the hair can produce "electric" sparks. Nevertheless, there are a number

of phenomena that in no way correspond to the theory of electromagnetic energy.

First of all, there are the effects of body "magnetism." Many
physicians and lay therapists make practical use of these magnetic
forces. Yet we are not convinced that these forces, which emanate
from organic, colloidal, non-metallic substance, are iron-magnetic.
In what follows, we shall provide experimental proof that the
energy in the living organism is not identical with iron magnetism.

The electrical effects of a galvanic current are experienced by
the body as foreign, "unorganic." Electrical energy, even in the
minutest quantities, always causes disturbances in our normal functioning. The muscles, for instance, contract in an unnatural, "sense-
less," biologically inappropriate manner. There is no evidence that
an electric charge applied to the body ever produces an organic
movement bearing the slightest resemblance to normal movements
by entire muscle systems or functional groups of muscles. Electrical
energy generates a movement that lacks the most essential characteristic of biological energy, namely the movement of a group of
organs in a coordinated, functionally meaningful form. By contrast,
the disturbances of biological functioning by an electric current do
possess the character of electrical energy. The movements generated
are rapid, jerky, and angular, exactly like the oscillographic reactions produced by rubbing an electrode on metal (*cf. The Function
of the Orgasm*).

In a muscle-nerve preparation, the electrical impulse does not
manifest itself directly in the movement; otherwise the smooth
muscle would contract just as quickly as the striated one. Actually,
the contraction of the smooth muscle follows the slow, wave-like
rhythm characteristic of its functioning. Thus, an unknown "something," is merely stimulated by the electrical impulse, which inserts
itself between the electrical impulse and the muscle action, mani-
festing itself as a movement that is accompanied by an action
current. But the "something" itself is not electricity.

Our organ sensations clearly indicate to us that emotions

(which undoubtedly are manifestations of our biological energy) are fundamentally different from the sensations one experiences from electrical shocks. Our sense organs completely fail to register the effect of the electromagnetic waves that fill the atmosphere. In proximity to a radio transmitter, we feel nothing. A radio reacts when near a high-tension wire; we do not. If our life energy, which is expressed in our organ sensations, were electricity, it would be incomprehensible that we should perceive only the wave lengths of visible light and otherwise remain totally insensitive. We perceive neither the electrons of an X-ray machine nor the radiation from radium. Electrical energy does not convey a biological charge. Thus far, it has not been possible to determine the potency of vitamins with electrical measurements, even though they doubtless contain biological energy. The examples could be continued indefinitely. Another problem is how our organism keeps itself from being destroyed by the infinite number of electromagnetic fields surrounding it.

It is true that sensitive voltmeters react to our touch, but the magnitude of this reaction is so minute compared with the amount of energy produced by our organism that there does not seem to be any connection.

These are major contradictions which are impossible to resolve within the framework of known forms of energy. They have been well known to biology and natural philosophy for a long time. Attempting to bridge the gap, some people have put forward concepts that were intended to make the specific life function comprehensible. Most of these concepts were advanced by the opponents of mechanistic materialism, the vitalists. Driesch suggested an "entelechy," a life force inherent in all living matter and governing it. But, since it was neither measurable nor tangible, it ended up as a contribution to metaphysics. Bergson's *élan vital* attempted to take account of the incompatibility between the known forms of energy and living functioning. His *force créatrice* represents an explosive function of matter which manifests itself most clearly in the way life functions. Bergson's hypothesis was directed against both mechanistic materialism and teleological final-ism. In theory, it grasped correctly the basically *functional* character of the life process, but it lacked empirical validation. The force in question was not measurable, tangible, or controllable.

The famous German physiologist Pflüger assumed a connection between life energy and fire on the basis of the function of cyanide. His assumption was correct. Prominent biologists, among them the Viennese Kammerer, were convinced that a *specific biological energy* exists, possessing no immediate connection with electricity, magnetism, etc.

> If transgressing the frontiers of what is permissible, I should finally state what seems to me to be the most probable—an un-proven, and at the present time, unprovable, scientific credo—then I have to say: the existence of a *specific life force* seems to me highly plausible! An energy which is not heat, nor elec-tricity, magnetism, kinetic energy (including oscillation and radiation), nor chemical energy, and is not an amalgam of any or all of them but an energy belonging specifically to only those natural processes that we call "life." That does not imply that its presence is limited to those natural bodies that we call "living beings" but that it is present also at least in the formative process of crystals. A better name for it, to prevent misunder-standing, might be "formative energy" instead of "life energy." It possesses no supraphysical properties, even though it has nothing in common with physical energies already known. It is not a mysterious "entelechy" (Aristotle, Driesch), but a gen-uine, natural "energy"; however, just as electrical energy is con-nected to electrical phenomena, so this "formative energy" is linked to living phenomena and the development and change of forms. Above all, it is subject to the law of the conservation of energy and is fully capable of conversion into other forms of energy, just as, for instance, heat can be converted into kinetic energy and vice versa. [Paul Kammerer: *Allgemeine Biologie*]

Kammerer came across the problem of a formative "life force" during the course of experiments designed to demonstrate the heredity of acquired characteristics in salamanders. The "inherited substances" and "genes" postulated by the heredity theoreticians only obscured an understanding of the living process, and seemed to have been devised to block every access to it. Their theories might best be described as resembling an inverted pyramid, a veritable mass of hypothetical contentions precariously balanced on a small number of dubious facts. One typical example would be the unscientific, unwarranted, and moralizing conclusions drawn from the notorious "family Kallikak" study. In reading hypotheses on heredity, one consistently has the impression that there is more frantic ethicizing than there is science. The life process is smothered beneath a mound of mechanistic hypotheses. These theories finally degenerated into Hitler's pernicious race theory.

In the work of the vitalists, the life force became an elusive specter, while the mechanists converted it into a lifeless machine. Bacteriologists postulated the existence of a special germ "in the air" (yet to be seen) for every living organism. During the second half of the nineteenth century, Pouchet took upon himself the wearisome task of testing the accuracy of the air-germ theory. Pasteur showed experimentally that there are no living germs in liquids brought to certain temperatures. If living organisms were found, he ascribed their presence to air infection. Lange, in his book *Geschichte des Materialismus*, criticizes Pasteur's conclusions and cites Pouchet's experiments. Pouchet passed hundreds of cubic meters of air through water, then examined the water. He invented an apparatus that collected dust particles from the air and deposited them on glass plates. Pouchet then analyzed the dust. He conducted these experiments on glaciers in the Pyrenees, in the catacombs at Thebes, in the desert and on the sea in Egypt, and atop the cathedral in Rouen. He found many things, but only rarely did he find a spore of a fungus, and even more rarely a dead infusorium. Pasteur's refutation of the early theories of spontaneous generation was basically misunderstood. Questions about the origins of the *first* germs of life were taboo, and in order not to conflict with the doctrine of a "divine creation," it was usual to resort to the notion of a plasmatic substance descending upon our planet from outer space.

Not one of these schools of thought succeeded in approaching the functional problems of the life process, nor did they find a connection with experimental physics. The life process emerged from their theories as a mystery, a special preserve of "divine providence" hidden away somewhere in the midst of the vast realm of natural science.

But the sprouting of every plant, the development of every embryo, the spontaneous movement of muscles, and the productivity of every biological organism demonstrate the existence of incalculable energies governing the work of living substance. *Energy is the capacity to work.* No known energy can compete with the total work capacity of the living organisms on our planet. The energy accomplishing this work must have its origin in *non-living matter.* Yet, for thousands of years it has been ignored by science.

What prevented an understanding of this energy? It was first necessary to understand the manifestations of the unconscious and repressed sexual life. Freud's discovery of the function of sexual repression made the first breach in the wall that had blocked our comprehension of the life process. The second step was a correction of Freud's theory of the unconscious: The repression of human instinctual life is not a natural but rather a pathological result of the suppression of natural instincts, in particular, of genital sexuality. An organism that uses most of its energy to keep the natural life process imprisoned within itself cannot comprehend life outside itself. The central manifestation of life is expressed in the genital sexual function, to which life owes its existence and continuation. A society of human beings that has excluded the most essential manifestations of this function and made them unconscious is not capable of living rationally; indeed, everything it says appears distorted and pornographic. Only the mystics, far removed from scientific insight, have preserved contact with the living process. Once the living process became the domain of the mystic, serious natural science shrank from any concern with it. The literature of the biological and physiological sciences contains no indication of even an initial understanding of autonomic movement, such as may be observed in the worm, for example. This movement is too reminiscent of the despised sexual acts of the animal world. Mysticism and mechanistic biology thus stand in opposition. Meanwhile, the force of religious feeling itself betrays the existence of a powerful "something" experienced by man, which he is unable to define in words, or to manage. Religion, too, has mysticized the living process.

The problem enters the province of natural science only if and where there exists a measurable and controllable energy function that makes the basic life function understandable and, at the same time, does not conflict with physics. It follows that such a specific energy, expressing itself biologically, would have to possess these properties:

1. It would be fundamentally different from electromagnetic energy, and yet related to it.
2. It would have to exist in non-living nature independent of living organisms, if the principle of life originating from non-living matter is to hold true.
3. It would have to elucidate satisfactorily the relationship between living organisms and non-living nature (respiration, orgasm, nutrition, etc.).
4. In contrast to galvanic electricity, it would function in *organic substance, which does not conduct electricity,* and in animal tissue.
5. It would permeate and govern the *entire* organism instead of being limited to individual nerve cells or groups of cells.
6. It would have to explain simply the basic pulsatory function (*contraction* and *expansion*) of life, as it manifests itself in respiration and the orgasm.

7. It would manifest itself in the production of heat, a characteristic of most living organisms.

8. It would definitively clarify the sexual function; i.e., it would make sexual attraction comprehensible.

9. It would reveal why living organisms have failed to develop an organ sensitive to electromagnetism.

10. It would contribute to an understanding of the difference between protein that is dead and protein that is alive, and would explain what must be added to the chemically complex protein to make it alive. It would be capable of *charging* living matter; thus, it would have a *life-positive* effect.

11. Further, it would reveal the processes involved in the symmetry of form development and explain the basic function of form development.

12. Finally, it would make comprehensible why living matter exists only on the earth's surface.

The enumeration of these problems is intended to show the indispensable context within which any discussion of biophysics and biogenesis must take place.

CHAPTER II

Orgone Energy Vesicles (Bions)
and the Natural Organization
of Protozoa

EXPERIMENTAL FOUNDATION FOR UNDERSTANDING THE CANCER BIOPATHY

Orgone energy was discovered in a bion culture. My first task, therefore, is to give an account of the orgonotic phenomena that represent transitional stages of evolution between living and non-living matter.

Because of the functional relationship between bions and atmospheric orgone energy, it is essential that a discussion of orgone functions in bionous matter precede the presentation of the actual discovery of the orgone.

It is difficult to determine a date for the discovery of orgone energy. Orgonotic functions of attraction, penetration, pulsation, and lumination had already been observed in the period between 1936 and 1939, and had been subjected to investigation in a variety of bion preparations. However, I had no presentiment that I was working with manifestations of a specific biological energy. Experiments with bion cultures led to the discovery of orgone energy in SAPA (sand packet) bions during January 1939 and in the atmosphere during July 1940. It was only after I had worked on the purely physical functions of orgone energy (1939–1942) that I understood the observations I had been making on bions and bion cultures since 1936. The description in my book *Die Bione* (1938) conforms completely to traditional bacteriological and biological concepts.

Later knowledge of orgone functions caused me to modify much of what I had written in that book. For instance, cultures of cocci and bacilli derived from bions represent not, as I thought then, a more advanced stage in the development of the bion but, on the contrary, a *degeneration* of bions to a biologically sterile form incapable of further development. I found that bions actually develop in the direction of protozoal organization. On the other hand staphylococci, streptococci, T-bacilli, and rot bacteria are due to a *degeneration* of the orgonotic living plasma.

Mistakes, such as the one I just mentioned, and the subsequent necessary modifications are unavoidable in working in unexplored territory. The following account of the bion experiments is given in the context of knowledge of atmospheric orgone energy, and its perspective is therefore no longer biologistic but functional, based on energy principles.

"Bion" and *"energy vesicle"* designate one and the same microscopically visible, functioning formation. The term "bion" refers to the vesicles into which all matter disintegrates if made to swell. These vesicles represent transitional forms between non-living and living matter. *The bion is the elemental functioning unit of all living matter.* At the same time, it is the bearer of a quantum of orgone energy and, as such, functions in a specifically biological way. It is an *energy unit*, compounded of a membrane, a fluid content, and an amount of orgone energy, i.e., an "orgone energy vesicle." In what follows, I would like to give an account of the observations and experiments on which the far-reaching conclusions just summarized are based.

1. THE VESICULAR DISINTEGRATION OF SWELLING MATTER (PA BIONS)

Carbon is the fundamental substance that, when combined with oxygen, nitrogen, hydrogen, and water, forms the basis of the infinite variety of organic compounds as well as living matter. Our intention is to ignore the already well-known chemical reactions and simply concentrate on examining a particle of carbon under a good microscope equipped with apochromatic lenses. Reichert microscopes (the Z microscope), which permit magnification up to 5000x, were used for the experiments. The finer biophysical processes like expansion and contraction, vibration, and formation of a radiating bridge can be observed only at magnifications greater than 2000x, and are best seen at 4000x. What matters is not the resolution of fine structural details but rather the visualization of *movement*. For this purpose, we can use carbon, derived from blood charcoal (obtained from Merck & Co.) or from ordinary soot. Since the process of combustion converts all organic compounds to carbon, the origin of the carbon used for the experiment is not important.

First, we examine the particle of carbon dry, at a magnification of approximately 300x. What we see is a black, uneven structure

Carbon particle, dry

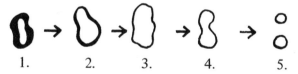

1. Thick wall of carbon, inelastic
2. Increased fluid content, swelling
3. Membrane thinner, elastic; blue color inside, vibrating
4. Indentation of carbon bion
5. Division into two bions

FIGURE 1.   Development of a carbon bion

which is motionless. In the dark-field, we observe an essentially striated structure interspersed with occasional vesicular formations. Along the margins, between the striated structure and the tiny oval-shaped vesicles, the light is strongly refracted.

We set the microscope at a magnification of approximately 2000x (objective 80x, eyepiece 16x, and inclined binocular tube, which increases magnification by 50%). The striated, vesicular structure can now be seen more clearly. There is not the slightest indication of movement.

We add a drop of ordinary water and look again, first at 300x then at 2000x. Essentially, there is no change. We see no movement; only here and there a round or uneven particle may be in motion. Its size seldom exceeds one micron in diameter. Overall, the field is "lifeless." There is no sign of contraction or expansion.

Using a spatula, we add finely pulverized carbon powder to water contained in a test tube. A portion of the powder sinks to the bottom, while the remainder floats on the surface. The water itself retains its clarity and no colloidal solution forms. The preparation is *not* sterile. Each day we draw off a drop of the fluid and examine it under the microscope. The object is to discover whether changes are taking place in the carbon, and if so, what kind. But a change is observable only after several weeks. The tiny individual spherical particles moving weakly across the field are becoming more numerous. In the dark-field, the larger particles of carbon display a very gradual increase in the number of spherical formations within them. However, the overall scene remains unalive. Months pass without much change. We are struck by the absence of ordinary air bacteria. (The test tubes are of course sealed with cotton plugs.) Macroscopically, the fluid appears unchanged. It is still clear. This is our control experiment. The experiment for the *production of coal bions* is as follows:

From now on, we apply strictly sterile procedures. All liquids are autoclaved at 120°C.; all dry substances and instruments are dry sterilized at 180°C.

Test tubes containing a preparation of 50% bouillon and 50%

0.1n KC1 solution are autoclaved. Then we heat a small amount of coal dust on a spatula tip in a gas flame to white incandescence. While the coal dust is still white-hot it is plunged into the sterile fluid. The fluid immediately turns black and only the heavy particles of coal sink to the bottom. The lighter particles remain suspended. A *colloidal solution* has been formed, in contrast to the control experiment. Over the course of a half hour, the black fades to gray. The solution remains colloidal for three to six days, then it becomes clear. All the particles have sunk to the bottom.

The preparation completed, we draw off a small drop, using sterile procedures, and examine it under the microscope in bright- and dark-field, again starting with a magnification of 300x (*cf.* Fig. 25, Appendix), then using 2000–3000x (for PA bions seen at this magnification, *cf.* Fig. 30, Appendix). What we see is fundamentally different from what was observed in the control preparation.

The structure of the individual coal particles is primarily vesicular. With continued observation, we are able to see small vesicles approximately one micron in diameter disengaging themselves from the margins of the larger particles and moving about freely in the fluid. When the preparation is successful, movement may be observed at the margins of the particles, expanding, contracting, vibrating, etc. But even the smaller particles that move about appear to change before our eyes if we observe long enough. First, they appear "hard," the membrane black and thick. Gradually, however, the membrane becomes thinner. On the inside, we see increasingly a *blue* and *blue-green* glimmer. The vesicles become more taut and show increasing internal movement. Wave-like vibrations may be observed in many vesicles. The thinner the membrane becomes, the more intense the blue and the more elastic the movement. Soon, on the same or, still better, on the following day, we can clearly see movements of *expansion* and *contraction.* No one who has studied these preparations for any length of time can doubt the living character of these movements. We distinguish movements of the vesicles *from place to place* and *inner* movements of their *contents*, fluctuations of the blue color, variations in brightness, protrusion and retraction. *The vesicles pulsate with an irregular rhythm.*

We pass a galvanic current of approximately 0.2–0.5 Ma. through the preparation. The vesicles move toward the cathode and therefore have a positive electric charge. After several days, when the particles are no longer in colloidal suspension, the cataphoretic phenomena fade or disappear altogether. The charge of the vesicles seems therefore to be a prerequisite for colloidal suspension and motility, as Pauli surmised. It is also a prerequisite for the capacity to form cultures (*cf. Die Bione,* pp. 54 ff.).

We try an experiment with biological stains, using Gram stain or carbol fuchsin. As a control, we stain plain coal dust. The unprepared coal does not accept any biological stain. The particles remain black. The *coal bions,* on the other hand, show a *positive* stain reaction (*blue* when Gram stain is used). It can also be observed that the staining is restricted to those particles that have attained a certain degree of bionous development (thin membrane, increased fluid, blue on the inside), while the undeveloped particles react neutrally, like those in the control preparation.

We examine the stained preparation at a magnification of 3000x, using oil immersion, and find that most of the blue vesicles that previously had every possible form have now become spherical. A new phenomenon is especially striking: alongside the large-sized vesicles, approximately one micron in diameter, there are tiny red bodies which were not visible at a magnification of 300x. The smallest of them are approximately 0.2 micron in length, i.e., only barely visible microscopically. They lie in groups around the larger round, blue vesicles and unstained crystals. They are elongated, and are pointed at one end like miniature lancets. They were not observed in the fresh, wet preparation, but can be found in a live state in other coal-bion preparations (photograph of blood-charcoal preparation at 5000x magnification, *cf.* Fig. 26. Appendix).

After long experimentation, it became clear that these Gram-negative bodies are of the greatest significance. They are the so-called T-bacilli, which play such a crucial role in cancer. More on this subject later.

Our conclusion is that bions are biologically active forms because, in contrast to the substance from which they originate, they react to biological stain.

There is another specifically biological characteristic of bions. Non-living substances viewed under the fluorescent microscope always show only their own characteristic color: coal, *black*, sodium chloride, *yellow*, etc. Coal bions viewed fluoroscopically show not a *black* but a *blue* glimmer, as does a staphylococcus culture or any organic cell tissue. This is additional proof of the biological character of the coal bions.

Before proceeding to an investigation of other properties of the energy vesicles, we must establish whether the blue vesicles develop exclusively from carbon or from other substances as well. If they were to be found exclusively in carbon, the fundamental question concerning the nature of biological energy in non-living matter would be easy to answer. But the problem is complex, because the more substances we examine and subject to swelling, the more the following conclusion is confirmed: *All matter heated to incandescence and made to swell consists of or disintegrates into blue-glimmering vesicles:*

1. *Cooked foodstuffs:* Muscle, when it is cooked, loses its predominately striated structure and consists of blue, motile vesicles. The same results are obtained with every kind of vegetable. Size and shape of the vesicles may vary, but the content invariably shows a blue glimmer.

2. *Egg yolk* consists of individual blue vesicles, sometimes in the form of a heap of vesicles surrounded by a membrane. *Milk* contains, apart from fat globules, blue bions. The same applies to *cheese*, especially those varieties processed with the aid of bacterial fermentation, e.g., Kephir, Roquefort, yoghurt; and casein of every kind. *Vitamins*, examined at a magnification of 2000x, consist of

blue vesicles, irregular in shape, which refract light strongly. *Egg white* when raw is without structure; when cooked, it disintegrates into heaps of blue vesicles. *Blood serum* reacts similarly and blood platelets along with the red and white blood corpuscles show an intense blue glimmer.

The structure of *moss* and *grass* is striated without vesicles, similar to that of animal muscle. When both are cooked, they disintegrate into blue vesicles, which look like algae. This raises the question whether the algae found in stagnant ponds are not the same as our bions, namely, matter disintegrated into energy vesicles. Blue vesicles abound in stagnant water, serving as foodstuff for protozoa. The bion experiments yield a surprising answer to this question, which we will discuss in a different context.

We try to find out more about the formation of bions. We mix certain structureless substances together in a certain sequence. First, we make the following solutions: (a) 100 cc. water + 50 cc. 0.1n KCl + 2 mg. dissolved gelatin + 50 cc. filtered bouillon; (b) a few drops of egg white in KCl; (c) a small amount of fresh lecithin in KCl. These solutions show no structure. Only the lecithin mixture shows space-enclosing membranes, without an inner structure. We now mix the three groups of substances. Within minutes, the blue bion vesicles are visible microscopically. Previously there had been no motion of any kind. But now the solution is swarming with moving forms. The gelatin combines a number of blue vesicles together into a heap, which contracts and expands. The effect is one of individual vesicles inside the heap straining to move in a variety of directions and thereby generating inner motility. In general, four types of motion can be distinguished:

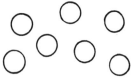

1. Non-moving vesicles

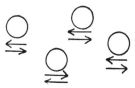

2. Vesicles moving back and forth in place

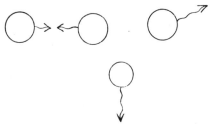

3. Vesicles moving from place to place

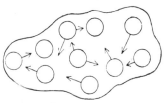

4. Heap of vesicles showing amoeboid motility, "protozoan" (amoeba)

FIGURE 2. Forms of movement visible in bions

If we now add finely pulverized blood charcoal, we can follow the development of highly motile coal bions. We witness the carbon absorbing the fluid containing egg white. The previously empty lecithin tubes fill with vesicles. The whole scene is one swarming with "life." We then autoclave the mixture; the movements become even stronger. Now the T-bacilli appear. The biological stain reaction (carbon fuchsin, Giemsa or Gram) is now positive.

In January 1937, I rendered an account of this experiment (No. 6) to the Academy of Sciences in Paris. In January 1938, I received word from Professor Lapique that, after one year, the autoclaved preparation still showed life-like movement and contained contractile forms. The news was all the more surprising since the preparation was sterile and sealed, air-tight. Here is Professor Lapique's letter:

Université de Paris   Sorbonne, le 25 Janvier 1938
Faculté des Sciences
Laboratoire de Physiologie Générale
1, rue Victor-Cousin (5ᵉ Arr.)

Monsieur le Docteur,

Chargé par l'Académie d'étudier votre communication du 8 Janvier de l'année dernière, j'ai d'abord attendu le film que vous annonciez. Puis, ne le recevant pas, j'ai examiné au microscope les échantillons que vous aviez joints à votre premier envoi. J'ai constaté, en effet, les mouvements d'apparence vitale que vous annonciez. Il y a là quelque chose de curieux, en raison du long délai depuis la préparation.

Je suis disposé a proposer a l'Académie de publier brièvement votre constatation en la faisant suivre d'une courte note de moi-même confirmant le fait avec une interprétation physico-chémique n'engageant que moi. Laissant de côté votre théorie électrique qui n'a rien a faire avec l'expérience, voulez-vous accepter que votre communication soit insérée simplement sous forme de l'extrait ci-joint qui en réalité, est un résumé de la partie importante? Il me semble qu'ainsi vous recevriez satisfaction pour votre désir de voir vos recherches prendre place dans nos Comptes-Rendus.

Veuillex agréer, Monsieur, l'assurance de ma considération distinguée.

DR. LOUIS LAPIQUE

Professeur honoraire à la Sorbonne

Membre de l'Académie des Sciences

Translation of preceding:

University of Paris,   Sorbonne, January 25, 1938

Faculty of Sciences

Laboratories for General Physiology,

1, rue Victor-Cousin (5ème)

My dear Doctor,

Requested by the Academy to study your communication of January 8 of last year, I first waited for the arrival of the film you were to send. Then since I did not receive it, I examined microscopically the samples you included with your initial communication. I have in fact verified the life-like movements that you described. That fact itself is remarkable considering the length of time that has elapsed since the preparations were made.

I should like to propose to the Academy the publication of your findings in brief, together with a short annotation by myself confirming the fact and offering a physical-chemical interpretation representing my own personal viewpoint. Would you agree to the publication of your contribution in the excerpted form attached, which is actually a résumé of the important part, while leaving out your electrical theory, which has nothing to do with the experiment? It seems to me that this arrangement would be in accord with your wish to have your research recorded in our bulletin.

Permit me to convey to you my sincerest respects,

DR. LOUIS LAPIQUE

Honorary Professor, University of Paris

Member, Academy of Sciences

I withdrew my consent for publication in the bulletin of the French Academy of Sciences on the following grounds:

1. The physical-chemical interpretation would have obscured the *biological* character of the experiment.
2. During 1937, I produced bion cultures that were confirmed experimentally by Prof. DuTeil in Nice.* This decisively important fact would not be published.
3. The résumé proposed for publication in no way represented the detailed report I had submitted to the Academy. Its publication could only have led to misunderstandings, and unsuccessful control experiments would have been the result.

Soft iron filings are the most suitable metallic substance for our experiment. Only a few minutes after introducing sterile filings into our standard bouillon–KCl solution, delicate vesicles develop from the iron particles. This process can be followed microscopically. A single iron particle is placed on a slide and a small amount of potassium chloride added. Within a short time, bions are produced whose motility lasts only approximately ten minutes. Like tiny magnets they order themselves along lines of magnetic force and cling to each other (*cf.* Figs. 27 and 28, Appendix).

A solution of iron bions becomes colloid within a few days. The particles consist of heavy, angular, intensely blue energy vesicles which become progressively "softer" and more elastic (*cf.* Fig. 3). The blue vesicles can form cultures, but this subject will be discussed later.

Humus is composed of mostly motile vesicles having an intense blue glimmer. Soil subjected to autoclavation disintegrates completely into energy vesicles. The progressive disintegration can be observed microscopically each day. (*cf.* Fig. 29, Appendix).

* Professor Roger DuTeil conducted control experiments on the bions at the university in Nice. [Ed.]

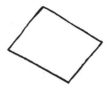

1. Angular form, showing in the dark-field a
   fine, vesicular structure with striations

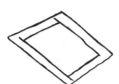 

2. Appearance of marked striations with typical
   rectangular and rhomboidal figures

3. Apparent softening and bending of striated structure

4. Advanced stage of development
   into bion heaps. Content between the structures shows
   intense blue glimmer. The heap
   already shows motility

5. Iron-filing bions of the
   PA type. Motile, contrac-
   tile, with a blue glimmer.
   Cultivatable

FIGURE 3.   Changes in the structure of iron filings in bouillon and potassium chloride during the swelling process

These experiments are difficult and require great patience and persistence. One cannot simply throw some substances into bouillon and wait for the development of bions, as did a biologist I knew. Nor can these experiments be performed without knowledge of the underlying process.

2. THE QUESTION OF "BROWNIAN MOVEMENT"

A few fundamental problems must be cleared up before we can draw any conclusions from our observations. The concept of "Brownian movement" has been invoked as an objection to the claim that specific *bio-energetic* forces account for the motility of bions. Physicists have known for a long time that the smallest colloidal particles are in motion, i.e., that they move in the field in various directions. These movements have even been calculated. They are attributed to collisions between the molecules in the solution and the larger colloidal particles.

This interpretation is purely *physical* and *mechanistic*. Nothing in it is consistent with the biological energy manifestations of pulsation. Can this interpretation be applied to the phenomena observed in bionous energy vesicles? An interpretation is valid only if it makes new phenomena comprehensible. It is invalid if it conflicts with the observations. And when it directly contradicts the observations and can be replaced by another interpretation that offers a more satisfying explanation of the phenomena, it is useless.

The mechanical Brownian movement is defended by physicists as a dogma. Insofar as it is directed against mystical interpretations of living phenomena this defense is justified. But experience shows just as clearly that the "molecular movement" interpretation is itself not without irrational motives. Otherwise, the physicist who sees all around him only Brownian movements of a purely physical nature would not so stubbornly refuse to consider a few facts that contradict his interpretation in certain instances. I do not believe I will ever be able to convince these physicists, but I know that the blind alleys into which the purely mechanistic viewpoint leads will one day force science to face up to new facts and arguments.

Doubtless, there exist movements of extremely fine particles that allow a mechanical interpretation. For example, I myself believe that the movement of the vesicles (*cf.* Fig. 2) back and forth in place is not of a biological nature. Whether molecules are moving them back and forth I do not know, since I have never seen molecules, any more than have the proponents of the purely mechanical Brownian movement.

Now, let us clarify what the physical-mechanical interpretation advocates. Since neither the particles nor the molecules ever disappear in the solution, the molecular impulses should, logically, continue indefinitely, as should the movement of the particles. In addition, all particles in approximately the same size range would have to be in motion. Finally, the only type of movement possible under these circumstances would be from place to place.

Contraction and expansion of the contents of the particles cannot be explained by the mechanical interpretation. *How could an impulse from a molecule outside the particle cause vibration or an expansion inside?* Later, we will become familiar with other properties of the bions that could not conceivably be explained in mechanical terms.

These observations can be seen only at magnifications of at least 2000x. This is the absolute minimum requirement. Actually, reliable conclusions require a magnification of 3000–4000x. Just as indispensable is the microscopic examination of a *living* preparation before it is destroyed by biological stain. The Copenhagen biologist A. Fischer became very upset and even somewhat hostile when he was unable to achieve a magnification greater than 1500x, as I had insisted he must in order to be able to see what I claimed as fact. The Giemsa stain of the bions done at his institute in 1936 was positive. Under the correct conditions, the following phenomena, which cannot be interpreted mechanistically, manifest themselves:

1. Movement is sometimes present, sometimes absent. It occurs, then stops. Bion vesicles appear at the margin of coal or moss particles and exhibit movement once there is a sufficient degree of tension and charge. Certain bionous preparations show no movement at all. What has happened to the molecular impulses in such cases? The molecules have not gone away and neither have the particles! And mechanistic science does not postulate a third factor in the origin of the movements. *The external motion of the energy vesicles must therefore be related to their inner charge.*

2. The internal motility of many bions, their expansion, contraction, vibration, and glimmering, is a fact that cannot be ascribed to external impulses, only to shifts in internal energy. Thus *the inner motility must also be connected with internal charge.*

3. Bion research comprehends living red blood corpuscles as orgonotic vesicles. Examined at a magnification above 2000x they are *blue* and pulsate. Dead red corpuscles are not blue but black. They are non-motile and do not pulsate.

    The motility of red corpuscles originates in the internal charge only, not in external impulses. With the disappearance of the blue, orgonotic color, motility also ceases.

The fundamental question of all biology concerns the origin of the inner impulses in the living organism. No one doubts that the living is distinguished from the non-living by the internal origin of the motor impulses. The internal motor impulse can be ascribed only to an *energy* active within the organism. The question of the origin of this energy itself is answered by the bion experiment.

The biologically effective energy, within the organism, that generates the impulses originates from the same matter as the bion.

I introduced the term "orgone" for the energy observable in motile, bionous matter, deriving it from the words "organism" and "orgastic." Henceforth, the expression "orgonotic" encompasses all energy phenomena and processes specifically pertaining to the energy governing living matter. Every living organism is a membranous structure containing a quantity of orgone energy in its body fluids; it constitutes an "orgonotic system."

Moreover, the purely physical-mechanical interpretation fails to clarify a single one of the specific biological reactions. We have freed ourselves from any suspicion that we are dealing with a supranatural life force transcending energy and matter. Therewith, we acknowledge a connection between the energy vesicles and Einstein's *functional* theory of matter and energy. We have observed some fundamental processes that indicate the manner in which orgone originates from matter, specifically, the processes of disintegration of matter and the swelling of the disintegrating particles. *The solution to the enigma of the way life functions is contained in these processes.* The essential objective functions of biological energy correspond to the essential functions of living matter. The basic functions of highly developed organisms are the same as those of the smallest bits of contractile plasma. Every mechanistic or chemical approach fails completely here. It is not a matter of substances, but of biological energy *functions.* In this viewpoint, we are in accord with many biologists. Üxküll, for instance, writes:

> Animal biology today owes its existence to the introduction of physiological experimentation into the study of lower animals. In these experiments the physiologists' expectations of new research horizons were not fulfilled. . . . The breaking down of living phenomena into chemical and physical processes did not advance matters at all . . . for all those scientists who see the essential element of biology in the life process itself and not in its reduction to chemistry, physics, and mathematics. [*Umwelt und Innenwelt der Tiere,* Berlin: Springer, 1921, p. 2]

3. THE T-BACILLI

In my account of the experiment on coal bions, I mentioned the discovery, using Gram stain, of tiny bodies, shaped like lancets. These bodies were given the name "T-bacilli," i.e., *Todes* bacilli, because of their dual connection with the process of dying:

a) *T-bacilli develop from the degeneration and putrid disintegration of living and non-living protein.*
b) *Injected in strong doses, T-bacilli are capable of killing mice within twenty-four hours.*

If staphylococcus cultures or rot bacteria (B-proteus, etc.) are allowed to stand for a sufficient length of time, a greenish margin forms around the edge of the culture. Against the light, this margin is seen to have a blue glimmer which tends to spread. At the beginning of the experiment, we established that the culture was pure, containing nothing but staphylococci. After a few weeks or months, we take a sample from the bluish-green margin, and find that although there are now very few cocci, the culture is swarming with a variety of much smaller bacilli moving in lively zigzag patterns. These are roughly 0.2–0.5 micron in length, and examined at a magnification of at least 2000x, appear slightly oval-shaped (*cf.* Fig. 4-c). Inoculated in bouillon, they develop a culture fluid with a strong blue-green glimmer and an acrid, ammoniacal odor. The longer the bouillon culture is allowed to stand, the denser it becomes and the deeper its blue or green-blue color. After a few days, rot bacteria cultures (B-proteus, B-subtilis, and staphylococci) (*cf.* Fig. 4-b) agglutinate at the bottom of the test tube or as a membrane on the surface. The agglutination of the T-bacilli, on the other hand, does not occur for months. In the case of a mixed culture, all other bacilli agglutinate very rapidly, whereas the T-bacilli remain alive.

a) Blue bions. About 2 to 10 μ

b) Staphylococci Streptococci   Bacilli

About 1 μ diameter   About 4 to 8 μ long

c) T-bacilli. About 0.2 to 0.5 μ

FIGURE 4. Typical forms of blue bions, black cocci and bacilli, and T-bacilli

T-bacilli can be obtained from degeneration of every kind of protein substance. To date, T-bacilli, identical in form and reactions, have been cultivated from fifteen different sources. *T-bacilli are therefore the product of degenerative putrid processes in tissues.* Following is a list of some sources of T-bacilli:

Blood of cancer patients: T-bacilli can be cultivated from the blood of patients with advanced cancer by simple inoculation in bouillon. In our laboratory, this process became one of our most important tests for cancer.

Cancer tissue: Every kind of cancer tissue, fresh or old, shows T-bacilli on microscopic examination, and yields T-bacilli cultures in bouillon and on agar. When boiled, it disintegrates almost totally into T-bodies with the characteristic red Gram-stain reaction.

Precancerous cells and tissue: These also yield T-bacilli; i.e., they disintegrate into T-bodies or already contain them fully developed. Epithelium from the vagina, tongue, skin, or from sputum is normally without structure. In the precancerous state, it shows extremely fine T-bodies on dark-field examination.

Degenerating blood (experiment): 2 to 3 cc. of blood are spread on a sterilized Petri dish and dried for twenty-four hours in an incubator. The dried blood is then dusted with blood charcoal that has been heated to incandescence. After a further twenty-four hours, enough potassium chloride and bouillon are added to cover the substance. Microscopic examination and biological stain reaction immediately confirm the presence of T-bacilli.

T-bacilli of every origin generate cancerous, destructive, and infiltrating growths in healthy mice. However, I would like to deal separately with this element of the bion experiment and restrict myself here to the essential, biologically significant reactions pertaining to the problem of orgone energy.

Bion preparations regularly yield two types of bions: the blue PA bions described earlier and the small black T-bacilli. These two types are antagonistic to each other in the biological experiment; *the PA bions are capable of killing or immobilizing the black T-bacilli.* This process occurs in the drop under the microscope as well as in the living mouse (*cf.* Fig. 4-a).

We place a drop of solution of earth and iron or coal bions on a hanging drop slide and add a small drop from a T-bacillus culture. At 400x in the dark-field, or more clearly at 2000x in ordinary light, we can see that the T-bacilli in the vicinity of the blue bions become agitated, spinning around and around, then remain on one spot, quivering, and finally become immobile. In time, more and more T-bacilli accumulate around the blue bions: they agglutinate. The "dead" bacilli seem to attract and to be lethal to those still living. The orgone energy experiments with cancer had their origin in this significant fact.

Subtilis or proteus bacilli, which are five to eight times the size of T-bacilli, are affected in the same way. In these organisms, the lethalness of the blue bions can be observed much more clearly. Ultimately, the whole field is covered with dead bacilli.

Between January 1937 and January 1939, injection experiments with PA bions and T-bacilli were carried out on 178 healthy mice. The following table shows the results:

Injection	Number of Mice	Dead in 1 Week	Dead in 15 Months	Sick after 15 Months	Healthy after 15 Months
T-bacilli	84	30	30	24	0
PA bions then					
T-bacilli	45	0	9	—	36
PA bions	39	0	0	—	39
T-bacilli then					
PA bions	10	0	8 (2 killed)	—	0
	178				

Of the 30 T-mice that died within fifteen months of the T-bacilli injection, 25 were carefully examined for cancerous growths. Seven mice revealed ameboid cancer cells in various tissues; 13 revealed destructive, infiltrative, cellular growths of a cancerous nature. The remaining 5 had chronic inflammatory growths. The cancer tumors were furthest advanced in the mice that had survived the T-bacilli injection for the longest period.

The connection between T-bacilli and cancer is of crucial importance and will be discussed later.

For an evaluation of orgone energy, the results of the experiments have the following significance:

1. *Theoretical:* At the basis of the life process, at the boundary between non-living and living, we encounter a way of functioning that is completely encompassed by our generally valid schema of biological functioning: *All life functions obey the natural law of the dissociation of the unitary and the functional antithesis and unity of the dissociated.*

Out of non-living matter A, motile bions B, containing orgone energy, develop. These bions divide into two groups: the PA group and the T-group. *The two groups have an antithetical relationship in that the PA bions paralyze the T-bions.* There is only one plausible explanation of this fact in the context of our knowledge of the physical functions of orgone energy: *The PA bions are fully developed, highly charged orgone units. T-bions, on the other hand,*

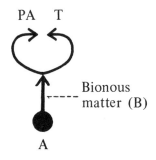

Bionous matter (B)

represent products of degeneration, appearing when tissues, cells, or bacteria begin to lose their orgone charge. They contain only small quantities of orgone and therefore are very weak orgonotic systems.

Since the stronger orgonotic system always attracts the weaker and draws off its charge,[1] the paralyzing of T-bions by PA bions is easily explained: The biophysical functional connection between PA and T is derived from the purely physical functions of orgone energy.

2. *Practical:* The T are produced either by *degenerative processes,* i.e., through loss of orgone energy in highly developed forms, or *they originate because of an insufficient amount of mass-free orgone inside the energy vesicle.*

T-bacilli were produced in my laboratory from the degeneration of the following tissues and bion preparations: dried blood, dried feces, autoclaved cancer tissue, autoclaved egg medium that had been dusted with incandescent charcoal and covered with potassium hydroxide, tongue epithelium damaged by dental bridgework, degenerated vaginal epithelial cells, degenerated spermatozoa, degenerated rot bacteria, coal bion preparations of all kinds, and from egg medium treated with potassium cyanide.

The deficient orgone content of T-bacilli manifests itself in a strange phenomenon which I would like to designate as "orgone hunger." The observations are as follows:

We filter blood that has been diluted about ten times with the usual potassium chloride solution. (A Berkefelt filter with a pore size of not more than 0.25 micron catches whatever T-bacilli might be present.) Microscopic examination at a magnification of 2000–4000x reveals only fluid, with no structures at all. We add to the serum a tiny drop of pure T-bacillus culture, containing no PA bions. Within a few minutes, an extremely exciting spectacle unfolds, one which in all probability holds the secret of "immune bodies" in the serum.

---

[1] This phenomenon, known as the reversed orgonomic potential, is discussed elsewhere from a purely physical standpoint.

At first, we see only T-bacilli moving around in the field. Before long, however, large blue vesicles appear here and there, with more and more T-bacilli surrounding them, exactly as in a mixture of PA and T. The T seem to have stimulated the formation of the blue PA bions; a control serum without T does not show any PA. The PA bions, once formed, exercise a paralyzing effect on the T, which begin to agglutinate.

A second, even more astonishing process now begins. The heap of agglutinated T is black; there is no evidence of blue. But within fifteen to thirty minutes, *this dead black heap begins to take on a strong blue coloring and to form membranous vesicles.* They are nothing other than PA bions. The dead T have drawn off orgone from the serum and transformed themselves into PA bions.

These two phenomena have not yet been thoroughly studied. On the one hand, they are connected to the immunity factor and, on the other hand, to the vesicular structuring or the vesicular disintegration of tissues that come into contact with the T-bacilli.

A few days after a healthy mouse is inoculated subcutaneously with T-bacilli, a non-purulent swelling appears on the skin, which, under microscopic examination, proves to be tissue in a state of vesicular disintegration. By the same process, the degeneration of epithelial cells in cancer is marked by the appearance first of T-bacilli; then of large numbers of blue PA bions in the surroundings.

At this point I would like to interrupt the account of these observations, which yield so much information about organismic orgone energy, and await the results of further experiments before deciding what conclusions to draw. Nevertheless, it is certain that *T-bacilli stimulate bionous disintegration* and that *cancer cells are organized from bionously disintegrated tissue,* just as amoebae and other protozoa are formed from moss bions.

THE T-BLOOD TEST

The biological vigor, i.e., functioning power, of a cell is determined neither by its structure nor by its chemical composition.

Disintegration of structure and chemical composition must be regarded as consequences rather than causes of the biological degeneration. The structure, along with the biochemical equilibrium of the cell, is the expression of the cell's biological vigor, but the biological function itself has hitherto been a mystery. The orgonotic charge of the cell now provides us with the possibility of determining it experimentally.

The red blood corpuscles of two persons can be alike in structure and chemical make-up while differing sharply in biological function. Under the microscope, both may have the same form; the red corpuscle count and the hemoglobin content may well be normal and identical for both persons.

Let us now expose blood samples from each person to the same destructive agent. We autoclave a few drops of blood from each person in bouillon and potassium chloride for thirty minutes at a temperature of 120°C. with steam pressure 15 lbs. per sq. in. Microscopic examination may now yield two very different results. The autoclaved blood of one person has disintegrated into large blue bion vesicles. The blood of the other person yields no blue vesicles, only T-bacilli. Gram stain confirms this difference: one blood sample produces blue, Gram-positive vesicles (*cf.* Fig. 31, Appendix), the other, red, Gram-negative T-bacilli (for T-bacilli from a sarcoma, *cf.* Fig. 32, Appendix). This conclusion may be drawn:

The former blood sample shows a strong orgonotic charge of the red cells. The charge reveals itself, after autoclavation, in the blue bions ("B-reaction"). The latter blood sample shows a weak or minimal orgone charge of the red cells. The lack of orgonotic charge manifests itself, after autoclavation, in the absence of blue bions and in the presence of T-bacilli, which result from the degeneration of the red corpuscles ("T-reaction").

The T-reaction is typical for cases of advanced cancer in which the orgone content of the blood has been totally consumed in the organism's struggle against the systemic disease (cancer biopathy) and the local tumor. This T-reaction is usually present *before* any symptoms of anemia and often reveals the cancer process long before a perceptible tumor has formed.

On the other hand, red corpuscles weak in orgone energy absorb it greedily when it is supplied to the organism by the orgone accumulator. Subsequent autoclavation tests yield a shift from the T-reaction to the B-reaction; i.e., the red blood corpuscles have become more resistant to autoclavation; they contain more orgone.

The red corpuscles can be charged by atmospheric orgone energy. (The effects of solar radiation are based on the same principle.) This can be confirmed experimentally. On a microscope slide, we mix biologically (i.e., orgonotically) weak blood with rot bacteria or T-bacilli. The blood, being energetically weak, does not destroy or agglutinate the bacteria or the T-bacilli. However, once the organism has been orgonotically charged (the degree of charge can be ascertained by means of the autoclavation test), the blood has a decidedly paralyzing and agglutinating effect on the same pathogenic micro-organisms. Smaller protozoa respond in the same fashion; that is, they are not damaged by orgonotically weak blood but are paralyzed by orgonotically strong blood.

The red corpuscle is an orgonotic system in miniature, contain-

weak   *strong*

Orgone margin narrow   Orgone margin wide
Blue color weak   Blue color intense
Membrane often shriveled
("poikilocytosis")

F I G U R E 5.   Red blood corpuscles showing weak and strong orgonotic charge (in the living specimen at 4500x)

ing a small quantity of orgone energy inside its membrane. At 4000x magnification, the red blood corpuscles show a deep blue glimmer and lively vibration of their contents. They expand and contract and are therefore not rigid, as is usually thought. They carry atmospheric orgone energy from the lungs to the tissues. The nature of the relationship between atmospheric oxygen and orgone energy can only be surmised at this time. Whether orgone is identical with the chemical particles of the air or fundamentally different from them is unknown.

The orgonotic charge is also revealed in the shape and structure of the red blood corpuscles. Cells with a weak charge are more or less shrunken and have a narrow blue margin which glimmers feebly. Once the organism is charged, the red blood cells swell, while the blue margin intensifies and widens, sometimes including the entire cell. No pathogenic micro-organism can survive in the vicinity of these orgonotically highly charged red blood cells.

How these facts are connected to immunity against infectious diseases, colds, etc., is still obscure; but finding the connection should not be too difficult. Probably, the orgonotic charge of the tissues and blood cells determines the degree of susceptibility to infections, the "disposition to disease."

The fact that during the process of destroying the pathogenic micro-organisms the erythrocytes gradually lose their blue coloration, turn black, and sometimes degenerate into T-bodies demonstrates that the orgone charge of the red blood corpuscles actually kills protozoa and bacteria. Examination of tissue from tumors in treated mice shows that when charged red blood corpuscles permeate cancer tissue it disintegrates into non-motile T-bodies. In this process, the red blood corpuscles disappear and only T-bodies can be seen. The cancer tumor shows large cavities which are filled with T-bodies, visible on dark-field examination at 300–400x. Macroscopically, the content of the cavities at first appears blood red, but gradually turns a rust brown due to hemosiderosis. The iron pigment has separated from the disintegrated corpuscles, which have lost their charge of biological energy. The typical secondary anemia of cancer patients is the expression of the loss of biological energy from the blood in the struggle against the T-bacilli and the cancer cells.

More details on this subject will be presented later in connection with our cancer experiments. What is important here is to learn how the orgonotic charge of the blood cells acts under a variety of conditions. To put it briefly: *Erythrocytes with a strong orgone charge act upon bacteria and small protozoa in exactly the same way as do earth, iron, coal, and other bions.* Since they originate in bone marrow, it must be assumed that the bone marrow has the capacity to generate bions constantly. Energy vesicles are basic to both animal and plant tissue. Taken together, these facts form the basis for the orgone therapy experiments on cancer patients. *The introduction of orgone energy from the outside relieves the organism of the burden of consuming its own body orgone in the struggle against the disease.* This is a further proof of the identity of atmospheric and organismic orgone energy.

Experiment reveals the following:

1. A grass infusion develops no protozoa, or very few, when kept from the beginning in the orgone accumulator. Clearly, orgone energy charges the grass tissue and prevents its disintegration into protozoa.
2. Fully developed protozoa are not destroyed in the orgone accumulator.
3. T-bacilli are not destroyed in the orgone accumulator but, on the other hand, a cancer patient's blood can be cleared of T-bodies within a few days if the patient is exposed to intense orgone irradiation.

4. LUMINATION AND ATTRACTION

It is a generally known fact, first discovered by Gurwitsch, that animal blood radiates. Since, from the point of view of orgone biophysics, erythrocytes are nothing but orgone energy vesicles, it is important to demonstrate the radiation microscopically. One of its most salient characteristics, as we discover in pure orgone physics, is "orgonotic attraction," which has no connection with iron magnetism. Observation of this orgonotic attraction is made possible by the following experiments, all of which consist of bringing together bions of various origins in the usual preparation of bouillon and potassium chloride and examining them under the microscope.

Seen bio-energetically, the destruction and agglutination of bacteria by various kinds of bions is quite simply the *attraction and subsequent withdrawal of orgone energy by the stronger orgonotic system, the PA bion.* By mixing different kinds of bions, we discover other important effects of orgone energy.

Let us experiment first with a sterile mixture of red blood corpuscles and earth bions. We use a drop of diluted blood and one of earth bion solution that is sufficiently thinned out to permit easy observation of each individual bion. No results can be expected at less than 2000x (a good 80x, apochromatic objective lens combined with a 16x eyepiece in a microscope with inclined binocular tube would serve the purpose). The use of a special water-immersion lens, which can simply be dipped into the solution, is advantageous. The work is easier and faster with direct water immersion and mechanical interferences are quickly offset. An effect from the metal need not be feared, since the phenomena is the same when a cover glass is used. But at this magnification and with the necessary use of hanging drop slides, cover glasses are inconvenient, since they break so easily. Any control experiment will prove that the immersion of the objective lens into the solution does not affect the results in any way.

THE RADIATING BRIDGE BETWEEN TWO
ORGONOTIC SYSTEMS

At first, the earth bions and red blood corpuscles move about separately. Gradually, however, grouping begins, with several erythrocytes gathering around one of the larger, heavier, earth bions and moving nearer and nearer until they are touching. At each point of contact, a strong radiation appears. At points where the bodies do not touch each other directly but are separated by approximately 0.5 to 1 micron, *a strongly radiating bridge is formed between the earth bion and the erythrocyte,* and apparently connects them. This bridge vibrates intensely, becoming alternately wider and narrower. Finally, the membranes between the bodies appear to be less distinct. With sufficient observation, it is possible to see clearly that the erythrocytes refract the light more strongly, that their blue color becomes more and more intense, and that they become larger and tauter and show a lively pulsation. In this manner, erythrocytes can be orgonotically charged just as effectively as the body is charged by orgone irradiation of the organism. If weak, deformed erythro-

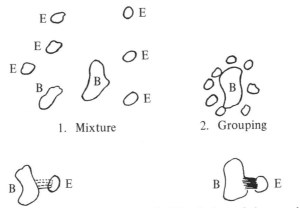

1. Mixture   2. Grouping

3. Formation of a radiating bridge   4. Dissolution of the membranes and orgonotic fusion

FIGURE 6. Phases in the formation of a radiating bridge and orgonotic fusion between earth bions (B) and erythrocytes (E)

cytes from the blood of cancer patients are used for this experiment, their expansion and radiation are more evident. Orgonotically weak erythrocytes exercise little or no influence on bacilli and small protozoa, but they do become effective when they are charged with orgone. The erythrocytes "drink their fill" of orgone from the earth bions.

The injection of sterile earth bions into cancer mice achieved the same effect as exposure to orgone radiation in the orgone accumulator: inhibition of the growth of the tumor, replacement of the tumor tissue by strongly radiating blood, and destruction of the T-bacilli. What actually occurs in the organism as a result of the bion injections can be seen in the microscopic study of the bion mixture. (Bion injection was the method of orgone application utilized in my laboratory before the discovery of atmospheric orgone energy, after which it was replaced by irradiation in the orgone accumulator.)

There is no fusion of earth bions and erythrocytes, only the formation of the radiating bridge. This is also true of iron bions, coal bions, etc. On the other hand, coal bions and bions produced from autoclaved blood or from any protein do interpenetrate. This *fusion* is extremely significant for an understanding of the experimental production of tumors in mice by means of tar.

5. FUSION AND INTERPENETRATION

Sexuality has in common with procreation the fact that *two living systems fuse orgonotically*. In single-celled organisms, *mutual penetration* of body substance follows the fusion that occurs in copulation. Fusion and interpenetration are not only energy processes but processes that involve substance as well. In the metazoan, however, these processes are much more complete in terms of energy than of substance. In the copulative act, the male organ penetrates the female. Both organs now form a functioning unit. In many hermaphroditic molluscs (snails, worms), penetration is mutual but restricted to the genitals. The union of two gametes to form a zygote, on the other hand, is a perfect example of total interpenetration and fusion of substance. Although in multicellular animals fusion is restricted to the genital organs and the reproductive cells, the orgonotic function is total; i.e., in copulation, two beings fuse temporarily into a single orgonotic energy system. (In the case of humans, this is true only if both partners are orgastically potent.)

Orgonotic fusion is regularly preceded by lumination. Orgonotic *cell lumination,* physiological *excitation,* and psychic *sexual emotion* are functionally identical processes. Psychic perception of a sexual object can cause physiological excitation (erection); conversely, physiological excitation (stroking, friction) can evoke sexual emotion. This psychosomatic process leads to orgonotic lumination of the entire organism. On the other hand, strong orgonotic lumination in an organism tends to intensify the urge for physiological friction with accompanying psychosexual emotion. Therefore, our diagram of biological functioning is again valid:

Psychic sexual emotion

Physiological (somatic) excitation

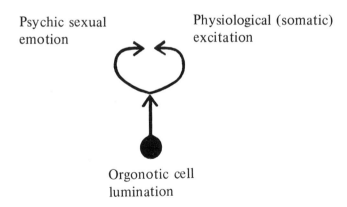

Orgonotic cell lumination

The concept that energy manifestations of the multicellular organism are present in each individual cell and, strictly speaking, have their origin there must be taken seriously. Orgone lumination of the individual cell is identical with the physiologist's and biologist's "cell excitation" and the depth psychologist's "organ libido" or "cell libido." We have taken an important step toward the understanding of these processes, since we now know that a demonstrable, specifically biological energy is active in the cells. The principal energy functions are formation of a radiating bridge ("sexual contact"), lumination, fusion, and interpenetration. Our purpose here is simply to observe the energy processes of fusion and interpenetration as they are revealed in the bions. Our sense of triumph when we witness the fusion of a coal bion and an earth bion is justified; the hypothetical concepts "cell excitation" and "organ libido" have become tangible realities.

After the coal bions are attracted to the heavier, and therefore less motile, earth bions and the radiating bridge is formed, the energy process continues to parallel every phase of copulation. The "excited," i.e., luminating, bions move ever closer to each other. At the point where the radiating bridges appear, the coal substance (in bion form) gradually begins to penetrate the earth bions. One has the impression that the earth bion absorbs the coal bion. Eventually, the smaller coal bions completely penetrate the earth bions. Their black membranes are clearly distinguishable from the brownish membranes of the earth bions. As a whole, this mixture of earth bions and coal bions appears brownish black. Then, gradually, the black disappears; the membranes of the coal bions dissolve. The earth bions take on a darker coloration and their blue vesicles emit a stronger radiation. Finally, all traces of the coal substance vanish.

Another way of describing this process would be to say that the earth bion "eats up" the coal bion. But it would make no sense to subdivide fusion into "eating" or "copulating" since, at this most primitive biological stage, biological energy functions without differentiation. It would be difficult to differentiate functionally between copulation and the incorporation of smaller protozoa by larger ones.

This statement is equally true of the multicellular animal when we describe energy processes and avoid the anthropomorphic trap of ascribing purpose. A suckling child is fulfilling a completely different "purpose" than is a woman who takes the male organ into her vagina. The first act "serves" the "preservation of the individual," the second the "preservation of the species." But these finalistic distinctions are incorrect when the problem is one of biological functioning. In terms of energy—and, biophysically, no other view is valid—the process taking place between the mother's breast and the baby's mouth is precisely the same as that between the erect penis and the vagina. This functional identity extends to the most minute physiological detail. Moralistic hypocrisy should not be permitted to obscure the significance of these matters by representing the "holy" suckling process as "asexual" so as not to "profane" it by identifying it with the "devilish, dirty, sexual act." It is not a matter of holy or unholy, but of biological functioning. We only now understand biophysically Freud's fundamental discovery that the nursing child's mouth is just as much a *sexually* excited organ as is the mother's nipple in excitation. This one insight will help more in diagnosing the inability of some women to breast-feed their children than all medical theories.

It is therefore a matter of indifference to us whether the earth bion has "eaten up" the coal bion in order to "strengthen" itself, thereby behaving in a "moral" or "rational" manner, or whether it has fused "sexually" with the coal bion. Instead we are concerned with the energy functions, which are fundamental in the process itself and common to all basic biological functions, whether we are considering ingestion, conjugation, copulation, the formation of zygotes, or the sexual act of the metazoon.

It should be noted that the orgone hunger of bions does have a satiation point. If a limited number of coal bions are introduced into a solution of earth bions, after a few days no coal bions are left. But if a large number of coal bions are added, not all of them disappear. Different species of bions display varying degrees of "orgone hunger." The behavior of sand bion cultures toward coal bions is, for instance, "gluttonous." Iron bions also fuse easily with coal bions. Bions formed from cooked organic substances, such as muscle, are far less greedy in their absorption of coal bions. This

indicates that the smaller the original amount of carbon contained
by a bion, the stronger its tendency to take in carbon. SAPA bions,
originating from sand, initially contain no carbon; iron bions contain
only traces of it. Muscle bions are, however, composed of carbon
compounds. Their hunger for carbon is therefore far less than that
of sand bions. I shall refrain from drawing far-reaching conclusions
about the origin of plasma on our planet and hold strictly to the
facts.

Coal bions are not the only ones that fuse with others. Fusion
also occurs between earth bions and iron bions, iron bions and
muscle bions, etc. Here is a broad field for fruitful research.

To summarize: *Orgone energy vesicles show the basic functions of completely developed living substance: attraction, lumination, a radiating bridge, fusion, and penetration.* These functions are
specific properties of the orgone vesicles; they are absent in bions
that have lost their orgone charge. These functions are therefore
determined not by substance but by energy. They are specific
functions of the orgone and have nothing to do with magnetism or
electricity.

We are now better prepared to approach the observations
provided by our investigation of the organization of protozoa and
cancer cells.

6. THE NATURAL ORGANIZATION OF PROTOZOA

I would like to begin this section with the excellent statement by the
biologist Üxküll, taken from the foreword to his book *Umwelt und
Innenwelt der Tiere:*

> Today, the word "science" has become a ridiculous fetish.
> It therefore seems appropriate to point out that science is noth-
> ing more than the aggregate opinion of living scientists. . . .
> In time all opinions are forgotten, rejected, or changed. For that
> reason, the question "What constitutes a scientific truth?" can
> be answered without exaggeration by saying "An error of

today." . . . We hope to progress from gross to smaller errors; but whether we are really on the right track at all is a matter of extreme doubt so far as *biology* is concerned.

In the summer of 1938, I published in *Die Bione* a number of photographs taken with fast-motion techniques and time exposures. They unequivocally demonstrated that single-celled organisms do not evolve from air bacteria that no one has ever seen but rather from bionously disintegrating moss and grass. The world of biology kept silent on this "error of today" and with just a few exceptions made no comment on the microphotos. Today, the facts speak for themselves (*cf.* Figs. 34, 35, 36, 37, 38, 39, 40, 41-a, b, c, 42, Appendix).

The animal is not a mechanical sum of organs, just as the organ is not a mechanical sum of cells. The animal in its totality—every organ and every cell, individually and collectively—is a self-contained orgonotic system characterized by the four-beat pattern of tension → charge → discharge → relaxation, and thereby a functional unit. It is a property of the living system that each one of its parts can operate according to the tension-charge formula independently *or* in connection with the organism in its totality.

In modern biological literature, since approximately World War I, the functional approach has slowly been making some headway against the substantive-mechanistic viewpoint. One of the crucial problems of biology is the fact that whereas the functions of structures (musculature, nerves, glands, etc.) are understandable mechanically, the functions of protoplasm are treated as though they were a miracle. Protoplasm is fundamentally different from a machine in the very fact that "fluid machines are inconceivable" (Üxküll). Protoplasm functions on the basis of characteristics not possessed by machines. It functions *without being structured*. It is preserved by a balance between assimilation and dissimilation, which is to say through *function* and not through material structure. When function ceases, the material state falls apart. *The substantive structure is itself dependent upon the function of the living plasm.* "The animal is an event" (Jennings).

These facts are inaccessible to the mechanistic-materialistic orientation of biology. What answer, then, does knowledge of orgone functions give to this riddle? One thing is clear: Any concept that deduces everything from "germ Anlagen," while assuming the eternal existence of germ plasm without investigating *its* origin, cannot enlighten us about plasmatic functioning. Such a concept, which sees everything to be already "materially" existent in the germ, is similar to the old notion of the "preformation" of all future generations in the germ cells. If, now, the *transformation of matter originally non-plasmatic into plasm* can be observed microscopically and on film, it is possible to arrive at conclusions about the development of plasmatic function itself. *We can, without hesitation, consider plasmatic function as identical with the function of tension and charge.* For all complex functions can be traced back to the alternation of expansion and contraction in the biological pulsation. Non-living substance does not pulsate. Living substance pulsates. *The solution of the enigma of biogenesis should be sought precisely at the point of transition between non-motility and pulsatory motility.* This transition point can, in fact, be observed microscopically and recorded on film.

The damage the metaphysical germ theory has done in biological research can be assessed by the following facts: Not one single biology textbook known to me contains a description of the *material* of protozoal infusions. We learn nothing about *what is actually happening* in the grass or moss. The protozoa are represented as simply present, a "finished product." The argument that no protozoa exist in moss that has been heated, so often raised against the concept of the natural organization of single-celled organisms, cannot be taken seriously. Its inadequacies were pointed out by biologists a long time ago and the stubborn adherence to it only betrays an interest that is *not scientific* but *religious*. We can now state that if heated moss contains no protozoa, it still contains blue bions.[2]

[2] In 1944, protozoa were obtained from grass that had been sterilized at 50, 60, 70, and even 80 degrees centigrade.

However, such bions are also to be found in unheated moss, which undergoes a process of gradual swelling.

Every authoritative book on biology contains the assertion—blindly copied by one author from another—that protozoa evolve from "encysted germs": protozoa can become spherical in shape, it is observed. The observation is correct, of course, but the interpretation of it is erroneous. Two separate processes are being treated as though they were one. One process is the assumption of a spherical shape by protozoa when they are damaged. The other process involves the evolution of spherical shapes in grass infusions that have no connection with the spherical protozoa. These spherical forms are the result of a gradual development of bions into a heap of bionous vesicles. The spherical heap of bions represents a typical stage in the natural formation of single-celled organisms.

Biology textbooks claim that the infusions are full of "algae," which in turn are supposed to have evolved from "germs." It is true that protozoa take their nourishment from these "algae." Yet, who has ever seen the germ of such "algae"? And how does it happen that these so-called algae can be found in large numbers, motile, in preparations consisting of only autoclaved blood or muscle tissue? The "algae" are nothing but our bion vesicles, into which every kind of organic tissue disintegrates on swelling.

There are no protozoal "germs" in the air (Pouchet). Biologists' notions to the contrary will appear to us no less remarkable than the phenomena that we ourselves are about to see. For while others are busy maintaining that protozoal "germs" are to be found in the air and that they "settle down" to start their evolutionary process wherever they "find" a "suitable" culture medium, we will take the trouble to observe an infusion microscopically for an hour a day from the moment of its preparation, at a magnification of 2000x.

As a preliminary, we conduct a simple experiment to see if we cannot perhaps find some of these "spores from the cosmos" which have drifted down and settled upon blades of grass or moss. Holding a few blades of grass in a pincette, we scrape "germs" into a glass of unsterile water. (The grass has been examined to see that it is not already in a state of vesicular disintegration but still has its usual cellular structure.) No matter how we conduct the experiment, *not a single protozoan nor a single cyst is to be found in the unsterile water into which we have dipped the grass blades.* What processes, then, are at work in the infusion?

Over the course of two to three days, the grass blades undergo vesicular disintegration, as does every other substance subjected to the swelling process (*cf.* Figs. 34, 35, Appendix). Even at a magnification of 4000x, there is not a trace of bacteria, cysts, or protozoa. However, the grass blades disintegrate more and more. After an additional two to three days, there is scarcely a blade left that still retains its original cellular, striated structure intact. Individual protozoa may well be present, but we direct our attention to the bions. Here and there, the bion vesicles can be observed to gather into heaps surrounded with membranes. Each step in this development can be followed. Occasionally, within a heap, individual bion vesicles begin to show delicate rotating or vibrating movements. They become increasingly taut and begin to look like cysts. However, they are not dried-up protozoa but *forms in the process of developing from bion heaps.* These bion masses, or heaps, take on a variety of sizes and shapes. The tauter they are, the more spherical they become. They have filled with fluid, and are thus mechanically tense. The first stage of the tension-charge function is complete. It is worth the trouble to examine a single formation for many hours at a magnification of 2000x, replenishing the fluid to keep it in focus. We can film this one formation in fast motion, which makes the work easier, but many interesting details are lost. The development of such a bion heap into a pulsating, single-celled organism takes one to two days. The protozoal germ vesicle (the bion heap) remains immobile for hours, but as the fast-motion film shows, it becomes tauter and more and more sharply delineated from its surroundings. Gradually, *a movement of the energy vesicles* begins to set in within the bion heap. The following types of motility can be distinguished:

1. *Rolling:* The energy vesicles inside the bion heap roll rhyth-

mically toward and away from each other, creating the impression of mutual attraction and repulsion. The causes of this rolling movement can only be surmised. Initially the vesicles of the disintegrating grass firmly adhere to each other. Their orgone charge is the same as that of the grass bions that do *not* develop into protozoa. As the spherical heap of vesicles swells and becomes tauter, more orgone has to be developed inside the individual vesicles, since, as with the coal bion, the swelling thins out the membrane and intensifies the orgone charge. Once the vesicles inside the bion heap have lost their mechanical adhesion to each other, the orgone charge can begin to express itself in motion, with the subsequent development of *orgonotic attraction* between the vesicles. The attraction effect exercised by the more remote vesicles results in mutual attraction and repulsion.

2. *Rotation:* In many bion heaps the entire contents of the vesicles begin to rotate in one direction. This movement can last for hours. It increases in intensity until, in the end, the whole mass, *including membrane,* is rotating. During this process, the membrane separates from the surrounding grass tissue.

3. *Confluence of the energy vesicles:* Not all bion heaps retain the vesicular structure of their plasm. In many kinds of amoebae, the boundaries between the individual energy vesicles disappear, and the plasm then forms a homogeneous mass with a blue glimmer. In others, the vesicular structure persists throughout the complete development. This is true also for cancer cells, which organize themselves from disintegrating animal tissue by precisely the same process as that by which protozoa are formed from grass or moss. *Cancer cells are nothing but protozoa that form in the animal organism from tissue bions.* The natural organization of protozoa in grass or moss infusions is *the* key to understanding the organization of cancer cells in animal tissue.

4. *Pulsation:* At a magnification of about 3000x, extremely fine movements of expansion and contraction can already be seen in the bion heap. Those forms in which the energy vesicles coalesce are apparently much more capable of pulsation than those which retain

the vesicular character of the plasm, as, for instance, the "org-protozoan" (vorticella) (*cf.* Figs. 39, 42, Appendix).

A variant of the confluence of bions can be seen in the primal vesicles of many paramecia. In this case, the small bions do not converge together into one mass, but instead form vesicles of medium size, and group in the interior of the larger body. The vesicles then start rolling and rotating movements around and toward each other, just like the bions from which they originate. *The more bions flow together, i.e., the more fluid the plasm, the more motile is the total organism.*

In addition to "finished" animals, evolving organisms and shapes at all stages of development may be seen—principally at the margins of the disintegrating moss or grass. As in the amoeba limax and B-proteus, the nuclei are formed by a distinct concentration of energy vesicles, which is revealed in a stronger lumination.

It is difficult for the observer to follow the transition from one stage of development to another because of fatigue. The device for making fast-motion films is an invaluable aid in this respect. For filming over the course of several days, a cover glass should be placed over the hanging drop slide in such a manner that a portion of its cavity remains uncovered. In addition, some fluid should be drawn over the edge of the cavity, forming a reservoir on the outside that can be used continually to refill the preparation without having to disturb the focus. Filming with the cover glass completely covering the cavity is impossible, first because it would cause the formation of air bubbles, and second because it would make the micro-organisms suffocate. Filming of the bionous structure and plasmatic motility in org-protozoa has thus far been successful at a magnification of 2300x. The fast-motion technique allows a process that took two to three days to complete to be viewed in a matter of minutes.

In all protozoa the development is identical, up to the stage when the bionous primal vesicles are formed. From that point on, the protozoa are differentiated according to a law not yet apparent. After years of observations, I cannot assume that the initial primal vesicles belong to any specifically individual forms. My own surmise is rather that the differentiation of forms sets in only at a certain point of common evolution (*cf.* Fig. 7). Here, further observation will make it necessary to amplify and correct a great deal. One of the greatest mysteries is why certain forms, once they have developed, reproduce thereafter in the same form. In this connection, the functional standpoint will have to enter into many battles with the metaphysical theory of heredity that substitutes ready-made "genes" for comprehension.

The primal cells that incline toward a rotating movement and possess a large vesicular structure usually develop into paramecia. The resting primal cells, in which the bion content liquifies, develop into flowing amoebae (amoeba limax) (*cf.* Figs. 36, 37, Appendix). The way in which both types separate from their matrix is likewise characteristic: the paramecia roll themselves free, while the amoebae simply flow away from the bion mass (*cf.* Fig. 38, Appendix).

The vorticellae, which I called "org-protozoa" because of their orgasm-like contraction and expansion, often adhere to the grass blade until fully developed (*cf.* Fig. 39, Appendix). But in some cases they detach themselves and swim around freely, sometimes with a tiny piece of bionous grass adhering to them.

When completely developed the protozoa absorb bions from the fluid by attraction. The attraction exerted by paramecia and colpedia on the energy vesicles is enormous and cannot be attributed to the mechanical movement of the cilia. For the vesicles in the fluid do not move past the body with the current, as would be expected from the action of the cilia; instead, once within a certain proximity to the paramecium, they are drawn toward it with great force. The impression is unmistakable. After it has contracted, the org-protozoan expands and opens wide at the mouth end; the bions in the fluid then stream into it with great force. The mouth closes, the protozoan contracts back to its spherical shape, and the energy vesicles inside start up a rhythmical, grinding movement.

Observation at 2000–3000x reveals interesting information

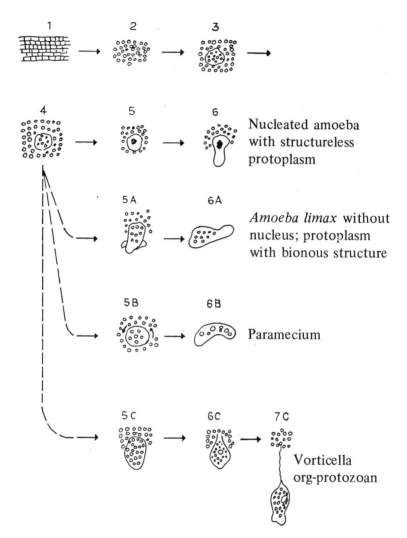

FIGURE 7. Development of various protozoa from the same membranous heap (1–4 = the common stages of development; 5–7 = the differentiation)

about the origin of the *internal* movement impulses. With absolute regularity, the vesicles, which have an intense blue color, begin a vigorous rotary movement at the point where a pseudopodium is about to be formed. Then the plasm starts to stream outward toward the periphery; i.e., expansion begins. Many of the blue vesicles are swept along in this process, losing their blue color and becoming black. This permits the following explanation: *The protrusion of the pseudopodium is preceded by a rapid, intense concentration of orgone, which is the source of the expansion impulse.* If the impulse is expressed in movement, then, clearly, orgone energy is being used up; there is no other explanation for the fact that the vesicles become black. I would not care to generalize this correlation, since the phenomenon just described is not to be found in all protozoa. There can be no doubt, however, that the energy for movement, in the form of expansion impulses, is provided by the orgone charge of the bions in the protozoan. The mechanistic interpretation based on Brownian movement fails completely here. Equally inadequate is the chemical concept of plasma as merely a highly complex carbon substance. *Living protoplasm is a complex protein governed by mass-free orgone.*

The body of the protozoan shows an *orgone energy field* which influences its surroundings. It affects bions, small bacteria, and other small protozoa, mostly by attracting or paralyzing them. (Charged erythrocytes seem to be orgonotically stronger than paramecia and amoebae, since they are capable of limiting the motility of these organisms.) From the standpoint of orgone physics, then, the protozoan consists of *a nucleus, a plasmatic periphery, and an orgone energy field, which together comprise an "orgonotic system."*

It should be pointed out that the origination of protozoa from bionous plant tissue does not contradict their procreation through division. *Development by natural organization and procreation through division occur simultaneously,* as can easily be observed microscopically.

There is probably nothing more suitable for the study of the functions of tension → charge → discharge → relaxation than protozoa. Their movements, their plasmatic currents, their expansion and contraction speak an entirely unequivocal language in terms of our formula of the life function. By using weak currents of electricity it is possible to change, accelerate, and even destroy these functions. But, as the development of the protozoan shows, the energy involved in these functions emanates from the bions that compose the protozoal primal vesicles. The locomotor functions of the amoeba must be ascribed solely to orgone energy, in view of the lack of all structural composition. The appearance and disappearance of pseudopodia are expressions of the expansion and contraction functions. The amoeba does not form a pseudopodium "for the purpose of" reaching an object, i.e., on the basis of a "goal" (finalistically speaking). It does it functionally, i.e., when a suitable object, by means of attraction, provokes an expansion impulse in the orgonotic plasma.

If only to protect future research, it is essential to maintain the principle that living matter simply *functions,* without "sense" or "purpose." If one resorts to "purposes," everything is easily explained. It is much more difficult to discover the nature of unknown functions. The "purposeful behavior" of the amoeba can be reduced to the function of orgone energy; e.g., it incorporates a bion vesicle because the stronger orgone charge of the protozoan attracts the weaker-charged free bion. It may be correct to say that the "purpose" of nourishment is thereby fulfilled, but this fulfillment is *an effect, not a cause,* of the act of ingestion. The protoplasm does not function according to mechanical, or metaphysical, finalistic principles, but on the basis of *orgonotic energy functions.*

In principle, all biological functions can be reduced to pulsation, i.e., to the alternation of expansion and contraction. Pulsation itself is a natural expression of the two antithetical functions of orgone energy, the dissociation and attraction of orgone-charged organic matter. On the basis of the processes that occur in the plasm of the amoeba, we must assume that the immediate state of matter has the following influence on the function of orgone energy:

The individual vesicles, with their orgone energy content, can arrange themselves in rows, as in moss, and form a striated tissue structure. This process is a product of the organizing function of attraction. With other protozoa, the energy vesicles converge and form a homogeneous mass. *Every concentration of orgone-charged matter, as a consequence of attraction, automatically triggers the impulse for dissociation, thus effecting a separation of the particles.* If the amoeba has already taken on spherical shape, then, at the point where the energy vesicles are most densely concentrated, a lively rolling movement appears. This movement evolves into an expansion, i.e., a separation of the vesicles. On the other hand, the separation of the vesicles from each other triggers the impulse for rapprochement through attraction. In this way, contraction takes place. As long as the plasm is sufficiently charged with orgone energy, every contraction induces an expansion, every expansion a contraction. This inner process appears externally as biological pulsation, whatever its rhythm. Since expansion is accompanied by swelling, and contraction by detumescence, the mechanical and orgonotic functions meet in the four-beat pattern: swelling (tension) → expansion (charge) → contraction (discharge) → detumescence (relaxation). But pulsation itself is essentially bound up with the alternation of *dissociation with attraction* and *attraction with dissociation* of the particles.

This process may be seen with particular clarity in the expansions and contractions of the vorticella (org-protozoan): after every contraction, a grinding or frictional movement of the vesicles begins in the body, culminating in an expansion. Connected with this expansion is the opening of the mouth end, which causes an attraction of energy vesicles from the fluid ("eating"), i.e., a charging. This is followed by a contraction to the spherical shape, i.e., a rapprochement of the inner vesicles. The process is endless.

We will encounter this biophysical functioning repeatedly. *Biological pulsation (i.e., contraction and expansion), the central phenomenon of living substance, is thus explained by the two antithetical, basic physical functions of biological energy: attraction and dissociation.*

SUMMARY

1. When matter is exposed to high temperatures and made to swell, it undergoes vesicular disintegration.

2. Although high temperatures, such as heating to incandescence (about 1500°C.) or autoclavation at 120°C., destroy life, they produce energy vesicles which may then develop into living organisms.

3. The energy function in bions originates from the vesicular disintegration of matter, not from an external source.

4. Energy vesicles are infinitesimal quantities of matter that contain a quantum of energy originating from this matter.

5. Bions are carriers of biological energy. They represent a transition from the non-living to the living.

6. The blue color of bions is a manifestation of this energy. With the disappearance of this color, the basic biological character of the bion ceases.

7. The bion experiments do not "create" artificial life. They merely reveal the natural process by which unicellular organisms and cancer cells derive spontaneously from the vesicular disintegration of matter.

EXPERIMENT XX[3]

ON THE ORGANIZATION OF PLASMATIC MATTER FROM MASS-FREE ORGONE ENERGY

In the following pages I would like to report on an experimental finding that owes its discovery to one of those accidents that

[3] Protocol begun January 2, 1945. Notarization of the protocol, March 8, 1945. Conclusion of the protocol, May 26, 1945.

often occur in the course of systematic experimental investigations and which when looked at more closely, usually prove to be completely logical consequences of experimental thought and work processes. The occasion in this particular case was a simple experiment (No. XX, 1944–1945).

For several years, I had been observing earth bion preparations which I kept alive by continuously replenishing the water. I noticed after a few months—in other cases, only after several years—the appearance in these preparations of small, rapidly moving forms, shaped like beans or the heads of spermatozoa and resembling living organisms. I was able to clearly follow the evolution of these forms from strongly radiating, slowly pulsating bions. As we already know, such living forms do not originate in the air. First, they are not found in air dust; second, they cannot be cultivated from air infection; and third, their appearance in the *non-sterile* earth-bion preparations only after months and years confirms their organization from the preparations themselves. In addition we found that autoclaved preparations, which were kept sterile, yielded the same living forms.

In December 1944, we acquired an apparatus designed for the quantitative measurement of the fluorescence of liquids, and also for colorimetry. The use of this apparatus was to be based on the following considerations:

Earlier experiments had demonstrated that orgone energy possesses the property of "lumination." It was to be assumed that fluids with a higher orgonotic potency, which is to say, those containing more orgone energy, would luminate more strongly than fluids with weaker orgonotic potency. Accordingly, the intensity of fluorescence in fluids would be considered as an expression of lumination. As a working hypothesis, the degree of fluorescence was made the measure of orgonotic potency. These assumptions were subsequently confirmed and led to practical and controllable experimental results.

Measurement of the fluorophotometric intensity, i.e., the orgonotic potency, of fluids that had contained earth bions for months and sometimes years showed immediately a far higher fluorophoto-metric value than that of ordinary water.

We now wanted to determine in what way the orgonotic potency, which we had measured fluorophotometrically, would change under various conditions. After first measuring their fluoro-metric content, we left several sealed ampoules of earth bion water in the laboratory itself, and put others in a small three-layered accumulator, in the X-ray room, in the open air, and buried in the ground. Our only purpose was to measure the fluorometric values again at the end of a specified time. *After three weeks, we noticed that the ampoules that had been left outside in the open and had frozen contained dense flakes after thawing.* We were about to throw away these particular ampoules as "contaminated," when it occurred to me to look at the flakes under a microscope. This proved to be a fortunate decision. To my great astonishment, I discovered that the flakes, which had formed in a crystal-clear, that is to say, an *absolutely particle-free,* fluid, were, when examined microscopically, intensely radiating particles of bionous matter. At a higher magnification (3000x), it was possible to observe contracting and expanding bions, with which we were already familiar. We repeated the experiment, filtering and freezing crystal-clear bion water, until all doubt was eliminated: *We had discovered a process by which orgone energy existing freely in water, i.e., not bound up in bionous matter, can organize itself into plasmatic, living substance exhibiting all the criteria of life.*

In the following account, I shall restrict myself to reporting the technique of Experiment XX and providing the verified facts. For the moment, I wish to refrain from discussing the experimental data in a larger theoretical context. Their implications are of extraordinary significance, but they are understandable only when considered within the total context of the orgone-physical function. This will be attempted elsewhere. Here, I would like merely to point to the advance that this experiment represents in the preparation of bions, i.e., of viable orgone energy vesicles. To summarize:

1. From 1936 to 1945, bions were prepared exclusively from fully organized matter (humus, grass, iron, sand, carbon, etc.). The advance represented by Experiment XX consists of the fact that now orgone energy vesicles, possessing all the properties of living matter, also can be obtained from mass-free orgone energy. We may therefore differentiate between the production of bions from matter already organized ("secondary bion formation") and the organization of orgone energy vesicles from unorganized energy ("primary bion formation"). The significance of this distinction for biogenesis and biochemical problems will be presented elsewhere.

2. Experiment XX also represents an advance on past bion experiments insofar as it provides a new, irrefutable proof of the life-specific nature of orgone energy.

THE FLUOROPHOTOMETRIC DEMONSTRATION OF ORGONE ENERGY IN EARTH BION WATER

1. Ordinary garden soil is sieved free of stones and lumps of clay. Examined microscopically after water has been added, the sieved earth shows no motility.

2. Distilled water and spring water are examined fluorophotometrically. If the fluorophotometric value of distilled water is set at 1, then water containing salts, i.e., spring or tap water, has a value of 3 to 4, as meaured in Forest Hills, New York. We take the fluorophotometric value of a fluid as the expression of its orgonotic lumination, i.e., its "orgonotic potency." The galvanometer connected to the fluorophotometer has a scale of equidistant graduations from 1 to 100. *The orgonotic potency of the fluid measured can then be seen as a multiple of the orgonotic potency of distilled water.* The table on page 64 lists the orgonotic potency (OP) values of a series of fluids.

3. Next the sieved garden soil is boiled in distilled water or

Fluid	(OP)
Distilled water	1
Rain water	3
Tap water	4
Sea water	8
Sand in H_2O, filtered	1
Iron filings in H_2O, filtered	5
Charcoal powder in H_2O, filtered	7
Earth in H_2O, filtered	8
Earth bions in H_2O, filtered	50 (average)
Grass in H_2O (after development of bions and protozoa), filtered	13
Urine	43
NaCl (physiol. sol.)	4
KCl (0.1 normal)	2
$CaCl_2$ ″ ″	2.5
HCl ″ ″	1
NaOH ″ ″	2
Ringer's solution	1.5
$HgCl_2$ (disinfectant)	3.5
Alcohol (95%)	3
Culture broth	45
50% Broth, 50% KCl	60
White sugar (saturated solution)	9
Brown sugar ″ ″	13
Maple syrup ″ ″	27
Dextri-Maltose ″ ″	41
Honey	73
Orange juice	7
Milk (pasteurized)	55
Milk (not pasteurized)	100+
Egg white	25
Tea	2
Whisky (blended)	11

ordinary tap water for one hour, or autoclaved for half an hour at 120°C. and 15 lbs. pressure.

4. The water is filtered off from the boiled earth, crystal clear. We call this fluid "bion water." In contrast with the original colorless water, this fluid is one or another intensity of yellow. The fluorophotometric measurement of the orgonotic potency of the bion

water is taken immediately after boiling and filtering. The value obtained, i.e., its OP, usually varies between 30 and 60 and averages about 45. In other words, the orgonotic lumination of bion water is, on average, forty-five times stronger than before boiling. Since the galvanometer records the reaction of the photoelectric cell to the fluorescent light rays, the rise in the fluorophotometric value of the water after boiling the soil indicates a higher energy content in the fluid. This can be estimated in micro-amperes. Understandably, however, the micro-ampere reading taken from the galvanometer is not the real measure of orgonotic lumination. It is simply the measure of the excitation of the photoelectric cell transformed into electrical energy. As I have demonstrated in another context, *electrical measurements record only an extremely small fraction of the actual energy values of orgone energy.*

5. That boiled bion water attains energy values approximating those of organic fluids such as bouillon, milk, or vitamins seems astounding and incomprehensible at first. But further consideration shows this result to be perfectly logical.

The boiling process transforms the substance of the soil into motile, *bionous* matter, and energy is freed from the matter, as is unequivocally demonstrated by the internal motility, the slow rhythmic pulsations, and the contractility of the orgone energy vesicles (in contrast to the non-motility of the particles of the same soil *before* the boiling process). But the transformation of the earth particles into bions and the release of the energy inside the particles were not the only effects. In addition, *this energy entered the water, because water attracts orgone and vice versa.* The orgonotic potency of the water therefore rose from its own basic value to the level of biochemical fluids of high orgonotic potency.

6. Experience has shown that boiled bion water develops rot bacteria even when immediately sealed air-tight. For this reason, in more recent experiments bion water has been autoclaved for thirty minutes at 15 lbs. pressure and 120°C. This procedure at first causes the OP to drop 5 to 8 points, but it recovers its initial level over the subsequent twenty-four to forty-eight hours. The auto-

EXPERIMENT XX

Date	Prep. No.	Procedure	OP before treatment	TYPE OF ORGANIZATION		OTHER FORMS PRESENT			Reproduction	T-degeneration
				Bion	Plasm	Single Cells	Bean Shapes	Protozoa		
Jan. 2, '45	XX 1 Org	Kept in Accumulator 20 days	46	+				+	+	
Jan. 3	XX 1 f	Frozen 21 days	38	++	+		+	++	++	+
Jan. 6	XX 1 c	Autoclaved, kept in room	41	+	+	+	+	++	++	+
Jan. 8	XX 1 x	Untreated, kept in room	40	+			+	+	+	
Jan. 25	XX 2 f	Frozen 4 days			+	+	+		++	++
Jan. 26	XX 3 cf	Autoclaved; frozen 4 days	52	+ ↓	++	++	+	+	++	++
Jan. 30	XX 1 g	Dried to crystals, put in distilled water		+		+	+	+	+	+
Jan. 30	XX 4 cf	Autoclaved; frozen 3 days	60	+	(+)	+	+		++	+
Jan. 31	XX 5 cf	Autoclaved; frozen 4 days	51	+	(+)	++	+		+	+
Jan. 31	XX 5 cg	Autoclaved; dried, put in distilled water	51		+		+		+	+
Feb. 5	XX 6 cf	Autoclaved; alternately frozen and thawed 6 days	57	+ ↓	+		+		+	++
Feb. 6	XX 6 cg	Autoclaved, dried, put in bion water	57	+					+	+
Feb. 9	XX 8 cf	Autoclaved; frozen 1 day		+	+	+	+		+	++
Feb. 9	XX 9 cf	Autoclaved; frozen 1 day	37	+ ↓	+	++	+		+	+
Feb. 9	XX 9 cg	Autoclaved, dried, put in bion water	37c	+					+	+

Date	No.	Description										
Feb. 12	XX 1 gg	1 g redried, put in tap water		+	+	+	+	+	+	+	+	+
Feb. 13	XX 10 f	Frozen 14 days	52	++	++	++	↓	++	+	↓	++	++
Feb. 13	XX 10 cf	Autoclaved; frozen 14 days	52	++	++	++	↓	++	↓		++	++
Feb. 13	XX 10 g	Dried, put in bion water	52	+	+	+					+	+
Feb. 13	XX 10 cg	Autoclaved, dried, put in bion water	52	+	+	+	+		+		+	+
Feb. 20	XX 11 f	Frozen 8 days	42	++	++	++	↓	+			++	++
Feb. 21	XX 12 f	Frozen 7 days; degenerated; refrozen 2 days	40	++	++	++	↓				++	++
Mar. 1	XX 13 f	Cloudy, full of rod bact.; frozen 4 days	44	+	+	+	↓	+	+	+	+	+
Mar. 1	XX 14 cf	Autoclaved; frozen 4 days	48	+		+				+	+	+
Mar. 2	XX 15 f	Frozen 15 days	61			++					++	++
Mar. 5	XX 15 g	Dried, put in bion water	61			++		+			++	++
Mar. 7	XX 16 c dil.f	Dilution 1 part bion water to 4 parts water autoclaved; frozen 5 days	55	+	+	+	↓	+	+	+	+	+
Mar. 7	XX 17 f	Contained a few rot bacteria and protozoa; frozen 5 days	67	+	+	(+)	↓	+	+	+	+	+
Mar. 8	XX 18 cf	Autoclaved; frozen 4 days	60		↓	+					+	+
Mar. 14	XX 19 cf	Autoclaved; cloudy, some rot bacteria; frozen 13 days				+		+			+	+
Apr. 6	XX 20 cf	Autoclaved; frozen 3 days	38	+	+	+	+	+	+	+	+	+

claved bion water is then refrigerated in sealed ampoules or in sterilized flasks stoppered with sterile cotton plugs.

THE ORGANIZATION OF BIONOUS AND PLASMATIC MATTER FROM THE ORGONE ENERGY IN BION WATER

Bion water, which is sterile, completely free of particles, and has a high OP, is put into several vials and test tubes two days after autoclavation or boiling. The vials are sealed air-tight and the test tubes stoppered with sterile cotton plugs. We divide the tubes into three groups: *Group A* is placed into a three-layered orgone accumulator, 1 cubic foot in size; *Group B* is left standing in the laboratory; *Group C* is put into the freezer compartment of the refrigerator. As a control measure, we store similar containers of sterile ordinary water with each group.

Two to eight days later, Group C is removed from the freezer. Before thawing begins, we are impressed by the fact that *the yellow color of the bion water has concentrated in the center of the ice in an opaque, brown-yellow spot.* The surrounding ice is completely bright and clear. As soon as the ice has liquefied, whitish and brownish flakes are observed in the previously crystal-clear fluid. Macroscopically, the flakes are approximately 1–5mm. in length and about 1mm. in width. The fluid itself is homogeneously yellow.

Groups A and B develop the same flakes, but much more slowly, taking three to eight weeks. Of the control groups, neither Group B (placed in the laboratory) nor Group C (frozen) develops flakes. However, control Group A (the sterile ordinary water stored in the orgone accumulator) does develop flakes over an extended period of time (several months), but they are much less dense and more imperfectly formed than those of experimental Groups A, B, and C.

Microscopic examination of the flakes always shows two basic types: smooth, plasmatic, well-defined forms, in which dark granules and occasional blue PA bions are scattered in varying densities; or bionous heaps of orgone energy vesicles with an intense blue glimmer and a sharp margin (*cf.* Figs. 43–47, Appendix).

The preparations, kept sterile, show, after a few days, and especially after two to three weeks, an increase in the number of flakes. Microscopically, it is possible to establish that the flakes grow individually through an accumulation of substance and that they also divide. The thread-like, winding, serpentine, bright flakes are transformed in the course of weeks into strongly radiating bionous heaps.

Culture experiment: To obtain a clearer and more demonstrable understanding of this process of growth and multiplication, some flakes are placed, under sterile conditions, in clear, sterile bion water. After one or two weeks, a culture formation can be clearly observed in the samples. The flakes have become more dense. In accordance with our previous experience, the OP of the culture fluid stays at approximately the same level, or even increases.

If we examine the preparations under the microscope at regular intervals (about once a week for several months), we can see quite gradual biophysical changes in the flakes. In some, there appear spherical bions measuring 2–3 microns in diameter, with a margin and a strong blue glimmer. Gradually, they stretch out until they eventually assume the following bean shape:

⌒ ⌒

Under favorable conditions, i.e., when no premature T-disintegration has occurred in the preparations, these "bean forms" develop into contractile protozoa which move in a rapid, jerky manner. For the most part the plasm of these protozoa has a granular and striated structure, though in a few instances it is smooth, without structure. Pure cultures of protozoa can also be obtained by inoculating the supernatant fluid without disturbing the flakes which lie at the bottom. The protozoa multiply in the new culture and without difficulty from culture to culture.

OBSERVATIONS AND TESTS TO DETERMINE THE BIOLOGICAL NATURE OF ORGONE FLAKES

1. *The thawed-out, flaky bion water preparation XX represents an unresolvable colloid:* If crystal-clear, yellow bion water of high orgonotic potency is evaporated, a golden yellow, smooth, opaque coating forms on the bottom of the vessel. Scraped off, this coating yields a powder consisting of small, yellow-to-brown crystals, which we have named "orgontin." These crystals cannot be dissolved again in either ordinary water or in water containing a high orgone content. They merely swell and react precisely like flakes obtained by the melting of frozen bion water. They, too, exhibit the phenomena of growth, multiplication, and protozoal formation.

2. *Microscopic observation of organization:* The flakes grow in length and width; bion heaps accumulate more bions from the fluid. Larger flakes sprout smaller ones and the small ones grow larger. The bions frequently arrange themselves in groups. As the flakes grow larger, they become darker, showing a brown to black color.

3. *Orgonotic attraction and sterilizing effect:* The orgone flakes react like all other bionous matter investigated so far. In the vicinity of rot bacteria, the flakes either kill the bacteria or, at least paralyze them.

4. *T-degeneration and putrefaction:* Like all organic or living substance, the orgone flakes degenerate by putrefaction and disintegrate into the T-bodies already familiar to us. Protozoa form more slowly and with greater difficulty in strongly degenerated preparations than in sterile ones. Degenerated preparations can, however, be freed of T-bacilli and rot bacteria again and again by repeated freezing. This seems to promote the capacity for the organization of motile protozoa.

5. Flakes that are dried and crushed into small particles burn

in a flame to a black, *coal-like* substance, thus reacting like living protoplasm and non-living organic carbon compounds. Even if the flakes are not burned, the identical black carbon substance that has proven to be combustible in the flame develops, probably through oxidation.

6. *Sugar content:* Bion water with a high orgonotic potency tastes sweet. Burning flakes give off an odor like that of caramel. (It has not yet been possible to conduct an exact biochemical analysis, but one is planned.)

7. All containers that have had contact for a considerable length of time with bion water or bion earth feel fatty to the touch.

8. Bion water reacts to weakening influences like autoclavation in the same way a living organism would react, namely, with *a falling-off of OP,* which is regained only gradually.

9. *Contractility of mass-free orgone in bion water:* There can be only *one* plausible explanation for the appearance of a concentrated, brown-yellow spot in the center of the crystal-clear ice. *Mass-free orgone energy reacts in freezing water exactly as does orgone energy in a freezing living organism: it contracts and withdraws from the point where the freezing occurs.* Mass-free orgone energy is therefore capable of contraction. In the process of contraction, matter is created, evidently through *condensation.* This process needs intensive study.

10. The orgone flakes develop into protozoa more rapidly when T-bacilli are added to the preparation. The appearance of plasmatic spindle forms of coarse structure, similar to the Ca III formations, can then be observed (*cf.* Chapter VI).

STAGES IN THE DEVELOPMENT OF PROTOZOA
IN STERILE, PARTICLE-FREE, BION WATER

1. After the bion water solution thaws, granulated plasmatic flakes of typically organic form appear.

2. Many of the individual granulae expand and develop into

spherical orgone energy vesicles with an intense blue glimmer. The majority of these groups of bions merge into larger formations by association or confluence.

3. In a matter of weeks, the spherical bions become bean-shaped, but are not yet motile.

4. These bean-shaped formations then become motile in two different ways: At 3000–5000x, the content of the energy vesicles reveals delicate movements of expansion and contraction; the formations stretch more and more, their membranes soften, and they begin to move about. The forms that have become markedly elongated develop serpentine, corkscrew-like movements. The accompanying sketches are drawn from life as seen with a magnification of approximately 240x.

5. When bion water fluid containing protozoa is inoculated with sterile bion water, the protozoa multiply and can be reinoculated ad infinitum. To these protozoa I have given the name *orgonomia*.

CONTROL EXPERIMENTS

1. The freezing of ordinary, *non-sterile* spring water or distilled water yields neither flakes nor protozoa. The organization of plasmatic matter must therefore be ascribed exclusively to the high orgone content as measured by the fluorophotometer.

2. When bion water of approximately 40–50 OP is distilled, a small number of flakes can be observed *immediately after cooling* and a large number after actual freezing. This is additional confirmation of the preceding statement.

3. Since sea water is extraordinarily rich in orgone, it is not

surprising that it also yields flakes and protozoal growth after filtration and autoclavation. Nevertheless, there is some slight mystery here. Sea water taken at Jones Beach, on the Atlantic coast of Long Island, New York, and measured one hour after extraction, was only approximately 8–10 OP. Earth bion water with so low an OP content yields no, or at best, deficient, bionous growth, and it is therefore difficult to explain why the low OP of sea water makes no difference. The phenomenon is undoubtedly important; unfortunately it is not possible to understand everything at once.

4. Water from autoclaved grass also yields flakes after freezing which multiply and grow.

GENERAL CONCLUSIONS

1. Humus contains orgone energy. The transformation of humus in water into earth bions causes a rise in the orgonotic potency of the water from 4 to between 30 and 70 (with the OP of distilled water set at 1).

2. Orgone energy in high concentration colors liquids yellow.

3. Orgone energy homogeneously distributed in a fluid at room temperature contracts when chilled or frozen to form a brownish yellow core in the ice.

4. Protoplasmic flakes, i.e., matter, develop from concentrated mass-free orgone.

5. Fluid with a high orgonotic potency develops protozoa by way of the formation of orgone energy vesicles.

6. The formation of plasmatic matter from concentrated orgone energy indicates a general process by which matter originates. Thus, we must consider orgone energy to be the primordial cosmic energy.

7. On the basis of our findings in Experiment XX, the development of living plasma on our planet preceded the organization of coal substance and carbohydrates. Coal is a product of the disintegration of living matter. Biochemical molecules did not exist prior to the development of plasmatic substance, but appeared as one of the mechanical constitutents in the process of plasmatic organization.

CHAPTER III

The Actual Discovery
of Orgone Energy

1. ABSURDITIES OF THE AIR-GERM THEORY

Until now, we have had to defend ourselves against an objection, or
to be more accurate, a slogan, to the effect that bions are a "quite
ordinary infection from the air." I have used three arguments
against this claim:

1. *The bion structures can be seen forming immediately
   after the preparation is made, whereas in the incubator
   several hours are required for air infection to develop.*
2. *Bion culture experiments are successful under sealed,
   air-tight, conditions.*
3. *In the bion cultures, certain forms not previously iden-
   tified are found, e.g., the SAPA bions.*

In order to discuss the manifold questions raised by the cultivation of bions, we must first refute the objection of air infection and
demonstrate the absurdity of trying to apply this argument today
either experimentally or theoretically. In the struggle for scientific
progress, new facts are less of an obstacle than obsolete concepts.

*The formations that I refer to as bions (PA and T) and bion
cultures are not present in cultures of air germs.* This claim can
easily be substantiated by the following series of experiments:

a) Dirt is scraped from the palm of the hand with a sterile
spatula and put into bouillon. After twenty-four hours in the
incubator, a *flocculent cloudiness* appears which, however, dis-

appears in the course of a few days or weeks. It is replaced by a thin membrane over the surface and a thick precipitate at the bottom. Under the microscope, we see tiny cocci, round to oval in form, with a blackish glimmer, and some bacilli having a serpentine movement, but no contractile amoeboids of the PA type, no nucleated cell forms, and (in the fresh preparation) no T-bacilli.

b) We put a few drops of ordinary tap water into bouillon. It frequently takes several days for cloudiness to develop (and sometimes culture growth does not take place at all). Microscopically, the same types of round, small cocci and bacilli can be seen.

c) We let a small bowl of water stand for half an hour in the open air by the side of a dusty road and then inoculate a sample of it on bouillon. Culture growth may not appear. If it does, the turbidity gives way, after a few days or weeks, to a membrane on the surface and a dense flocculent sediment at the bottom. Such culture growth as does occur may take two to three days to develop, appearing as small cocci and sausage-shaped bacteria with a slow, serpentine movement. *There are no formations of the type of our cultures (packet amoebae and T-bacilli).*

d) We let an open test tube containing bouillon stand vertical in our laboratory for half an hour, and then incubate it for twenty-four hours. By the end of this time cloudiness has developed, only to dissipate and eventually be replaced by a membrane over the surface and a flocculent sediment at the bottom. Once again we find the tiny cocci already familiar to us, plus rows of streptococcal forms and occasional club-shaped formations. Also seen are the previously mentioned sausage-shaped bacilli having a serpentine movement. *There is no sign of our bion types.*

e) We let a sterile agar culture stand open in our laboratory for half an hour. After twenty-four hours in the incubator, a growth consisting of typical, small, non-contractile heaps of vesicles has developed. Occasionally, bacilli are also present. But there are none of our bion types. If the agar plate is left open no longer than is necessary for inoculation, we should be convinced that it is extraordinarily difficult to bring about an air infection.

f) We conduct a variation of the control experiment by collecting dust from the surface of a cupboard or from an open oven with a spatula and putting it into our standard solution of bouillon and 0.1n KCl, thus exposing it to the same conditions as those of the bion culture. The findings, again, are familiar. A growth usually appears after twenty-four hours; sometimes, however, only after forty-eight or seventy-two hours. We find no bions, just elongated, thread-like bacteria, spirilla and spirochete-like forms, as well as small, non-contractile, rapidly moving cocci. Inoculated on agar, the culture yields, as a rule, only bacillary forms with a serpentine movement. Like all other non-sterile cultures, this culture forms a membrane and after a certain time flocculates. When egg medium is used, massive dust infection occurs, usually mold.

These control experiments on the problem of air infection can be done repeatedly, in any variety of ways. They inevitably yield two facts:

1. *Air contains only certain forms of larger bacilli and simple cocci.*
2. *Bions cannot be cultivated directly from the air no matter what the culture—bouillon, agar, or egg media.*

The control experiments reinforce a third fact: *The case for the danger of air infection has been greatly overstated by those who use it as an argument against the idea of bionous organization of non-living matter.*

Having made doubly certain that our bion cultures have nothing to do with "air germs," we would now like to undertake a critical investigation of the concept of "air germs" itself. Let us summarize the conclusions that follow from the claim that protozoal organisms cannot originate from any other source but germs that are present in the air:

1. *For each and every kind of protozoal and bacterial organism there is a specific corresponding germ.* In other words, there are as many types of germs as there are micro-organisms, which is to say,

millions of types. Such a claim is contradicted by the fact that the cultivation of air bacteria yields only a minimal fraction of the forms actually known to pathology. This discrepancy alone raises a number of questions that would need direct answers from the proponents of the air-germ theory. For instance, have cholera vibrios, plague bacilli, or syphilis spirochetes ever been cultivated directly from the air? The truth is that these forms have hitherto been cultivated only from animal tissue and a theory of their origin has merely been tacked on. As long as there exist forms of microbes, and now also bions, that cannot be cultivated directly from the air, the hypothesis of air infection will *not* be valid.

2. *Refutation of the metaphysical air-germ theory:* The bion experiment, which has been filmed, established the fact that single-celled organisms, such as protozoa, evolve by natural organization from the vesicular disintegration of moss. The metaphysical theory of sporogenesis, on the other hand, claims that protozoa originate from germs omnipresent in the air which develop in places favorable to their growth. As yet, not one of its proponents has been able to authenticate this germ theory, and its fundamental inaccuracy can be demonstrated by the following experiment.

If the protozoa originate from germs attached to moss and hay and can be made to form in infusions after a few days, the following procedure should demonstrate that fact. Non-sterile dried hay is washed in ordinary water, by either passing the water through a filter containing the hay, or by swishing a piece of hay through the water a few times with pincers, thereby preventing the smallest particle from getting into the water. Thus "contaminated," the water shows no protozoal growth, nor any trace of it. On the other hand, an infusion of hay or moss exhibits the progressive swelling of the tissue and all of the other stages in the evolution of protozoa, from the first vesicular disintegration, occurring along the margins, to the formations that grow out of the tissue and disengage as completely formed protozoa.

If the adherents of the air-germ theory insist upon its authenticity, they must take the trouble to demonstrate experimentally, first, that the spores from which the protozoa are supposed to evolve can be isolated by stripping them off from the matter to which they are supposed to be attached, and second, that they are capable of developing into protozoa.

But even if we assume for a moment that all known forms of microbes, and the new bion forms, could indeed be found in the air, would the expression "air germs" represent a scientific explanation for the origin of these forms? We could very well reply: True, these forms are present in the air, but where did they come from?

If this question is thought over carefully, the scientific worthlessness of the air-germ theory will have to be admitted. If our claim that micro-organisms form themselves from inorganic material and disintegrating organic substances is correct, then we have a valid explanation for the *origin of air germs*. There can be nothing else in the air except inorganic and dead organic substances. Furthermore, at most only the spores of a few primitive organisms have been found; no one has ever *seen* the germ or spore of an amoeba or of a paramecium. The slogans that are substituted for the actual experience of seeing, and propounded as absolute theological theses, e.g., *omne vivum ex vivo* and *omnis cellula ex cellula,* cannot be regarded, in the context of these considerations, as serious scientific statements; they are merely an emotional protection against very hard facts.

Now that we have demonstrated the absurdity of the air-germ theory as it dominates medical thinking today, we would like to show just how damaging it is to the understanding of a large number of vastly important phenomena in medicine, e.g., how medicine, by its dismissal of the concept of natural organization, robs itself of every possibility to observe simple and obvious facts, to investigate them in detail, and to use them in a practical way.

1. It is common medical knowledge that living organisms are constantly being formed in the animal organism, e.g., the red and white corpuscles in the bone marrow and the lymphatic system, and the egg and sperm cells in the epithelia of the gonads. The discrepancy between this acknowledged fact and the germ theory has

not so far, strangely enough, disturbed the scientific world in the least. Erythroblasts form, and from them erythrocytes develop; the female ova form in the follicles of the ovary, the sperm cells, from the spermatogonia. The transitional forms evolve from the epithelia of the organs in question. *One cell form is transformed into another fundamentally different form.* This process occurs in cancer, and is one of the central factors of the entire cancer problem. The formation of biologically independent entities from biological organisms of a different kind goes on continuously within the body. But precisely this process must remain incomprehensible without acknowledging the transformation of organic tissue into independent protozoal formations.

2. There are various kinds of micro-organisms on the mucous membranes and orifices of the human body. Intestinal bacteria, for instance, presumably reach the alimentary canal from some infection external to the body. But why the bacterium coli is to be found only in the colon, and not, say, on the mucous membrane of the throat as well, remains a mystery. Why pneumococci find their way from the air to the lungs but not into the alimentary tract is equally mysterious. Furthermore, *if, in fact, thousands of varieties of deadly bacteria are present in the air and consequently on the mucous membranes, it is completely unfathomable that the human species did not become extinct a long time ago.* The magic formula used for answering this particular puzzle is the notorious "disposition." But the concept of "disposition" reveals precisely what the air-germ theory conceals. For instance, it is incomprehensible how hundreds of thousands of cultivable micro-organisms fatal to mice are found in cancer tissue freshly extracted from the inside of a bone. How did they get into the bone? The information that they "came in from the air and nested in the mucous membranes" and then "traveled in the bloodstream from there into the bones" can hardly be taken seriously, because the question it fails to answer is, why the air bacteria, in their complex wanderings, chose to settle precisely in the cancerous bone, and why all kinds of infectious diseases were not set in motion along all the pathways of the human body. The

fact that there are pathogenic organisms in the throat that are harmful only at certain times and for certain persons is a marvel that cannot be adequately explained by "disposition" or "latent virulence," because these are merely words. The important issue is to establish exactly what is going on *within the organism* that makes it possible for the micro-organisms to exercise their effect at certain times and not at others.

3. In the literature on micro-organisms, the frequent repetition of the statement that certain organisms flourish only in certain culture media is striking. The fact is, it is no less than mystical to assume that the amoeba germs, which, according to theory are everywhere in the air, seek, of all places, muddy pools of stagnant water and the underside of plant leaves, or in other cases are unable to develop during the spring in fresh moss, whereas they appear in large numbers on the autumn moss. It is difficult to understand how one can fail to notice the illogicalness, inconsistency, and factual inaccuracy of such thinking.

4. In the context of these considerations, we may venture on a problem likely to arouse all kinds of passions. According to the air-germ theory, the bacillus that causes cholera or bubonic plague is buzzing around in the air all the time but does not appear under normal conditions of careful hygiene. It zooms in from the air to cause epidemics—in which hundreds of thousands of human lives may be lost—in time of war, or in those densely populated areas where hygienic precautions and habits are poor. But are we really to believe that in these epidemics the *biological condition* of people exposed to the chronically poor hygienic environment, or to the horrors of extended warfare, plays no part at all? Is it really possible that all the responsibility must go to the bacillus, none to the living organism in which it wreaks its devastations? What reason is tl.ere for ascribing so much importance to the bacterium and so little to the human organism? I am afraid the "air germ" is a good deal easier to fight than the biopathies! Without wishing to offer here an answer to all the questions raised, I would nevertheless like to stress

that the biopathic condition of the victims of cholera and bubonic plague deserves much more attention than the respective bacterium, about whose origins there is no clarity even today.

To summarize: *Not only is the air-germ theory false and incapable of providing enlightenment about central phenomena of biology and pathology; it actually hinders a factual comprehension of the mechanisms of disease. It has become a dogma which, like all dogmas, eschews thinking and inquiry.* We can now see how much the bion theory and the facts on which it is based contribute to the clarification of those problems not explained by the air-germ theory.

Let us now turn our attention to a specific bion culture in which the actual discovery of orgone energy was made.

2. THE CULTURES OF RADIATING SAND-PACKET BIONS (SAPA)

In order to thoroughly refute the theory of air infection, I started, as early as 1936, to autoclave bion preparations for half an hour at 120°C. By this procedure, disintegration into vesicles turned out to be more complete than when I simply used the process of swelling. The blue bions appeared more rapidly and the biological stain reaction (Gram, carbol fuchsin) more intense. In May 1937, I began to heat coal and earth crystals to incandescence in the Bunsen flame before introducing them into the culture medium that induces swelling. This heating process accelerated the formation of bions still further. Now the bionous disintegration of matter could be carried out in the space of just a few minutes, with the certainty of complete sterility. I no longer needed to wait for days and weeks for the process of swelling at room temperature to yield bions. To bring about the swelling of the substances, I used caustic potash and potassium chloride solution. Over the course of two years (1937–1939), experiment after experiment confirmed the vesicular disintegration of swelling matter and the organization of bacteria and cells from the bions.[1]

In January 1939, one of my assistants was demonstrating the incandescence experiment to a visitor in the laboratory in Oslo. By mistake, she took the wrong container from the sterilizer and instead of earth she heated ocean sand to incandescence. After two days a culture had started to form in the bouillon–potassium chloride solution which, when inoculated on egg medium and agar, yielded a yellow growth. Under the microscope this new kind of culture appeared as large, scarcely motile, packets of energy vesicles glimmering with an intense blue. The culture was "pure"; i.e., it consisted of only *one* kind of formation. At a magnification of 400x, its formations looked like the *sarcinae* occasionally found in water. Examination at magnifications of 2000x and 4000x showed strongly refracting formations consisting of packets of six to ten vesicles between 10 and 15 microns in size. We repeated the experiment eight times over the course of a few months, and five times we obtained the same formations (*cf.* Figs. 48a and b, Appendix).

These bions received the designation SAPA (*sa*nd *pa*cket). They possessed properties of extreme interest.

The effect of the SAPA bions on rot bacteria, protozoa, and T-bacilli was much more powerful than that of other bions. Brought together with cancer cells, they killed or paralyzed the cells even at a distance of approximately 10 microns. At this proximity to SAPA bions, the amoeboid cancer cells would remain rooted on one spot as though paralyzed; then they would spin around frantically and, finally, become motionless. This process was recorded on film.

For four weeks, I examined the SAPA bions every day for several hours. After a few days, my eyes began to smart whenever I looked into the microscope for any length of time. In order to isolate the basis of this problem, I began to use a monocular tube. Now it was only the eye I used for looking through the microscope that hurt. However, after a while, a violent conjunctivitis developed in

[1] *Cf. Die Bione* (1938).

both eyes; they became very sensitive to light, and I was obliged to see an ophthalmologist. To him, my account seemed "fantastic." He treated me, prescribed dark glasses, and forbade microscopic work for a few weeks. My eyes improved, but by this time I knew that I was dealing with a radiation phenomenon. Several months before this event, the Dutch physicist Bon had written to ask me whether I had ever noticed any radiation in bions. I had replied in the negative. For many years, Bon had been quarreling with his colleagues because of his insistence that life is a manifestation of radiation. I was directly confronted with this fact, and did not know how I should approach it. Of course I had been trained in the basic theoretical problems of physics, but I had never had any practical experience with radiation. This created great difficulty, but at the same time had its advantages. The radiation I had discovered turned out to be new; it possessed highly unique properties. Traditional methods of radiation research were to yield negative results. Orgone radiation required the development of special, hitherto unknown, methods and research procedures that could be worked out only gradually, step by step, with observations over a long period of time. Routine, schematic methods failed.

I first tried a very primitive method of testing the cultures for radiation by placing the test tubes against the palm of my left hand. Each time, I thought I felt a fine prickling, but was not sure of the sensation.

Then I placed a quartz slide, on which I had put a small quantity of SAPA culture in potassium chloride solution, on the skin and let it stand for about ten minutes. Where the culture lay (separated from the skin by the quartz slide), an anemic spot with hyperemic margin developed. I repeated this experiment with all my students, whose vegetative reactions were well known to me. Those who were vegetatively very alive always gave a positive result. The emotionally weaker ones showed little or no reaction. These results were an indication of something, but were still far from being clearly understandable.

I sought help from the radium physicist of the Cancer Hospital in Oslo, Dr. Moxnes. He tested one of the culture tubes with the radium electroscope. *It gave no reaction.* The physicist declared that there was "no radiation." Since his electroscope was equipped for radium only, I objected that the only conclusion that could be fairly drawn from the test was that there was no *radium activity,* not that there was no radiation of any kind. There could be no doubt about the skin reaction, and I was puzzled about the kind of radiation with which I was dealing. The speed of the skin reaction suggested enormous energies. X-ray and radium radiation take several days after exposure to produce reddening of the skin, but the SAPA cultures reddened the skin within a few minutes. As will become evident later, there was in fact a completely logical reason for the negative reaction of the electroscope.

The following events solved the riddle bit by bit:

After two more weeks, the palm of my left hand was highly inflamed and very painful. There could be no further doubt that the cultures were exercising a biological effect.

As time went by, it struck me that the air in the room where the cultures were kept was becoming very "heavy" and causing headaches whenever we closed the windows, if only for an hour.

One day, during the course of an experimental procedure, I noticed that all metal objects, such as scissors, pincers, needles, etc., had become highly magnetic. This phenomenon, so obvious today, was incomprehensible to me. I had never before observed it and was not prepared for it. But since the electroscope of the Oslo physicist had shown no reaction, I was prepared for surprises.

I experimented with photographic plates in various ways: In a dark room I placed culture preparations on uncovered plates, on plates in plateholders, on plates wholly or partly covered with lead, and, in addition, for control purposes, I put some plates without cultures in the same room. To my amazement, *all* the plates became fogged. On some plates, there was a blackening corresponding to the glued cracks in the wooden plateholders; on others, I saw marked blackening where the plate had not been directly affected by the culture but where the lead covering was pervious. To my surprise, *the control plates in the same room were also fogged.* I could not understand it. It seemed as if the energy was active not just around the edges of the plateholder and through its joints; *the radiation seemed to be omnipresent.* However, it was also possible that there had been some experimental oversight.

Over the course of two decades of clinical and experimental work, I had learned not to ignore such seemingly incidental ideas as "energy present everywhere." I value these flashes of insight, which if combined with strict, objective controls, lead to the ultimate goal. My surmise turned out to be correct: *orgone radiation is indeed present everywhere.* But at the time this idea had no concrete meaning.

The experiments with the photographic plates seemed to have reached a dead end. If the effect was omnipresent, the phenomena could not be isolated and controlled. Since all objects were exposed to the radiation, there could be no possibility of a comparison with some object not influenced by it.[2]

I transferred the cultures to dark basement rooms and continued my observations there. To intensify the effect, I prepared dozens of cultures. The observations made in the dark had something uncanny about them. Once my eyes had become accustomed to the darkness, the room appeared not black but *grayish blue.* I saw fog-like vapors, streaks of blue light, and dots darting about. Light of a deep violet color seemed to come from the walls and the objects around the room. Looked at through a magnifying glass, these light impressions intensified and the individual streaks and dots grew larger. Dark glasses weakened the impressions. But when I closed my eyes, the blue light impressions continued. That was disconcerting. I did not know at this point that orgone energy radiation irritates the optic nerves in a particular way and generates after-images.

After only one or two hours in the basement, my eyes would hurt and be inflamed. One evening, however, I spent five consecu-

[2] Later, in the fall of 1940, I finally succeeded in demonstrating SAPA radiation on film.

tive hours in the basement room. After two hours, I began to see quite distinctly a radiation from the palm of my hand, the sleeve of my shirt, and (looking in the mirror) the hair on my head. Gradually, the blue glimmer surrounded my body and objects in the room like a hazy, slow-moving, gray-blue luminous vapor. I admit I felt frightened. I telephoned Dr. Bon in Holland that night and told him of the experience. He warned me to take precautions. But since the radiation seemed to be present "everywhere" and to pervade everything, I did not know how I could protect myself.

I had our friend Dr. Havrevold participate in the dark-room observations. Though *completely uninformed,* he confirmed the majority of my observations. Over the next few months I subjected one person after another to the skin test and to the observation in the dark. The descriptions provided by the subjects were so completely in agreement that no possible doubt could remain about the existence of the radiation. The most difficult task was that of *isolating the objective phenomena in the room from the subjective sensations in the eye.* As the investigations proceeded, however, a variety of techniques for making this distinction evolved. For instance, I had subjects reach for luminous objects in the dark or determine where my arm was at a given time. I had them turn their eyes away from the light impression until its after-image had disappeared, then try to find the light impression again. The radiation was very irritating to the optic nerve. A businessman who had obtained a piece of equipment for me and who served once as a subject said: "I feel as if I've been staring into the sun for a long time."

This comment by a layman provided much food for thought. It seemed especially relevant to the conjunctivitis that many of the subjects developed. One day the idea "sun energy" suddenly occurred to me, providing a simple solution which sounded absurd only at first: *SAPA bions had originated from ocean sand. But ocean sand is nothing more than solidified solar energy. The incandescing and swelling of the sand had released this energy once again from its material state.*

I overcame the emotional reluctance I felt to accepting such a conclusion. If the radiation in question were directly connected with solar energy, then many phenomena could be easily explained; e.g., the irritation of the eyes, the conjunctivitis, the rapid reddening of the skin and its subsequent tanning. (I had conducted the experiments during the winter and early spring of 1939, had not been exposed to the sun, yet had a deep tan over my entire body.) I felt extremely vigorous, as "strong as a bear," and vegetatively alive in every respect. Gradually, the fear of dangerous effects from the radiation disappeared and I began to work with it without any further worry about protective measures.

There was no doubt of the existence of an energy possessing extraordinarily high biological activity. It remained only to discover what its nature was and how it could be measured. One of my colleagues told an assistant at the Bohr Institute in Copenhagen about the SAPA bions. This person considered the notion of the production of bions from sand so "fantastic" that I decided not to expose my new radiation discovery to the danger of a biased investigation, prejudiced from the start by fundamental disbelief.

Furthermore, there was nothing I could really offer as starting points for the qualitative and quantitative determination of the radiation, apart from the biological effects and subjective sensations. The negative reaction of the cultures with the Oslo physicist's electroscope was another warning to me that caution was advisable. Moreover, the recent press campaign of Oslo pathologists and psychiatrists against my orgasm and bion research had destroyed any possibility of friendly cooperation. So, at first, there seemed to be no avenue to a quantitative investigation. Everything would have to be left to the spontaneous development of the facts and to chance. This "chance" soon appeared.

I had begun reproducing well-known electroscopic phenomena obtained from friction between various materials. One day I started to set up an electroscope experiment involving high voltage. For insulation, I put on a pair of rubber gloves kept in a glass cabinet in my laboratory. When I brought my hands near the electroscope, there was a strong deflection of the leaf. *It curled upward, shifted sideways toward the glass wall of the electroscope, and stuck to it.* I knew of course that insulators can be "charged." What was really astounding was the *sideways deflection* of the leaf and its tenacious *adhesion to the glass wall, i.e., the fact that non-magnetic aluminum was sticking to glass,* which was an insulator and had not been subjected to friction. I had not rubbed the insulator gloves. So where did the effect come from? Then I realized that the gloves had been lying near a number of SAPA cultures. To confirm this possibility, I placed one rubber glove in a shaded place in the open air and the other in a metal box containing bion cultures. Then I exchanged and tested them at various intervals. The rubber glove that had been exposed to the open air for about fifteen minutes did *not* influence the electroscope; whereas the previously neutral glove, placed for half an hour with the cultures, did in fact show a strong electroscopic reaction. The same result was achieved on several consecutive evenings.

Lengths of hard rubber, rubber gloves, paper, cotton wool, cellulose, etc., absorbed energy from the cultures and caused the leaf of the electroscope to curl without the application of any friction. Humidity, shade combined with a strong breeze, or touching the substances with the hands for several minutes caused the effect to disappear.

Thus a start had been made toward a qualitative understanding of the radiation. It was an indisputable fact that the cultures were charging the rubber and other organic substances; I was able to charge them by bringing them into contact with the cultures and to discharge them by exposing them to fresh air or putting them in water.

The situation became more complex when I acquired a *new* pair of rubber gloves and found that they, too, caused a reaction of the electroscope, without having been exposed to the cultures or previously rubbed. It was therefore clear that the energy not only was in the cultures but also was present "elsewhere"! This discovery spoiled the unequivocal nature of the culture reaction, but seemed important. Again, I had the feeling that I had had during the experiments on the photographic plates: *the radiation is present everywhere.*

It was then that I remembered the statement of my experimental subject: "I feel as if I've been staring into the sun for a long time." *The radiation must be related to solar energy. If the radiation is present everywhere, it can come only from the sun.* I placed a pair of uncharged gloves in the bright sunlight. After an exposure of from five to fifteen minutes to sunlight, without prior friction, the rubber gloves elicited a strong reaction from the aluminum leaf of the electroscope. I now had double proof of the solar origin of the energy—first, because the heating experiment had released solar energy from the sand; second, because solar radiation had charged the insulators. Protracted irradiation of insulators with an ultraviolet lamp produced the same effect.

But if bions and the sun emit the energy in question, then it must also be present in the living organism. I placed uncharged rubber gloves directly on the abdomen of a vegetatively alive patient, carefully avoiding friction. The result was positive. Five to fifteen minutes after contact with the abdominal skin, the gloves registered a strong reaction at the electroscope. I repeated this experiment with several students and patients. The result was always positive. With people who were vegetatively sluggish or whose exhalation was shallow, the reaction was weaker. The results improved if the breathing was deepened.[3]

Now I was able to understand several previously incomprehensible phenomena. Obviously, I was dealing with an unknown energy possessing a specific biological activity. It originates from matter heated to incandescence and made to swell. It is presumably released through the decomposition and disintegration of matter (as with radiating bions). Furthermore, it is radiated into the atmosphere by the sun and is therefore present everywhere. This clarified the apparent contradiction that the electroscope reacted

[3] *Cf.* "Drei Versuche am statischen Elektroskop," in *Experimenteller und klinischer Bericht,* no. 7, 1939.

not only to the rubber charged by the SAPA bions but also to the rubber gloves that had not been near the culture.

The newly discovered energy is found also in the living organism, *which absorbs the energy from the atmosphere and directly from the sun.*

It was the same energy with which my blue bions, from any source, killed bacilli and cancer cells. The only difference was that in bions the energy was contained within the small blue vesicles.

The energy was named "orgone," in reference to the history of its discovery through the study of the orgasm and to its biological effect of charging substances of organic origin.

Now I was able to understand the blue-gray vapors that I had seen in the dark around my head, hands, and white coat: *organic matter absorbs orgone energy and retains it.*

The electroscope of the Oslo physicist had not reacted to the cultures because orgone energy can influence an electroscope *only indirectly, by way of charged insulators.*

3. VISUALIZATION OF ATMOSPHERIC ORGONE ENERGY

It was necessary to study the radiation of SAPA bions by the least complicated means. For this purpose, an enclosed space had to be constructed that would *contain and isolate* the radiation emanating from the bions and prevent its rapid diffusion into the surroundings. Organic matter could not be used because it absorbs radiation. However, on the basis of my observations, I was certain that metal would reflect the radiation and hold it within the enclosed space. But the radiation could also penetrate the metal and disperse outward. To prevent this, the apparatus had to be *walled with metal on the inside and with organic matter on the outside.* The radiation generated by the cultures on the inside would be reflected by the inner metal walls, while the outer surface of organic matter (cotton and wood) would prevent, or at least reduce, the transmitting of the radiation by the metal to the outside. The front wall of the apparatus was to have an opening fitted with an eyepiece to enable the radiation to be observed from the outside.

The apparatus was constructed, and a dozen or so culture preparations were put into it. For magnification, I adapted a device used for viewing film, assuming that the rays would strike the cellulose disk of the viewer and thus become visible on it. The experiment was successful. I was able to distinctly observe blue moving vapors and bright, yellow-white streaks and dots of light. The phenomena were confirmed by several persons who served as subjects in repetitions of the experiment. The results now seemed conclusive enough for publication. But just at this point a completely incomprehensible finding intruded. I had expected that after having been emptied and thoroughly ventilated, the box-like apparatus would not show any light phenomena. Otherwise, my contention that the visible rays emanated from the cultures would be invalidated. I did not doubt for a moment that a control experiment would confirm my assumption.

I was astonished when I saw the same rays, blue vapors, and bright streaks of light, in the empty box. I took it apart completely, dipped the metal plates into water, replaced the cotton, ventilated for several days, and then repeated the experiment. I was assuming that the covering material had absorbed radiation from the cultures and was now producing after-effects during the control experiment. But I was wrong. *I simply could not remove the radiation phenomena from the empty box,* and I was at a loss to explain why. What was the origin of the radiation in the box if it contained no cultures? To be sure, the light phenomena were not so intense as when the cultures were present, but they were there nevertheless.

I had another box constructed, with a front wall of glass and no organic covering; I was careful to keep it away from rooms where there were SAPA cultures. Since this box had no covering of organic matter, there could no longer be any question of a residue of absorbed energy.

It was all to no avail. The radiation was still there. After several days of complete bafflement, I remembered that a similar phenomenon had occurred with my rubber gloves and the electroscope. Rubber, exposed to the cultures, had charged the electroscope; then water and ventilation in the shade had eliminated the phenomenon. Reexposure of the rubber to the cultures had promptly and consistently restored it. But even rubber gloves that had never been near the cultures had produced the phenomena *without prior friction*. At that time, I had had to conclude that the energy the cultures emitted was one that was present everywhere. I now drew the same conclusion from the fact that the box, even without cultures, clearly emitted radiation. *Where did it come from?*

Today, with orgone energy measurable and in practical use in the treatment of cancer patients, my earlier puzzlement seems unintelligent. From the very beginning, I had had the feeling that the radiation was present everywhere, and surely the incident with the charged rubber gloves that had never been exposed to cultures should have made me anticipate the presence of radiation in the empty box. It is very easy to be clever after the fact, but for the first two years I doubted every one of my observations. The idea that "radiation is present everywhere" and the impression of "spontaneously charged gloves" were not very convincing and, in fact, drew my attention away from the radiation itself. In addition, the constant doubts, objections, and negative findings of physicists and bacteriologists greatly inhibited me from taking my observations as seriously as they deserved to be. Because of the smear campaign against me in the Norwegian press, which was just dying down at the time that I discovered the radiation, my self-confidence was not very great. It was certainly not strong enough to support the flood of insights that poured in on me. My observations were calling into question seemingly unshakable convictions in biology and bacteriology: the air-germ theory, "body electricity," the idea that protoplasm is merely highly complex protein, the mechanistic as well as the vitalistic view of life, etc. Only the spontaneous development and logic of my experiments sustained me.

It is interesting and useful to look back on such times of uncertainty, when what have become facts of everyday work seemed to be the strangest of phenomena. It provides the courage necessary to go on in spite of disturbing and apparently negative findings in control experiments; not to invalidate new facts with superficial controls; *always to check negative control findings personally;* and, finally not to give in to the temptation of saying, "It was just an illusion." The existence of the radiation was proven beyond doubt. I could not expect to be able to explain each individual phenomenon with one stroke. Consequently, I could not allow myself to give way to the doubts and emotional upheavals such a confusion of findings arouses.

Naturally it was unsatisfactory to say that radiation in the absence of cultures corresponded to the electroscope's reaction to rubber that had never been near the cultures. This explanation was simply a temporary bridge across a void I was not yet able to fill.

For several weeks, I observed the radiation in the empty box. It remained unchanged; it was not affected by sunshine or rain, fog or clear weather, high or low humidity, night or day. It could not, therefore, be the result of direct solar radiation, as was the charge of the rubber exposed to the sun. It came from "everywhere," but there was no way of determining what the "everywhere" was.

During the summer of 1940, I took a holiday and traveled to Maine. One night, while I was still struggling with this riddle, I observed the sky above a nearby lake. The moon was low on the western horizon. Opposite, in the eastern sky, there were strongly flickering stars. I noticed that stars at the zenith flickered less intensely than those near the eastern horizon. If, as theory has it, the flickering of the stars is the result of the diffusion of light, then the flickering would have to be uniform all over the sky; if anything, stronger near the light of the moon. But exactly the opposite was true.

I began to look at individual stars through a wooden tube, at one point unintentionally aiming the tube toward a deep-blue spot in the sky between the stars. I was amazed to see a lively flickering followed by flashes of fine rays of light in the circular field of the tube. The phenomenon gradually faded as I moved the tube in the direction of the moon, being the most intense in the darkest portions of the sky *between* the stars. It was the same fine flickering and flashing, with dots and streaks of light, that I had observed so often in my box. I inserted a magnifying glass in the tube to enlarge the rays. Suddenly my box lost its mystery. The phenomenon had become quite understandable: *The radiation in my culture-free box originated in the atmosphere. The atmosphere contains an energy of which I had no previous knowledge.*

What I saw that night could not have been "cosmic rays." No one had yet seen cosmic rays with the naked eye. Moreover, physicists contend that "cosmic rays" come to the earth from outer space; i.e., they do not have their origin on our planet. It is true that recently there have been objections and challenges to this hypothesis. But even if the cosmic rays of the physicists should be of *planetary* origin, they would merely be identical with orgone rays. The so-called great power of penetration of the "cosmic rays" would then simply be explained by the fact that *orgone energy is present everywhere.*[4]

Looking at earth and rock through the tube, I observed the same phenomenon, sometimes stronger, sometimes weaker. It was also present in clouds, only in this case it was more intense. Now I

[4] Rudolf W. Ladenburg, in "The Nature of Cosmic Rays and the Constitution of Matter," (*Scientific Monthly,* May 1942), states: ". . . the origin of the primaries of the cosmic rays is still a great puzzle. *We do not know the processes responsible for the production of such immensely energetic particles.* Some of them carry a million times more energy than the most energetic particles we can produce artificially. And as to the question of the constitution of matter our answer is still rather incomplete. We know that all matter consists of atoms, that the atoms consist of tiny nuclei surrounded by electrons and that the nuclei consist of protons and neutrons. *There must be strong forces acting between the protons and neutrons holding the nuclei together. But we do not know what they are. They are not of electrical nature* as we have seen, and many theories have been tried for understanding these forces. The discovery of the meson in the cosmic rays has raised some hope for reaching the goal, but this fundamental problem is still far from being solved." (Italics are mine.—W. R.)

understood: *During my control experiments on SAPA radiation I had discovered atmospheric orgone energy.*

I shall now try systematically to describe orgone energy so that anyone can discover it for himself, without having to travel the tortuous path down which my bion experiments led me. This description, which will reveal many properties unknown to us in any other form of energy, should make clear the logic that connects the "blue bion" and its energy function with atmospheric energy. Atmospheric orgone energy could doubtless have been discovered without SAPA bions. Yet, because of this complex detour, by way of the bion radiation, we had an insight of profound significance: *The energy that governs everything that is alive is necessarily identical with atmospheric energy;* otherwise it would not have led to the discovery of atmospheric orgone energy.

CHAPTER IV

The Objective Demonstration
of Orgone Radiation

1. ARE THERE SUBJECTIVE IMPRESSIONS OF LIGHT?

When we were children the light phenomena we saw with our eyes shut were a constant source of fascination. Small dots, blue-violet in color, would appear from nowhere, floating back and forth slowly, changing their course with every movement of the eyes. They floated quite slowly in gentle curves, looping periodically into spirals, in a path somewhat as follows:

It was a delightful game to change the shape and track of the light dots by rubbing the eyes through our closed lids; we could influence even the color of the dots, the blue becoming red, green, or yellow. Part of the fun was to open the eyes suddenly, look into the bright light of a lamp, then close the eyes again and see the after-images. With a little imagination we could turn these forms into all kinds of things: rainbows, balloons, animal heads, human figures.

But such childish pleasures lost their interest as we grew up and studied physics, mathematics, and biology. We had to learn that such subjective optical phenomena were "unreal," something to be distinguished from objectively measurable, physical manifestations of light and its seven colors. In time, our concern for what could actually be measured and weighed obliterated the strong impressions of our sense organs. We no longer took them seriously. The practical everyday world demanded concentration on concrete details exclusively; fantasy only interfered. But the subjective light impressions remain, and the question must nag at many whether such clear phenomena as light impressions observed with the eyes closed do not, after all, represent a reality. The illusionary nature of these optical sensations is not so obvious as it appears.

We were educated to regard such things as these light impressions as "purely subjective" and therefore "not real." They could be of no concern to scientific research and were relegated to the realm of "human fantasy." Man's fantasy life, of course, is far removed from reality, being inspired by subjective desires and, moreover, unstable—which is why scientific research had to develop an objective, realistic foundation through experiment. The ideal experiment makes judgment independent of subjective fantasies, illusions, and wishes. To put it succinctly, man has no confidence in his faculties of perception. He prefers, with good reason, to rely on the photographic plate, the microscope, or the electroscope when examining phenomena.

Yet in spite of the progress made by turning from subjective experience to objective observation, an important quality of research has been lost. What we observe objectively may well exist in reality, but it is dead. In the interest of scientific objectivity, we kill what is alive before making any statements about it. The result is necessarily a mechanistic, machine-like image of life, from which life's most essential quality, its specific aliveness, is missing—an aliveness uncomfortably reminiscent of the intense organ sensations experienced in childhood. Every kind of mysticism—yoga, the fascist "surging of the blood," the receptivity of the spiritualist medium, or the ecstatic, divine epiphany of the dervish—is grounded upon these subjective organ sensations. Mysticism claims the existence of forces and processes that natural science denies or disdains. One moment of sharp deliberation tells us that *man cannot feel or imagine anything that has no real, objective existence in one form or another, for human sense perceptions are only functions of objective natural processes within the organism.* Could it not be that behind the "subjective" light impressions of our closed eyes there exists a reality after all? Is it not possible that through our subjective ocular sensations we perceive biological energy of our own organism? This thought seems strange, daring. But let us see!

To dismiss these subjective light impressions as simple "fantasy" is incorrect. Fantasy is an active property of an organism governed by certain natural laws and must therefore be "real." Not so long ago medicine rejected all functional and nervous ailments as unreal and imagined, because it did not understand them. But headache is headache, and light impression is light impression, whether we understand it or not.

Naturally we reject mystical claims based on *misinterpretation* of organ sensations. But that is not to deny the existence of these sensations. We must also reject a mechanistically fragmented natural science, because it separates organ sensations from the vital processes of the organs. *Self-perception is an essential part of the life process.* It is not a case of nerves being here, muscles there, and organ sensations somewhere else. The processes within the tissues, and our perception of them, form an indivisible *functional unity.* This must be one of the essential, experimentally documented, theoretical guidelines of our therapeutic work. Pleasure and anxiety express a particular state of functioning of the total organism. It is therefore important to make a clear distinction between functional thinking and mechanistically fragmented thinking, which can never penetrate to the essentials of the life process. Let us note four important principles of a *functional* view of nature:

1. Every living organism is a self-contained, functional unit, not merely a mechanical sum of organs. The fundamental biological function controls the total organism just as it governs each individual organ.
2. Every living organism is a part of surrounding nature and is functionally identical with it.

3. Every perception is based upon the correspondence of a function within the organism with a function in the external world, i.e., upon orgonotic harmony.
4. Every self-perception is the immediate expression of objective processes within the organism (psychophysical identity).

Little can be expected from philosophical speculations on the reality of our sensations if they exclude the principle that the observing, perceiving ego (subject) and the observed, perceived object together form a functional unity. Mechanistic research divides this unity into a duality. In its total rejection of sensation, contemporary mechanistic empiricism is beyond redemption. *Every important discovery originates in the subjective sensation or experience of an objective fact, i.e., in orgonotic harmony.* What is required is to objectivize the subjective sensation, separating it from its stimulus and comprehending the origin of the stimulus. As orgone therapists, we do this every hour of every day when we try to understand the bodily expressions of the patient by identifying ourselves with the patient and his functions. Once we comprehend these expressions emotionally, we let our intellect work and objectivize the phenomenon.

Now, with this understanding of orgonotic harmony, let us return to our childhood fantasies and impressions of light. How can we establish *objectively* whether these impressions "seen" with our eyes closed correspond to real processes?

2. FLICKERING IN THE SKY MADE OBJECTIVE (THE ORGONOSCOPE)

First of all we try to determine whether similar phenomena can be perceived with *open* eyes in broad daylight. If we observe carefully for a sufficient length of time, we discover that they can. We gaze at a screen, a wall, or a white door. *We observe a flickering.* The impression is of shadows or foggy vapors traveling more or less rapidly and rhythmically over the surface of things. Rather than disregarding this observation as a mere "subjective ocular impression," we resolve to establish *objectively* whether this flickering is taking place merely in our eyes or all around us.

Devising a method of differentiating is not easy, however. We begin by closing our eyes. Instantly the flickering seems to change into a movement of small dots, shapes, and colors. We open and close our eyes repeatedly until we are convinced that the phenomena we perceive with our eyes closed are *different* from those we observed while looking at the wall opposite us.

We look into the blue sky, as though gazing into the far distance. At first we see nothing. But if we continue to observe, we discover, to our surprise, a rhythmical, wave-like flickering, clearly perceptible across the blue sky. *Does this flickering exist merely in our eyes, or is it in the sky?* We continue to observe the phenomena over several days, under varying weather conditions and at different times of the day. It is striking that the flickering in the sky varies a great deal in kind and in intensity. Next we experiment at night. Since our observations are now unhampered by diffused daylight the wave-like flickering is even *more distinct.* Here and there we believe we catch a glimpse of a lightning flash in the form of a streak or dots. The flickering and delicate flashings are also to be observed in dark clouds, where they are more intense. As we observe the sky over a period of weeks, we notice that the flickering of the stars varies in intensity. On some nights, the stars shine clearly and calmly; on others their flickering is subdued; on still others, it is extraordinarily vivid. Astronomers ascribe the flickering of the stars to diffuse light. There was a time when we accepted this explanation unquestioningly. However, now that the actual existence of a flickering in the sky has become a crucial question for us, we must ask ourselves whether the flickering of stars may be related to the flickering in the sky *between* the stars. If so, we have taken the first step toward demonstrating the objective existence of an unknown something in the atmosphere. The flickering of the stars is certainly no subjective ocular phenomenon: observatories are built on high mountains in order to eliminate it. The unknown something that makes the stars flicker must therefore be moving close to the surface of the earth. But it is certainly not diffuse light; otherwise the flickering would not vary in intensity as it does. Such "explanations" only obscure facts. Let us defer the answer.

The longer and more precisely we observe the flickering in the sky and across the surface of objects, the more imperative it becomes to delineate a limited field. We construct a metal tube 1 to 3 feet long and 1 to 2 inches in diameter, with a dull black interior. We look through it at the walls in the day time and the sky at night. The tube isolates a circle which appears *brighter* than the area around it. Keeping both eyes open and looking through the tube with one eye, we see a dark-blue night sky within which is a disk of brighter blue. Within the disk itself we perceive, first of all, a flickering movement, then, unmistakably, delicate dots and streaks of light appearing and disappearing. The phenomenon becomes less distinct in the immediate vicinity of the moon; the darker the atmosphere in the background, the clearer the phenomenon.

Are we perhaps this time victims of an illusion? To find out we insert a plano-convex eyepiece with a magnification of approximately 5x in the viewing end of the tube and look through. The bright circular field is now broader; the dots and streaks of light appear larger and more distinct. *It is impossible to magnify subjective light impressions; therefore, the phenomenon must be objective.* Moveover, no flickering is perceptible along the dark interior walls of the tube; the flickering is confined strictly to the bright section of the disk, and therefore cannot be "subjective" sensation. We have isolated a limited area and are now in a position to examine the phenomenon carefully under conditions that eliminate diffuse light from the atmosphere as a factor. But first we shall make some improvements in the primitive orgonoscope we have improvised:

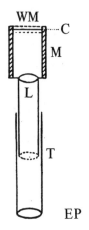

C: cellulose disk, exterior surface dull
WM: wire mesh, on both sides of disk
M: metal cylinder, about 4" long, 2" wide
L: biconvex lens, about 10x, focused on disk
T: telescopic tube, 1' to 2' long, about 2" wide
EP: eyepiece, 5x, for additional magnification

FIGURE 8. The orgonoscope

We point our tube toward the dark night sky in front of the mirror of a good microscope equipped with apochromatic lenses. We use a 10x object lens and a 5x eyepiece. Our eyes need to be accustomed to the dark for about twenty-five minutes. The microscope reflects the light phenomena in the sky with total clarity. Every single flash of light is clearly discernible. We remove the eyepiece from the tube. Now the flickering is seen in smaller scale, but it is more intense; we are no longer able to distinguish individual flashes of light.

Can the phenomena be ascribed to the haze in the atmosphere?

Let us try observing the phenomenon on foggy or hazy nights. It does not take long to see that the phenomena are either very weak or have disappeared completely. *Fog or haze does not cause flickering in the circular field. The movement of light particles in the field of the microscope has nothing to do with the movement of fog.*

By careful observation, we are able to establish that the light and wave phenomena extend across the entire sky and become weaker only when close to stars or the moon because of the stronger light. They are at their most intense on clear nights and when humidity is relatively low. When the humidity rises above 50 percent, the radiation phenomena decrease in intensity. In other words, *humidity absorbs the radiation in the atmosphere,* just as it absorbs the SAPA radiation.

At night we direct our tube at various places—on the ground, the pavement, loose earth, a lawn, walls, etc. We see the same movements of light particles. They are more pronounced on soil than on asphalt. We point the tube at thick shrubs from a distance of about 10 cm., moving the tube slowly away from the foliage and then back to it. Without doubt, the phenomena are more intense at the leaves than in the surroundings. They seem to come from the leaves themselves. We look at a variety of flower blossoms. The radiation phenomena are more intense close to the blossom than at the stalk.

Earth, walls, bushes, grass, animals, the atmosphere, all show the same phenomena. The conclusion to be drawn from these findings is inescapable: *The radiation phenomena are present everywhere, with variations only in the density and intensity of the energy.* Perhaps we would have wished to find them present in some places and not in others. Then, the discovery would not have been so overwhelming. But we have to stay with the facts, however strange they now begin to appear.

3. ENCLOSING THE RADIATION AND MAKING IT OBJECTIVELY VISIBLE

Orgone radiation is everywhere. This fact makes it difficult to devise experiments with it. To describe a phenomenon accurately, it is necessary to isolate it and determine its meaning by comparing it with a different phenomenon. We must create an enclosed space in which the energy can be isolated.

We wish to ascertain whether anything new can be learned in a completely darkened room. We allow about half an hour for our eyes to become fully accustomed to the darkness. During this time, all subjective light impressions disappear and we see nothing but *black*, that is, *nothing*. We look through our tube into the darkness. We see *nothing!* This experiment only confirms the fact that in absolute darkness blackness prevails. The radiation has disappeared and we are about to give up all concern with this "stupid problem." At this point many people would go no further. But that is not research. We cannot simply ignore the fact that we had established, *beyond any doubt*, the existence of a strange phenomenon in the open air. It cannot have ceased to exist. Nevertheless, conviction and proof are two different things.

Since the properties of our atmospheric radiation are unknown to us, we are obliged to work with apparatuses that are used in known realms of energies. We might use a Faraday cage, an enclosure that has walls made of iron or copper wire mesh, whose function is to provide an enclosed space that cannot be penetrated by electromagnetic waves from the outside. The cage itself is free of electromagnetic fields because all electromagnetic waves converging upon it from the outside are caught by the copper mesh and grounded. (If you drive across a bridge with a metal superstructure, your car radio stops working. The principle is the same as in the Faraday cage.) Delicate experiments with the oscillograph can be conducted in the cage without risk of interference.

We now build such a cage, in a corner of the basement. We line the copper wire walls with sheet iron on the inside, in order to reduce to a minimum the contact between inside and outside air. We leave just a few cracks or holes to admit enough air for breathing. We then sit down in the completely darkened cage and allow our eyes to accustom themselves to the darkness.

Over the course of approximately half an hour, the blackness gives way to an indefinable glimmer. Strange light phenomena irritate our eyes. The impression is of fog-like vapors of gray-blue color wafting slowly across the interior of the cage. If we fix our eyes on a single spot on the wall, we see moving light phenomena. The longer we stay in the cage, the more distinct the light phenomena become. Within the gray-blue vapors, light dots of a deep blue-violet color are observed. They are reminiscent of the familiar subjective visual phenomena that occur immediately prior to falling asleep. Again the problem arises: Are the phenomena inside or outside our eyes? When we close our eyes, the deep-violet dots do not disappear. Are the optic nerves irritated, or are the light phenomena not real? Theoretically, the phenomena should disappear when our eyes are closed and reappear again when our eyes are reopened. Subjective after-images do exist, of course, but the matter is not so simple as that. How is it that the optic nerves become irritated in complete darkness and why are we unable to "free our eyes" of the phenomena?

The more prolonged the observation, the more pronounced the phenomena become. For example, on dry, sunny days, lightning-like flashes can be seen in the metal enclosure. In order to eliminate any doubt about the existence of atmospheric orgone energy, I urge my students to acquaint themselves thoroughly with these phenomena.

Many experimental subjects developed a slight conjunctivitis if they stayed in the Faraday cage for an hour or more. Since, under normal conditions, the eyes rest in complete darkness, there must be something in the cage to irritate the eyes, excite the optic nerves, and render the conjunctivae hyperemic. We repeat the observations in the dark cage until we find some means to resolve these important problems. For instance, *can the blue-gray and deep-violet light phenomena be enlarged with a magnifying glass?* We discover that a good magnifying glass does indeed enlarge the dots and make them more distinct. They manifest themselves in two ways: *they fly either directly at us or past us.* In the first instance, we observe the following sequence of light impressions:

Every individual light dot seems alternately to expand and contract as though pulsating. The light dots flying past us follow a trajectory something like this:

Because of the shape its path takes, we have called it a spinning wave (*Kreiselwelle*). Its significance will in time become clear. The blue-violet dots seem to come from the metal walls in rhythmic intervals.

After two or three hours in the cage, we notice a blue-gray sheen around our white coat. The contours of another person can be made out, blurred but plainly visible. Let us not be disconcerted by the mystical and ghost-like character of this phenomenon. There is nothing mystical about it. The radiation seems to adhere to cloth and hair. We put some good fluorescent material, such as zinc sulfide, on a swab of cotton wool and fasten it to the wall opposite us. We were not mistaken. The area of the cotton swab appears lighter than its surroundings. Through the magnifying glass, we see the radiation distinctly enlarged; flickering and the fine light rays already familiar to us can be observed.

A paper disk of zinc sulfide has been left in the cage for several days. We now bend it slowly. It emits strong radiation. For control purposes, we expose a similar zinc sulfide disk to fresh air or bend it for a long time. In either case, the light phenomena disappear. We now leave the control zinc sulfide disk in the orgone room for a few days. When we bend it, the light phenomena are again found to be present. *The paper disk soaked in zinc sulfide has absorbed orgone energy.*

The purpose of our next experiment is to make the orgone energy inside the cage visible *from outside*. We cut a window about 5 inches square in the front wall of the apparatus. On the inside metal wall, across the opening, we place a fluorescing glass plate of the type used to make X-rays visible.[1] In the outer wooden wall we attach a metal tube equipped with an eyepiece containing a biconvex lens capable of magnification of 5–10x. Tube and lens are both removable, so the fluorescing disk can be observed with or without magnification.

Inside the cage, we mount a green light bulb of the type used in developing highly sensitive photographic plates. The bulb, rheostatically controlled, provides a constant dim light as background for the radiation. In this experimental arrangement we are following the pattern provided by nature: the orgone radiation is clearly visible against the dim light of the night sky. To reproduce the flickering of the stars, we drill a few holes about 1/8 inch in diameter in the wall. Then we observe the apparatus from outside in total darkness.

Through the holes we are able to perceive a *strongly flickering light;* its color is *blue.*

There is a great deal of movement observable on the fluorescing disk: rapidly moving streaks of light and single flashes of light

---

[1] Fluorescence, as distinct from luminescence, designates the property of a substance to produce light while being acted upon by invisible energy particles. In the case of luminescence the light effect persists for shorter or longer periods of time even after the substance has been removed from the effective rays. Zinc sulfide is a fluorescing substance, calcium sulfide a luminescing substance.

in the form of dots and lines may be clearly distinguished. After a while we see deep-violet vapors that appear to stream from the openings. The area of visible radiation is a sharply defined square against the black of the cage. The flickering and the various light phenomena are visible only within the contours of this square. Through the magnifying glass, the light phenomena are much more distinct. It is possible, in fact, to distinguish the individual rays. In dry, clear weather the phenomena are more distinct and intense than on damp and rainy days. The observation of radiation in the Faraday cage is greatly enhanced by the use of the orgonoscope.

How does the energy get inside the cage? The wire mesh should ground all electromagnetic energy. The interior of the cage should be free of all electrical charges; otherwise, it would be impossible to use it for conducting delicate electrical experiments without interference. A further problem confronts us:

Can the energy in the cage be electricity? We have now two main tasks before us:

1. To comprehend the properties of the radiating energy, "orgone," now made visible.
2. To investigate the connection between orgone energy and electricity.

4. THE ORGONE ACCUMULATOR

Here I have to interrupt the account of the course of the development of the orgone therapy experiments in order to answer a question that must have been constantly in the mind of the attentive reader. It concerns the "orgone accumulator," which has been discussed without being mentioned by name and without any explanation of how the accumulation of atmospheric orgone energy is brought about and how it is measured.

This question cannot be answered as exhaustively here as it really deserves to be. Orgone energy is a completely new form of energy fundamentally different from electricity and magnetism. Investigation and definition of its properties is the task of orgone physics in the realm of non-living nature. This research is as yet only in its earliest stages. The trained reader will know the concepts applicable to electricity, but these cannot be applied to orgone energy. The new physical concepts developed during the course of our orgone experiments need a detailed presentation accompanied by a series of definite, purely physical experiments. However, such an account would exceed the scope of a report on experimental orgone therapy, and it must therefore be deferred. In the present context, the information of most immediate interest to the reader is that concerning the mechanism of accumulating and measuring orgone energy. At the risk of being misunderstood and misinterpreted by the electrophysicists, I would like to discuss the three basic findings that demonstrate the accumulation of orgone energy in the orgone accumulator and make its measurement possible.

THE MECHANISM BY WHICH ATMOSPHERIC ORGONE ENERGY IS CONCENTRATED

The orgone accumulator consists of a casing of organic material: wool, or preferably celotex, etc. The inner wall is lined with a thin layer of sheet iron.* This arrangement makes possible a concentration of atmospheric orgone energy much greater than the atmospheric concentration. The mechanism of this concentration depends upon two facts:

1. *Organic material of every kind attracts orgone energy and absorbs it. Conversely, orgone-containing material attracts small organic particles and holds them.*

* The number of layers, each consisting of organic material on the outside and metal on the inside, can be increased. Thus, there may be any number of layers. As many as twenty layers have been used. [Ed.]

2. *Metallic material, especially iron, attracts orgone energy but then repels it again quickly. Conversely, orgone-charged metal repels metallic particles.*

These two facts fundamental to orgone physics can be demonstrated experimentally and repeated at will in the following way. Under a glass hood, used to protect the arrangement from air currents, a metal sphere is placed on a cork or rubber plate. We suspend a small piece of cork on one side of the equator of the sphere, at a distance of 2–3 mm., and a small piece of tin foil on the other side, at the same distance. Neither the cork nor the tin foil should be touching the iron sphere; both should hang freely. The sphere is connected to an electroscope by a wire.

We then charge a polysterene rod (a rubber rod produces too weak a charge) by stroking our hair with it once or twice, *without rubbing*. After having been charged with orgone energy in this way, the rod is now brought close to the glass hood of the experimental apparatus or, better still, to the metal point of the electroscope connected to the sphere. If the orgone charge is strong enough and the relative humidity does not exceed 50 percent, the cork will move toward the metal sphere and adhere to it for a period of time. This reaction means that *the energy transferred from the hair to the rod has enabled the metal sphere to form around itself a field of energy in which organic material is attracted and held.* Other experiments show that the converse of this statement is equally true: *organic matter attracts orgone energy and absorbs it.*

A non-charged polysterene rod will not influence a small piece of tin foil. *An orgone-charged rod, on the other hand, will attract the tin foil and hold it fast.*

From this we draw the conclusion that *orgone energy and organic substances attract each other, as do orgone-charged organic and metallic substances.*

On the other side of the sphere, where the tin foil is suspended, the effect is different. *The tin foil is first attracted to the metal sphere but then immediately repelled and kept at a distance. The*

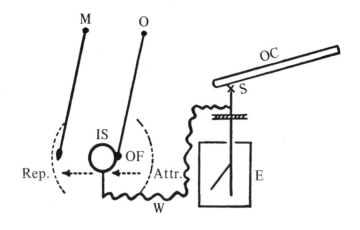

O: organic material
M: metallic material
OF: orgone energy field
IS: iron sphere
Attr.: attraction
S: spark to tip of electroscope
Rep.: repulsion
E: electroscope (orgonometer),
    grounded or not grounded
W: wire connection
OC: orgone carrier (polysterene rod)
----: direction of deflection

FIGURE 9. Demonstration of the orgonotic attraction of organic material and the repulsion of metallic material in the orgone energy field of a metal sphere

effect upon each other of two metallic substances in the orgone energy field is one of repulsion. A further conclusion to be drawn is that *metal, especially iron, attracts orgone energy. However, it does not absorb it but repels it.* (The experiments I have outlined can be carried out only with low humidity.)

These findings are fundamentally new. They do have a relation with the confused concept of "friction electricity" and with the equally confused theory of "static electricity." All this has been explained in detail elsewhere. The simple experiment I have described demonstrates two basic functions of orgone energy: the *attraction* of organic substances and the *repulsion* of metallic substances in the orgone energy field. The application and significance of these findings for the orgone accumulator will be evident from the following experimental studies.

THERMIC MEASUREMENT OF ATMOSPHERIC
ORGONE ENERGY (THERMIC ORGONOMETRY)

The metal walls of our orgone accumulator are "cold." If we hold the palm of a hand or our tongue at a distance of about 10 cm. from the metal wall long enough, we will experience a sensation of *warmth* and a delicate *prickling*. In addition, a salty taste is detected on the tongue. If we put a thermometer in the same place, or better still, above the top of the accumulator, and a second thermometer outside the accumulator, we notice, to our surprise, a difference of 0.2° to 0.5° C. compared with the room temperature.

Neither the subjective feeling of warmth nor the temperature difference as measured objectively can be due to "heat" radiated from the wall, since the temperature on the metal wall is lower than the temperature at a distance of up to 10 cm. from it. And there are no sources of heat on the wall or behind it, under the accumulator or inside it. We are therefore obliged to risk an hypothesis and see where it leads.

We know that radiation in general consists of *moving energy particles.* Let us therefore assume for the moment that the cold metallic walls of the accumulator radiate or reflect energy. We must assume the following: If we hold the palm of our hand or a thermometer at a distance of 6 to 10 cm. from the wall, we *block* the movement of the energy particles. *When the kinetic energy of the particles is blocked, it manifests itself as a sensation of warmth or as an objective rise in temperature as registered by the thermometer.* This hypothesis is completely in accord with the physics of all radiation. The blocking of electrons flying from the cathode of an X-ray tube toward the anticathode generates warmth and light phenomena.

We construct a small orgone accumulator. Six iron plates, each 1 square foot, are built into a cube. On the outside of the top metal plate we mount a cylindrical container measuring about 15 cm. in length, into which we can insert a thermometer. The temperature *inside* the accumulator can be read through a hole in the container. To insulate the inside of the cylinder against the room temperature, we wrap it with cotton, wood, or some other substance that conducts heat poorly. In addition, we screen the thermometer container from the outside with a glass lampshade. No organic substance should be placed between the thermometer and the upper metal plate.

The basic consideration guiding our construction is the following: The radiation particles *inside* the box are being bounced back and forth between the metal walls. They are blocked on all sides. Since heat rises, the most favorable spot for temperature change to be registered is above the top metal plate. A *difference in temperature* must exist between the enclosed air in the cylinder above the accumulator and the air in the room. Let us call the temperature of the air in the room T, that of the air in the cylinder $T(o)$. If our hypothesis is correct, the temperature differences, expressed as $T(o) - T$, must be *positive* and constantly present. We do not yet know how great it is. Measurements taken over several days indicate a constant difference in temperature varying between 0.2° and 1.8° C. The arithmetical mean of the temperature differences, ob-

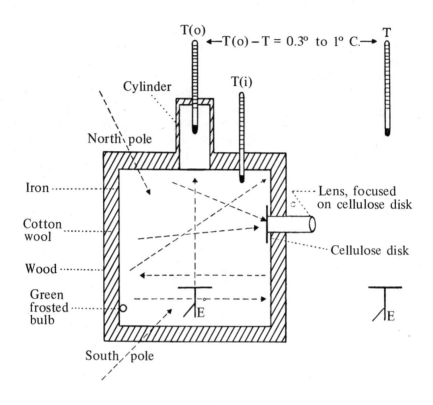

T(o): temperature in cylinder; T(i): temperature inside accumulator;
T: control (temperature of air in room)
E: electroscope   ----→: direction of radiation   Size: 1 cubic foot

FIGURE 10.   Basic design of orgone accumulator (section)*

* In accumulators designed for therapeutic purposes, the wood is usually
replaced by celotex, the cotton by glass wool, and the sheet metal by steel
wool, except for the rigid sheet metal used for the innermost layer. [Ed.]

tained from measurements taken several times a day for a number of days or weeks, amounts to approximately 0.5° C. Since we have introduced no constant source of heat into the box, the temperature difference must have its origin in the blocking of the radiation particles. Let us now summarize what we were able to learn thus far about the orgone energy:

1. *Organic substances absorb the energy.*
2. *Metallic substances reflect it.*
3. *Blockage of the kinetic energy by any metallic obstacle causes a rise in local temperature.*

At this point we notice a deficiency in our construction. The bare metal walls, which are exposed to the outside as well as to the inside, radiate the energy and the heat produced to the *outside* and to the *inside* simultaneously. In order to better separate the air inside the accumulator from the atmospheric air surrounding it, we wrap the metal box with an organic material such as cotton wool. To make the construction more solid and to improve its appearance, we build a second box around it out of thin plywood or celotex. We make the inside accessible through a door in the front wall.

Thus *the outside of the apparatus consists of organic material, the inside of metallic material.* Since the former absorbs the energy and the latter reflects it, an *accumulation of energy* results. The organic wrapping absorbs the energy from the atmosphere and transmits it to the metal on the inside. The metal radiates the energy toward the outside into the cotton and toward the inside into the open space of the accumulator's interior. The movement of the energy toward the inside is unimpeded, while that toward the outside is blocked. For that reason, the energy can oscillate freely on the inside, but not to the outside. In addition, a part of the energy given off by the metal toward the outside is absorbed by the cotton wool and fed back to the metal. How the energy penetrates the

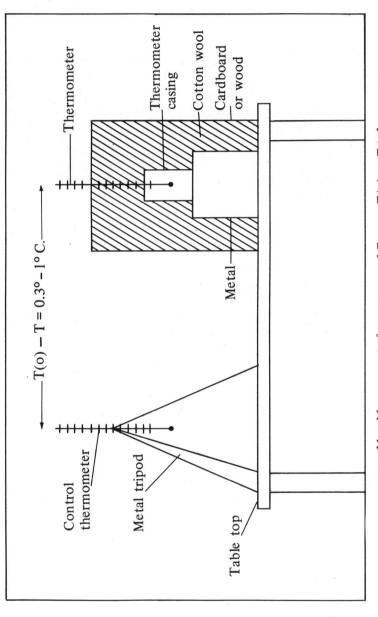

FIGURE 11. Measurement of temperature difference $T(o) - T$ indoors

metal, we do not know. We only know that it does, since the subjective and objective phenomena are significantly more intense inside the accumulator than they are outside it.

After the metal has been covered, the temperature difference $T(o) - T$ is found to be *more constant* and, on the average, *greater. We have designed an accumulator which confines and concentrates the orgone.*

As a control of these results, we take measurements inside, outside, and above a box of the same size but constructed solely of wood or paper. We establish to our complete satisfaction that with such a box temperatures are completely equalized: all the temperatures are the same. *Temperature differences* occur only when we line the inside of the box with metal.

Measurement of the Orgone in the Open Air

During the summer of 1940 I buried a small orgone box in the earth in my garden and subsequently observed a constant temperature difference. But it was not until February 1941 that I discovered just how much greater this difference was than that recorded in closed rooms.

One sunny but cold, windy day, February 15, 1941, I buried an accumulator in the soil to a depth of two-thirds of its height, and in such a way that the box thermometer (I) was still *above* ground level. The box, along with the thermometer casing on top, was set in a second box of cardboard. I filled the space in between the boxes with cotton and woodshavings, then covered the whole apparatus with a wool blanket. (The space where the temperature is measured must, of course, be well protected against the low outside temperature in order to hold the heat produced.) I put a control thermometer (II) through a hole in a glass jar and buried the jar to a depth of about 4 inches in the soil so that the bulb of the thermometer was *below* the ground level. I set a second, uncovered control thermometer (III) 1 inch into the soil. I also used this

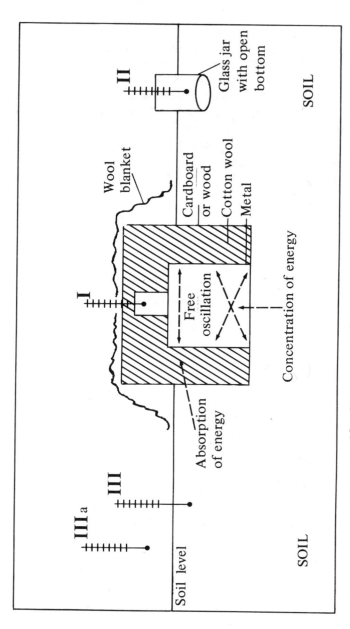

II

Glass jar with open bottom

Wool blanket

Cardboard or wood

Cotton wool

Metal

I

Free oscillation

Concentration of energy

Absorption of energy

SOIL

IIIa

III

Soil level

SOIL

FIGURE 12.   Measurement of temperature difference $T(o) - T$ in the open air (experiment undertaken February 16–17, 1941)

Reading Number	Weather	Time	Air Free	Air Protected	Soil	Air in Glass Jar in Soil	T—Org Above Soil	T(o) − T Compared with Air	Remarks
1	Sun, cold wind, clear	Feb. 16, 1941 12:30 P.M.	3.6°	5.0°	0.5°	1.5°	11.6°	+8.0°	Apparatus with thermometer wrapped in cardboard, front left exposed. Two-thirds underground, begun 12 noon.
2	Sun, cold wind, clear	1:00 P.M.	3.4°	4.6°	0.3°	1.5°	11.4°	+8.0°	
3	Sun, cold wind, clear	1:45 P.M.	2.1°	3.5°	0.4°	1.3°	9.5°	+7.4°	Wool blanket over apparatus.
4	Apparatus in shade	2:30 P.M.	0.3°	0.6°	0.4°	1.3°	6.5°	+6.2°	
5	Apparatus in shade	3:30 P.M.	0.2°	0.3°	0.3°	1.3°	2.9°	+2.7°	Wool blanket over apparatus; elimination of sun radiation.
6	Apparatus in shade; freezing temperature	4:00 P.M.	−0.6°	0.6°	0.2°	0.4°	+0.6°	+1.2°	Wool blanket over apparatus; effects of freezing temperatures.
7	Apparatus in shade; freezing temperature	5:00 P.M.	−0.9°			0.2°	0°	+0.9°	Wool blanket over apparatus; effects of freezing temperatures.
8	Nighttime; freezing temperature	12 midnight	−2.1°			−0.4°	+1.7°	+3.8°	Measurements interrupted; wool blanket removed.
9	Early morning; cloudy	Feb. 17, 1941 9:30 A.M.	−1°	−1°	0°	+0.7°	+1.8°	+2.8°	Apparatus remains in open overnight. Wool blanket cover restored in early morning.
10	Heavy snow	11:30 A.M.	−1°	−1°	0°	0.9°	+2.3°	+3.3°	Thermometer exchanged with each following reading.
11	Heavy snow	12:15 P.M.	−0.9°	−0.9°	0°	0.7°	+1.3°	+2.2°	
12	Heavy snow	1:00 P.M.	−0.7°	−0.7°	0°	0.7°	+1.3°	+2.0°	
13	Heavy snow	2:00 P.M.	−1.0°		0.3°	0.7°	+1.2°	+2.2°	
14	Heavy snow	3:00 P.M.	−1.1°		0.3°	0.7°	+1.2°	+2.3°	
15	Heavy snow	4:00 P.M.	−1.2°		0.2°	0.6°	+1.0°	+2.2°	
16	Heavy snow	5:30 P.M.	−2.0°		0.1°	0.2°	+0.5°	+2.5°	

second control thermometer (IIIa) to measure the temperature of the air above the soil, at about the height of the box thermometer, sometimes with and sometimes without protective covering against the wind. The three thermometers were constantly interchanged. (Figure 12 and the accompanying table on pages 118–119 illustrate the arrangement and the results of this experiment.)

In this arrangement, $T(o) - T$ is much greater than in the closed room, probably because of the elimination of the effects of secondary orgonotic radiation from walls and table tops, which would reduce the difference. *In the open air and without sun, $T(o) - T$ varies around $+2°$ C.*

In order to be certain of these results, I continued the experiment overnight and on the following day, February 16 to February 17, 1941. I left the apparatus just as it was in the open air but took away the wool blanket; i.e., I let the apparatus get as cool as possible in the freezing nighttime temperatures. At 9:30 A.M. on February 17, the temperature of the air was $-1°$ C., the soil temperature, $0°$ C. I wrapped the apparatus once again in the wool blanket and inserted the thermometer, which had just registered the temperature of the air at $-1°$ C., into the cylinder on top. The mercury began to climb and after a while reached $+2.3°$ C. The air temperature still remained constant at $-1°$ C., and the soil temperature at $0°$ C. The air inside the buried glass registered $+0.9°$ C.

This experiment was conducted for the purpose of refuting a specific objection by a distinguished physicist. In January 1941, a few months after the discovery of the remarkable temperature difference, Albert Einstein set up a small orgone accumulator in his home in Princeton, New Jersey. In a subsequent letter to me, he confirmed the existence of a temperature difference at the accumulator, but discovered, in addition, a temperature difference between the underside and the top of the table on which the accumulator stood. This finding naturally undermined the validity of the reading at the accumulator. One of Einstein's assistants, Leopold Infeld, concluded that the temperature difference at the accumulator was

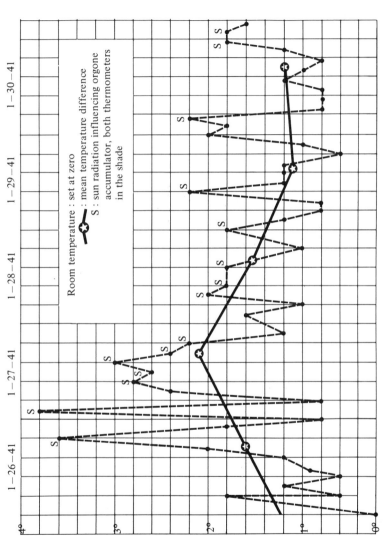

FIGURE 13. Temperature difference from measurements taken inside a room with open window

to be ascribed to the fact that in the basement room, where the observations were made, there would be an increase in temperature "due to the convection of heat from the ceiling to the table top." However, this assistant failed to check his interpretation of the previously confirmed temperature difference *by simply taking measurements in the open air and in the soil,* where there can be no question of "convection of heat from the ceiling to the table top."

I believe these findings are unequivocal:

1. *The soil and the atmosphere contain an energy measurable as heat in our apparatus.*
2. *This constant energy-heat source can attain high thermic values only with a certain arrangement of materials.* In order to effect a *rise* in the temperature difference, there must be *organic material on the outside* and *metallic material on the inside.*

This experiment also demonstrates the significance of the arrangement of material in connection with soil and solar radiation. In the shade, where the influence of radiation from the sun has vanished, $T(o) - T$ drops, relative to all control measurements, from about $+5°$ C. to about $+2°$ C. The control thermometer encased in a glass jar and therefore only minimally exposed to the radiation of orgone energy in the soil registers a difference of only approximately $1°$ C. The accumulator, on the other hand, the most efficient apparatus yet constructed for the absorption and accumulation of orgone energy, registers much higher values—*greater than $+2°C.$*

The temperature *drop* in the open air under freezing weather conditions affects the box thermometer in spite of the insulation. Nevertheless, the temperature difference remains constant within certain lower and upper limits owing to the fact that the $T(o)$ and T temperatures *fall at a parallel rate.* The results of experimental readings taken over a period of approximately three hours were as follows:

$$\left.\begin{array}{l} T(o) = 11.4° \\ T\,(\text{air}) = \ \ 4.6° \end{array}\right\} T(o) - T = 6.8°$$

$$\left.\begin{array}{l} T(o) = \ \ 9.5° \\ T\,(\text{air}) = \ \ 3.5° \end{array}\right\} T(o) - T = 6.0°$$

$$\left.\begin{array}{l} T(o) = \ \ 6.5° \\ T\,(\text{air}) = \ \ 0.6° \end{array}\right\} T(o) - T = 5.9°$$

Experimental Conclusions

1. *When the apparatus is constructed and arranged as described, without a constant source of heat of any known kind, there exists, under all circumstances, a temperature difference between the thermometer of the apparatus and the control thermometer.*

2. *Measurement in the open air demonstrates a radiation from the soil which manifests itself in temperature differences of varying degrees according to the arrangement of the component materials.*

The temperature difference in the open air varies with increases and decreases in the intensity of solar radiation, and also with the time of day. On summer days, under a strong sun, differences up to 20° C. are not uncommon. The org-thermometer is, of course, never exposed directly to the sun's rays.

The thermometric measurement of orgone radiation from the soil can also be accomplished using other arrangements. The one essential ingredient of such experiments is strict and clear definition of the comparative basis for the measurements. $T(o)$ can be measured against T of the air or soil. The $T(o)$ of the air must be distinguished from the $T(o)$ of the soil. In the same way, the distinction must be made between measurements taken inside a metal cylinder placed vertically over a metal plate and those taken inside a metal cylinder without a metal plate. The following diagrams will illustrate a few principal methods of measuring orgone energy temperatures:

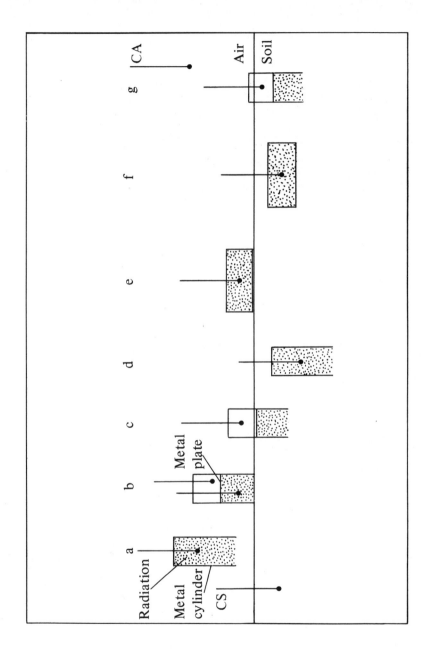

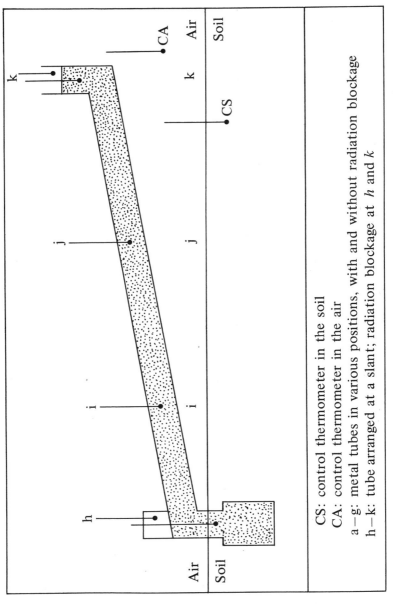

CS: control thermometer in the soil
CA: control thermometer in the air
a—g: metal tubes in various positions, with and without radiation blockage
h—k: tube arranged at a slant; radiation blockage at h and k

FIGURE 14. Different methods of measuring $T(o) - T$ in soil and the atmosphere

The results may be summarized as follows: The temperature rise in a metal tube is greater above a metal cross-plate than without a cross-plate.

In rainy weather, the temperature differences are either minimal or they disappear completely.

With strong sun radiation, the temperature differences reappear and reach high values.

To obtain the effect of orgone radiation, we leave the tubes open. To produce the *temperature difference* we close the tubes with metal plates and take the measurements *above* the plates.

The experienced theoretical physicist will readily view the constant orgonotic temperature difference as a finding that would invalidate the *second law of thermodynamics*. It is true there is a process in nature in the direction of increasing entropy, which is to say "the universe is running down." However, there is another energy process, an *orgonotic* process, which functions in the opposite direction, toward a restoration of the energy that is being lost in the process directed toward increasing entropy. This problem will have to be elaborated in a separate context.

DEMONSTRATION OF ORGONOTIC ATTRACTION IN THE ENERGY FIELD OF THE ORGONE ACCUMULATOR

Arrangement: We bring a good magnetic needle close to an orgone energy accumulator with 1 cubic foot of interior space, in the following manner: 1) toward the center of the four upper edges; 2) toward the center of the four lower edges.

Result: The magnetic north pole fixes itself consistently toward the middle of the upper edges, while the magnetic south pole fixes itself toward the middle of the lower edges.

Conclusion: The reaction of the energy field of the orgone accumulator is orgonotic and not magnetic in nature.

Proof: 1) The magnetic attraction emanates only from certain parts of the iron, namely from the ends rather than from the middle; the middle is not magnetic. 2) The poles of magnetic attraction (south or north) are not interchangeable, except by remagnetizing a weak magnet by means of a stronger one. If the attraction effect of the orgone accumulator were iron-magnetic in nature, then the magnetic needle would always move toward the center of the edges regardless of how we moved or turned the accumulator. But the actual reaction of the magnetic needle is different. *No matter which edges are made the lower, side, or upper edges, the magnetic needle always reacts in the way described,* i.e., its north pole fixes itself consistently toward the center of the four upper edges, its south pole toward the center of its four lower edges. The attraction emanating from the orgone accumulator is therefore not bound to specific parts of the material and consequently cannot be magnetic in nature. The reaction is clearly dependent upon the position of the orgone accumulator in the field of the orgonotic atmosphere of the earth. The conclusion that must be drawn from careful consideration of all experimental and theoretical facts is that the energy field of the earth is not magnetic but orgonotic in nature and stands in a well-defined relationship to the magnetic north and south poles of the earth.

The probability is that magnetism itself will prove to be a particular function of cosmic orgone energy. Many scientists already doubt the magnetic nature of so-called earth magnetism.

USE OF THE STATIC ELECTROSCOPE FOR THE DEMONSTRATION AND MEASUREMENT OF ORGONE ENERGY: ELECTROSCOPICAL ORGONOMETRY

The measurements of the temperature difference $T(o) - T$ show that a radiating energy exists inside the accumulator. But they say nothing about the *nature* of this energy. Furthermore, the subjective light phenomena yield little knowledge about the quality of the radiation even though they are extremely impressive and convincing.

Over a period of months, several times a day we systematically measure the discharge of the electroscope, inside the accumulator, in a room, and in the open air. The following premise underlies our experiment with electroscopic measurements: Charged leaf electroscopes discharge *more rapidly* in strongly ionized air than in weak air or air that is not ionized. (By "ionized air" is meant air containing electronegative units, i.e., "electrons.") The air in a room can be "ionized" by X-rays or by the ultraviolet rays from a sunlamp. Air at high altitudes is much more strongly ionized than air in the lowlands. Strongly ionized air causes this rapid discharge because it acts as a conductor between all the parts of the electroscope, so that the charge of the metal walls and that of the leaf are more easily equalized than in non-ionized air which is a poor conductor. The electroscopic measurements in the study of cosmic rays are based on this principle.

The following possible results may be expected from measuring the electroscopic discharges *outside* and *inside* the orgone accumulator:

1. *The electroscope discharges with equal speed inside and outside* the orgone accumulator. This would mean that *no difference* exists between the charge of the air inside the apparatus and the charge outside of it. Thus, there is no greater concentration of atmospheric orgone energy inside, in which case the temperature difference phenomenon would remain incomprehensible.

2. *The electroscope discharges more rapidly inside than outside the orgone accumulator.* This would mean that the air inside the apparatus is more strongly *ionized* than the air outside; i.e., it contains more negative electric charges (electrons). *Our orgone energy would then be identical with negative electricity.* That, too, would make the phenomenon of the absorption of orgone energy by organic materials incomprehensible.

3. *The electroscope discharges more slowly inside the orgone accumulator than outside it.* This would imply that *orgone energy is*

something other than negative electricity. It would then be necessary to explain the slower discharge of the electroscope inside the accumulator in order to conclude that the electroscope is registering a *concentration of orgone energy.* Only in this third case would the subjective phenomena, the temperature difference, and the speed of discharge of the electroscope be consistent with each other and understandable. Our orgone theory then would be considerably advanced, since several manifestations of the energy would now be derived from *one single* principle.

The measurements taken systematically inside and outside the accumulator do in fact demonstrate that the electroscope discharges *more slowly inside than outside.* Postponing for the moment any discussion of the why and how of our observation, we simply record it as a fact from which we conclude:

1. *The energy tension inside the accumulator is different from that outside it. This implies a difference in potential between the inside and the outside.* What we do not know is whether the potential is higher inside than outside or the reverse.

2. *The energy within the apparatus cannot have its origin in a stronger ionization of the air inside;* otherwise the electroscope would discharge *more rapidly inside,* not more slowly. If, then, the *presence* of the energy inside the accumulator is unquestionable, but is not due to electrons, what is it? *It could be another form of energy. In any case, it is not negative electricity.*

Although equal or more rapid discharge inside the accumulator would be easily accounted for within the framework of known theories, it is difficult to explain the slow discharge which we had not anticipated.

At this point we are aided by the fact that we charge the electroscope by drawing off energy from cotton wadding or cellulose. We can also charge it from our hair (which must be *dry*) by use of a polysterene rod or a cellulose disk, both of which absorb this energy from the hair. The energy is present in the air both inside and outside the apparatus, but in *different concentrations,* as is demonstrated by the difference in the speed of discharge. The electroscope has access to the air through the disk at the top and other holes, and its casing is grounded. The energy transmitted to it by solar radiation or from our body is released back into the surrounding atmosphere in the process of discharge. We now feel justified in considering the following assumption:

The lower the energy tension of the air is, relative to the charge of the electroscope, the more rapidly will the electroscope release the energy with which it was charged. The higher the energy tension of the surrounding air is (i.e., the smaller the difference between the energy tension of the electroscope and that of the surrounding air), the more slowly will the electroscope discharge.

This assumption is in accord with the laws of energy in general. Water flows faster between two vessels positioned one over the other the greater the height between the two. The speed of the flow depends on the steepness of the drop or, in other words, on the extent of the difference in positional (potential) energy. *The metallic plate of the electroscope can discharge more rapidly into air of low energy tension than into air of high tension.* Here I am deliberately trying to make the difference in speed of discharge comprehensible in terms of the traditional theory of potential difference. It has been shown elsewhere that another, purely biophysical interpretation does better justice to the facts.[2]

This characteristic of our energy is new. It is not explained by ionization: the electroscope would discharge more rapidly in air with a high electrical charge. The fact that this energy *cannot, therefore, be electricity* is inescapable but disquieting, because an energy that influences an electroscope and is not electromagnetic energy sounds implausible.

[2] *Cf.* "Orgonotic Pulsation," *International Journal of Sex-economy and Orgone Research,* October, 1944.

We must consider another possible objection, which would be that the spontaneous discharge of the electroscope is slower inside than outside the accumulator because the circulation of air inside the apparatus is slower than that outside. Hence, the exchange of air ions takes place more slowly inside the accumulator than outside of it, thus causing the slower discharge. According to this viewpoint, the phenomenon could therefore be explained in the context of the theory of ions, i.e., of electricity.

This objection is easily tested. We measure exactly the speed of discharge of our electroscope outside of the accumulator. Then we charge the electroscope again to precisely the same level and accelerate the circulation of the air around it with the aid of an electric fan. Result: *The fan does not affect the speed of discharge. The difference in the speed of discharge cannot be ascribed to the circulation of air. Our energy behaves differently than electricity. The speed of electroscopic discharge depends solely upon the atmospheric energy tension which, in turn, is determined by the density or concentration of orgone particles per cubic unit of air.*

As our observations have shown, the energy in the apparatus is more concentrated than in the open air. The designation "accumulator of atmospheric energy" is therefore accurate.

In theory, enclosed electroscopes should not lose their charge. The fact is, however, that they do discharge spontaneously. This phenomenon is called by physicists "natural leak" and is ascribed to the humidity of the air. *Thus, we are in reality measuring the phenomenon designated as the "natural leak" of the electroscope.* We do not hermetically seal off the air inside the electroscope, but *intentionally* allow access to the outside air. We thus determine precisely the same phenomenon that the physicist, in measuring the effect of an electrical radiation source, tries to exclude. Insofar as he is unsuccessful in doing so, he subtracts the ion effect from the results, because until now the "natural leak" has not been understood. *The spontaneous discharge of the electroscope "without apparent reason" is nothing other than the normal effect of atmospheric orgone energy.*

There is still another possible objection: The electroscope discharges more slowly inside the accumulator than outside it only because the inner metal walls insulate the interior of the accumulator against the effect of radioactive substances. This objection is refuted as follows:

1. No matter where the accumulator is placed, the phenomenon of the slower discharge in the interior of the apparatus is always present, as is the temperature difference. It is improbable that "radioactive substances" are *ubiquitous.*

2. If the effect were to be ascribed to radioactive substances outside the apparatus, then the discharge would have to be more rapid in a simple wooden box than in a wooden box protected against radioactivity by metal plates on the outside. In reality, the discharge of the electroscope is more rapid *when the wooden box is lined on the outside with metal plates.* This fact refutes the objection and is further confirmation of the accuracy of our finding.

QUANTITATIVE DETERMINATION OF THE ORGONE

Orgone energy manifests itself in temperature differences and in variations in speeds of electroscopic discharge in the orgone accumulator. These facts can be used as the basis for *quantitative* orgone measurements. First, we determine that a single unit of orgone energy shall be known as 1 org. *An org may be defined as the quantity of orgone energy in a space of 1 cubic foot, which corresponds to the maintenance of a temperature difference* $T(o) - T$ *of 1° C. for one hour, according to the formula*

$$1 \text{ org} = (T(o) - T) \cdot t \cdot f^3$$

$T(o) - T$ being the temperature difference in degrees centigrade, t, the time in hours, and f^3, the volume in cubic feet.

The *quantity* of orgone energy, i.e., the number of orgone energy particles per unit of space (org), has to be distinguished from the *orgone tension* (op). We define as 1 op that atmospheric orgone charge which in the time unit of one hour (T, $60t'$, and $3600t''$) decreases the charge of a static electroscope by one unit ($Eo - Er = 1$).

If 1 op (atm) designates the unit of atmospheric orgone tension, Eo the charge of the electroscope, Er the remaining electroscope charge after the reading, ($Eo - Er$) the amount of discharge, and t the time in hours, then the following formula represents the atmospheric orgone tension in the open air

$$op = \frac{t}{Eo - Er}$$

The op *inside* the orgone accumulator can be distinguished from the op of the atmosphere by adding the designation "accu." Op can also be expressed directly in hour-org, minute-org, or second-org, according to whether a unit of charge of the electroscope discharges in an hour, a minute, a second, or in fractions or multiples of these time units, as in this table:

$$
\begin{array}{rll}
1 \text{ hour op} & = 60 \text{ minute-org} & (60'\,0) \\
0.75 \quad\;\; \text{op} & = 45 \text{ minute-org} & (45'\,0) \\
0.5 \quad\;\; \text{op} & = 30 \text{ minute-org} & (30'\,0) \\
0.25 \quad\;\; \text{op} & = 15 \text{ minute-org} & (15'\,0) \\
0.16 \quad\;\; \text{op} & = 10 \text{ minute-org} & (10'\,0) \\
0.1 \quad\;\; \text{op} & = 6 \text{ minute-org} & (6'\,0) \\
0.05 \quad\;\; \text{op} & = 3 \text{ minute-org} & (3'\,0) \\
0.015 \quad\;\; \text{op} & = 1 \text{ minute-org} & (1'\,0) \\
0.00025 \text{ op} & = 1 \text{ second-org} & (1''0) \\
\end{array}
$$

Suppose, for instance, one unit of the electroscope charge discharges in thirty minutes. The op is then

$$op = \frac{0.5\,(t)}{1(Eo - Er)} = 0.5$$

or

$$op = 30'\,\mathrm{org}$$

If, for example, the total charge of the electroscope $Eo = 5$ org (equivalent to 630 volts) is discharged in twenty minutes, then

$$op = \frac{0.33\,(t)}{5 - 0(5\,Eo - Er)} = 0.066$$

or

$$op = 4'\,\mathrm{org}\,(4\ \mathrm{minute\text{-}org})$$

The choice of one or the other method of calculation is entirely a matter of convenience.

The orgone charge of the static leaf electroscope can also be expressed in electrostatic units. One "electrostatic unit" is set internationally at a value of approximately 300 volts. We charge an electroscope with energy from the hair until the electroscope leaf is deflected 45° or 90°. The same effect can be obtained by applying a high voltage to the electroscope. *One unit of org-charge then corresponds to the voltage necessary to produce the same deflection of the electroscope leaf.* By this method, we find that *one single* gentle stroke of the hair can draw off energy amounts equivalent to hundreds of volts.

The instrument used in making these measurements is a static electroscope with an aluminum leaf. The voltage calibration of this electroscope in the laboratory of the Radio Corporation of America showed the following values:

Scale Divisions		*Volts*	
1		135 ⎫	
2		180 ⎬ approximately 45 volts	
3		225 ⎪ per division	
4		270 ⎭	
5		330 ⎫	
6		390 ⎪ approximately 60 volts	
7		450 ⎬ per division	
8		510	
Standard: 1 org. { 9	120 volts {	570 ⎭	
10		630 ⎫	
11		730 ⎬ approximately 100 volts	
11 1/2		780 ⎭ per division	

Using the method of stroking a cellulose disk over the hair, we always charged the electroscope up to the *tenth* scale division, that is to an energy load equivalent to approximately 630 volts, then let it discharge two scale divisions, i.e., the orgone equivalent of 120 volts, into the surrounding air. *The scale divisions (8–10) thus correspond to 1 org unit charge, i.e., 120 volts.* If an electroscope that has been charged to the tenth scale division with an orgone energy equivalent of 630 volts discharges in one hour (sixty minutes) 1 org (=120 volts), then the orgone tension (op) of the surrounding air is 1 hour-op or *60 minute-op.* In other words, the electroscope discharged into the air at the rate of 2 volts per minute.

The unit 1 org was determined by the constant temperature difference $T(o) - T$ in one hour in an accumulator of 1 cubic foot. Electroscopically, 1 org is defined as the equivalent of 120 volts. Whether these two determinations of the unit 1 org are equivalent is still unknown.

The fact that the curves representing $T(o) - T$ and the atmospheric orgone tension (op atm) are parallel would appear to indicate this. However, further investigation will be required to arrive at a definite answer.

I would now like to report the results of a few measurements, which reveal some extremely interesting facts about the orgone tension in the atmosphere and the relationship of this tension to the tension in the accumulator. Certainly what I am presenting here are only rough outlines; more intensive work over an extended period of time is needed in order to fill in all the details. But the essential

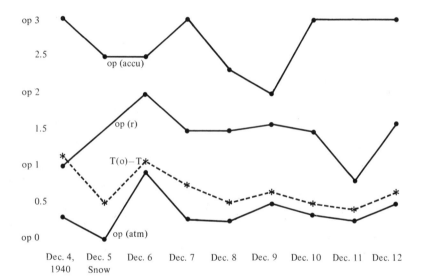

FIGURE 15. Measurements of the atmospheric orgone in the open air, in the orgone accumulator, and in the orgone room. Broken line represents $T(o) - T$. Op 1 corresponds to $T(o) - T = 1°\ C$

points are clear. Figure 15 graphs three superimposed orgone tension curves: *op* (*atm*) represents the curve of daily variations in atmospheric orgone tension, measured regularly at 12 noon; *op* (*r*) depicts the daily variations of orgone tension in the room in which the orgone accumulator stood at the time of the measurings; *op* (*accu*), the third and uppermost curve, shows the variations in orgone tension inside the accumulator, measured between 12 noon and 1 P.M. Curve *T*(*o*) − *T*, drawn as a broken line, presents the variations in temperature difference at the accumulator, measured daily between 12 noon and 1 P.M. from November 29 to December 22, 1940, in an orgone accumulator of 1 cubic foot, and beginning December 24, 1940, in an orgone accumulator of 25 cubic feet (2′ × 2.5′ × 5′), built for human beings. (See also Fig. 16, pp. 138–139.)

The overall pattern of the curves provides the following observations:

1. The tension curve of the room *op* (*r*) is higher than that of the atmosphere in terms of minute-org; the tension curve of the accumulator *op* (*accu*) is higher than that of the room and that of the atmosphere *op* (*atm*); i.e., *the concentration of energy is at its greatest in the accumulator.*

2. *The temperature difference curve T*(*o*) − *T runs with its ups and downs more or less parallel to the tension curve op* (*atm*).

3. *The rise in tension in room and accumulator usually occurs about one day after the rise of atmospheric tension.*

4. *The atmospheric tension curve is low on rainy and snowy days, high on sunny days. The atmospheric tension varies between close to 0 and approximately 1.* The atmospheric tension drops more or less steeply one or two days before snow or rain. The temperature differ-

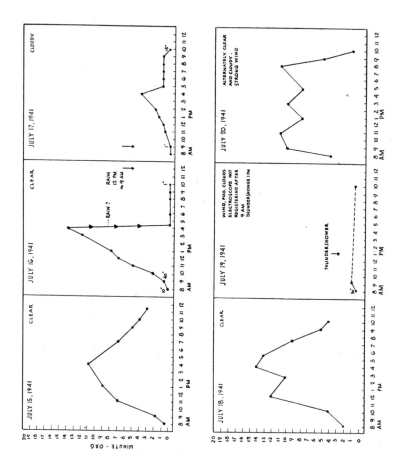

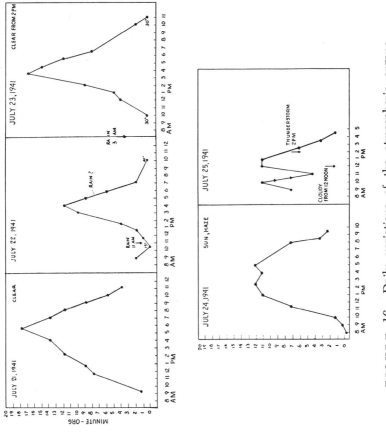

FIGURE 16. Daily variations of the atmospheric orgone tension between July 15 and July 25, 1941

ence curve also falls before or during a period of precipitation.

Thus, there is a connection between the degree of concentra-
tion of atmospheric orgone and weather formation. A thorough
grasp of this relationship naturally is of great importance to us in
our work with the accumulator in orgone therapy.

Let us now dispose of a probable objection to the curves in
Figure 15: The assumption of a special orgone energy is not necessary to account for the drop in the *op (atm)* curve, i.e., the more
rapid discharge of the electroscope before the onset of precipitation.
This phenomenon can easily be explained within the context of the
theory of "electricity in the air"; quite simply, the accelerated discharge of the electroscope is due to the fact that the air is more
strongly ionized before rain or thunderstorm. Indeed, this misgiving
was in my mind too, but I was unable to get around the fact of the
slower discharge of the electroscope inside the accumulator.

Total refutation of this particular objection emerged during
experimental measurings conducted in the months of July and
August 1941 in my laboratory at Oquossoc, Maine. Over a number
of weeks I measured not only the daily variations at 12 noon but
also the variations in the atmospheric energy tension during the day
from 8 A.M. to approximately 12 midnight, hourly, in all kinds of
weather. *These measurements showed unequivocally that the dis-*
charge of the electroscope is dependent, not upon variations in the
"electricity in the air," but upon variations of the atmospheric
orgone tension.

Figure 16 graphs the daily variations of atmospheric tensions
from measurements taken between July 15 and July 25, 1941.
During the early morning hours the discharge of the electroscope is
far more rapid than in the period between 12 noon and 4 P.M.; it is
slowest at midday. This is due, of course, to the intense solar radiation at midday. Thus, completely in accord with our other observations, it is due to *the higher concentration of orgone energy* at that

time of day. It would not be sensible to assume that the atmospheric air in the early morning and late evening is more strongly "ionized" than it is in the noonday sun. The electroscope discharges *more rapidly* in the early morning and late evening than at noon. Just the opposite would be expected if the laws of "air electricity" were being followed. The highest concentration occurs around 4 P.M. On days when there are no clouds from early morning to late evening, the curve rises and falls in a more or less regular pattern. Changing weather, on the other hand, causes considerable fluctuations in the curves, as occurred, for instance, on July 20, when, between 9 A.M. and 8 P.M., there was a repeated rise and fall in the intensity of concentration not found on days of steady sunshine. We also notice that *a rapid change from high to low concentration of atmospheric energy regularly occurs about three to ten hours before a rainfall or a thunderstorm.* The electroscope discharges very rapidly in the open air and in the orgone accumulator (slightly less quickly in the accumulator than outside), and the temperature difference $T(o) - T$ becomes very small or entirely disappears. Measurements taken at regular intervals over an extended period indicate that the curve of electroscopic discharge patterns itself in undulations approximately parallel to those of the temperature difference curve.

At two o'clock in the afternoon on July 25 there was thunder with rain. During the morning, the tension had fallen between 10 and 11 A.M. from 12′ org to 5′ org. A similar drop was registered on July 16, when the tension fell from 14 minute-org to 10″ org *between 4 P.M. and 4:30 P.M.*—within the space of *thirty minutes.* At midnight there was a heavy downpour.

The same occurrence was recorded on July 22, when the tension dropped from 12′ org to 2′ org between 4 P.M. and 7 P.M., and by 10 P.M. was only 30″ org. At 3 A.M. on July 23 a strong, steady rain began.

On July 19 the weather was windy and very cloudy, and the tension did not rise above 1 minute-org. At 10 A.M. the electroscope could not be charged and at 1 P.M. a violent thunderstorm started which lasted until 3 P.M. By contrast, a sunny day can be relied upon to follow days showing a regular tension curve and relatively high levels of orgone concentration during the evening hours (1 to 3 minute-org). The daily variations are very important for orgone therapy. If we expose patients to orgone energy in doses calculated according to hour-op or minute-org, then the duration of exposure will have to be different in the early morning hours than at noon or during the late evening. This will be necessary as long as we are unable to regulate the tension of the orgone independent of the weather.

Control measurements taken at regular intervals since the summer of 1941 confirmed the most important findings: Orgone energy tension varies with the time of day; it drops or disappears altogether before or during rainfall or snow; electroscopic reactions occur in direct contravention of the theory of ionization of the air.

The reader trained in physics will have posed the question: *What relation does orgone energy have to so-called static electricity?* This question was discussed elsewhere.[3]

5. DEMONSTRATION OF ORGONOTIC PULSATION IN THE REALM OF NON-LIVING MATTER

The following observations and experiments were carried out for the purpose of demonstrating the presence of specifically biological orgone energy in the *purely physical* realm. This undertaking succeeded, thereby removing any possibility of a mystical, otherworldly, philosophical concept of the specific biological energy. The observations and experiments in question are very simple and easy to carry out.

[3] *Cf.* "Orgonotic Pulsation," *op. cit.*

THE OSCILLATIONS OF A PENDULUM IN
THE PULSATING ORGONE ENERGY FIELD
OF A METAL SPHERE

Experiment: A metal sphere of iron or steel, about 4 to 6 cm. in diameter, is placed on a stable surface,[4] a solid table for instance. A much smaller sphere, about 1 cm. in diameter, is suspended pendulum-wise at about 0.5 cm. from the equator of the larger sphere. For definite reasons the length of the pendulum thread should be exactly 16 cm. My experience is that the best results are obtained by making the pendulum sphere out of a mixture of soil and iron filings (i.e., a combination of organic and metallic material) molded together in water and then put into an extremely thin-walled glass sphere. The bigger sphere and the pendulum sphere are then covered with a cellulose cover to protect them against air currents.

Observation: In dry, sunny weather the pendulum sphere oscillates toward the center of the larger metal sphere, spontaneously. When the relative humidity exceeds about 70 percent, or when it rains, the swings of the pendulum grow smaller until they stop altogether. They resume their spontaneous movement with the return of good weather. The swings of the pendulum will become greater if the observer's own organism has a strong and far-reaching orgone energy field. The oscillations continue without stopping, no matter where the apparatus is placed. They are determined only by the laws that govern any pendulum, the number of oscillations varying per unit of time, depending on the length of the pendulum and its height above sea level.

Conclusion: This experiment demonstrates *the existence of a pulsating orgone energy field* around an ordinary iron sphere capable of causing a freely suspended pendulum to oscillate. *The*

[4] This arrangement is advantageous but *not* indispensable. Movements of a pendulum caused by the instability of the base on which it stands are easily distinguishable from orgonotic pendulations.

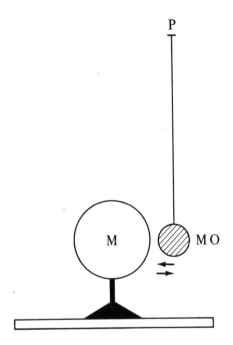

M: metal sphere
P: pendulum
MO: pendulum sphere (metal and organic matter)
⇄: direction of oscillation

FIGURE 17. Demonstration of orgonotic pulsation in the atmosphere

natural orgone energy field, in the realm of non-living matter, pulsates.

THE PULSATION OF ATMOSPHERIC ORGONE ENERGY

Observation and Experiment: My experiment was set up as follows: A telescope with an aperture of 3 1/2 inches and a length of 4 feet, capable of a magnification of 185x (supplied by E. Vion, Paris, France), was so positioned on the shore of the lake that the opposite shore, about 4 to 8 miles away, could be clearly observed. Observations were made toward all four points of the compass. They were carried out over two months during the summer of 1944 and four weeks in the summer of 1945, at my cabin on Lake Mooselookmeguntic, near Oquossoc, Maine. During these two periods I conducted observations at approximately half-hourly intervals every day from early morning to late evening. For reasons that will be appreciated, only the daily mean and the changes were actually recorded. The observation is the following: When the telescope is pointed south, it is possible to observe against the background of the opposite shore of the lake, at a magnification of only 60x, a wavy, pulsating movement traveling, with few exceptions, always *from west to east.* The west-east movement is constant, whether the lake is rough or smooth, whether or not there is wind, and whether the wind is from west to east or south to north, strong or weak. The further the telescope is turned toward the west or the east the more difficult it is to see the movement. It can no longer be seen when the telescope is trained due west or east. The speed of the wavy movement varies greatly at different times. It is independent of the air temperature. The "something" in the atmosphere is moving faster than the earth; otherwise its movement could not be seen. Every time a severe thunderstorm formed in the west, the direction of the undulating movement was reversed, or ceased altogether. I have never seen it move from south to north or north to south.

This telescopic observation is supported by an observation that can be made with the naked eye when there is absolutely no wind or breeze, and the surface of the lake is completely smooth: a pulsating of an infinite number of separate sections is perceptible over the water, while the "whole" moves in more or less rapid pulsations from west to east.

These observations, simple to make with a little practice and patience, are in accord with the confirmation of the pulsating orgone energy field around a metal sphere, and with the basic concept of orgone biophysics of the *fundamental pulsatory function of orgone energy*. In addition, the rotation and pulsation of atmospheric orgone energy from west to east is in clear and unequivocal conformity with certain astronomical observations known for a long time. I intend to discuss elsewhere, in detail, the implications for astronomy of the phenomenon just described. However, the preliminary conclusion is that *the earth is surrounded not only by an air atmosphere of a definite chemical composition but also by an envelope of orgone energy.* This "orgone envelope" rotates from west to east, faster than the earth. More precise research still needs to be done on the relationship of the reversal of this rotation to local weather formation. The rotating orgone envelope has no connection whatsoever with waves of haze or air movement, being independent of these processes.

This account should be regarded as a preliminary finding which will be confirmed and refined when social and financial circumstances permit. However, it might be relevant here to report that a pulsation in the atmosphere has been successfully recorded by oscillograph. I would like to reserve the presentation of this phenomenon, and further research on the subject, for a later time.

6. DEMONSTRATION OF ORGONOTIC LUMINATION AT
THE ORGONE ENERGY FIELD METER

Experiment: The different pole of the secondary coil of an induction apparatus (an old diathermy apparatus, for instance) is connected by ordinary electric appliance wire to an iron plate, 2 feet long and 1 foot wide. The iron plate is insulated on the underside with wood. A similar metal plate is then mounted above and parallel to the first at a distance of 6 to 12 inches and in such a way that it can slide up and down. The top side of the upper metal plate is insulated with a piece of plastic celotex, or like material the same size as the plate and 1/2 inch thick. Electric wire connects the two iron plates to a simple cylindrical bulb of about 40 watts set between them. The primary current of the induction apparatus is maintained at the minimum level necessary to make the bulb glow. How this glow is obtained will depend, of course, on the nature of the induction apparatus used.

Observation: 1. An argon gas tube (fluorescent tube) held in the hand and moved toward the upper metal plate luminates. The distance from the plate at which it starts to glow depends on the strength of the primary current. The light goes out when we place the gas tube on the upper plate and take away our hand. The lumination returns as soon as we move our hand close again, and it becomes particularly strong if we touch the glass of the tube. The lumination is most intense *between* the two metal plates, and fades steadily as the distance from the apparatus is increased. The lumination is intermittent. By this method we can determine exactly the energy field of the orgone energy field meter.

2. The cylindrical bulb between the two metal plates begins to luminate more intensely when we gradually lower our hands toward the upper plate. The lumination becomes especially intense if we actually lay our hands on the upper plate. (To prevent the possibility of electrical shocks there should be no metal on the surface of

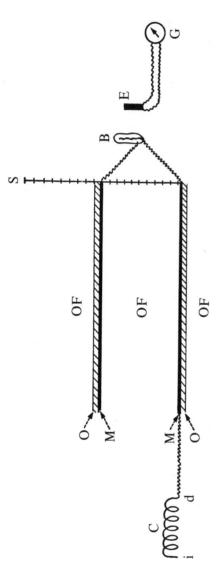

C: secondary coil system; i: indifferent pole; d: different pole
O: organic material
M: metallic material
OF: luminating orgone energy field
S: centimeter scale
B: 40–60-watt tungsten bulb
E: electric eye
G: galvanometer

FIGURE 18.   Diagram of orgone field meter device

the plate.) The more body surface we bring close to the upper plate, the stronger the lumination becomes. By carefully adjusting the strength of the primary current, we can even perceive pulsations of the heart, in the form of slight fluctuations in the intensity of the lumination.

3. A static leaf electroscope shows no deflection when we approach its plate with the palm of the hand. But if we put the electroscope in the energy field of the apparatus, on its upper plate, and then move the palm of the hand toward the plate of the electroscope—without touching it, of course—the electroscope leaf will be influenced.

4. A freshly cut branch with many leaves makes the bulb luminate, although the lumination is weaker than that elicited by the hand. A live or freshly killed fish placed upon the upper metal plate produces the same effect. Note that the longer the fish has been dead, the feebler the lumination. Eventually it fades completely. The same gradual decrease in intensity is also true for the branch.

5. There is no lumination when we bring an old piece of wood close to the upper plate. (We, of course, make sure that the wood is long enough so that our own orgone energy field does not come into contact with the orgone energy field of the apparatus.) An iron plate held above and parallel to the upper plate does make the cylindrical bulb luminate, however.

6. The argon gas cannot be made to luminate in the energy field of an X-ray machine of 60–80 kilovolt.

CONCLUSIONS

1. In contrast with simple, electrical high-tension voltage, the secondary coil of an induction apparatus develops an orgone energy field that can be demonstrated by the lumination of an inert gas, such as helium, argon, or neon, without any direct wire contact being necessary.

2. *The orgonotic lumination is the result of the contact between two orgone energy fields.*

3. The lumination effect can be achieved only by contact between an orgone energy field and the field of a *living* organism, not through contact with non-living, organic matter. This means that the living organism is distinguished from the non-living in that it has an orgone energy field.

4. By installing a sensitive electric eye opposite the cylindrical bulb, the luminating energy can be transformed into electrical energy and measured in electrical units by means of a galvanometer. The orgone field meter can thus be used for the determination of the intensity and range of the orgone energy field of a living organism.

7. A MOTOR FORCE IN ORGONE ENERGY

In the summer of 1947 certain observations were made from which a most significant conclusion has been drawn:

1. Using several accumulators or a specially built orgone room, a high concentration of atmospheric orgone energy can be obtained. This is demonstrated by Geiger-Müller counters registering 40–80 impulses per minute, at a threshold voltage of 700–800 volts.

2. Geiger counter tubes that have absorbed orgone energy by being kept in an orgone atmosphere of high concentration for several weeks can produce 25 to 100 impulses per second in the impulse counter, at a "rotation threshold" of 900–1000 volts. This rate of impulses amounts to an even rotation of the pointer in the impulse counter. In other words:

3. *Orgone energy is capable of developing a motor force.* Upon completion of control experiments, the relevant details will be published. But it is evident, at this point, that there is a motor force in orgone energy that provides an explanation for the locomotion of living organisms.

CHAPTER V

The Carcinomatous
Shrinking Biopathy

1. DEFINITION OF BIOPATHIES

The cancer tumor is merely a visible symptom of the disease we call "cancer." Localized treatment of the cancer tumor by surgery or irradiation with radium or X-ray therefore constitutes treatment of a symptom only, not of the disease itself. In this regard, death from cancer is not the result of the presence of one or more tumors. It is rather the final result of the systemic biological disease "cancer," which is caused by a disintegrative process in the total organism. Medical literature gives no information about the *nature* of this systemic disease. So-called *cancer disposition* indicates merely that deadly processes, uninvestigated up to now, are at work behind the cancer tumor. The typical cancer cachexia, the last stage of the disease, should be regarded only as the ultimate, visible phase of the unknown systemic process "cancer."

The term "cancer disposition" is meaningless. We would therefore like to replace it with the term *carcinomatous biopathy,* or *cancer biopathy.* The purpose of the following chapter is to demonstrate the process that is at the basis of the cancer biopathy.

The term *biopathies* refers to all disease processes caused by a basic dysfunction in the autonomic life apparatus. Once started, this dysfunction can manifest itself in a variety of symptomatic disease patterns. A biopathy can result in a carcinoma (carcinomatous biopathy), but it can just as easily lead to angina pectoris, asthma, cardiovascular hypertension, epilepsy, catatonic or paranoid schizophrenia, anxiety neurosis, multiple sclerosis, chorea, chronic alcoholism, etc. We are still ignorant of the factors that determine the direction in which a biopathy will develop. Of prime importance to us, however, is the *common denominator* of all these diseases: *a disturbance in the natural function of pulsation in the total organism.* Fractures, local abscesses, pneumonia, yellow fever, rheumatic pericarditis, acute alcoholic poisoning, infectious peritonitis, syphilis, etc., are, accordingly, *not* biopathies. They do not develop from disturbances in the autonomic pulsation of the total life apparatus; they are circumscribed and can only secondarily bring about a disturbance of the biological pulsation. The results of recent orgone-biophysical research, however, have raised questions about the exclusion of pneumonia and some heart diseases from the realm of biopathies. Further investigation will prove or disprove my assumption that the *disposition* to pneumonia, or to valvular heart diseases caused by "rheumatic fever," may be due to a chronic extension of the bony chest structure, resulting from the typical inspiratory fixation of the chest. For the present, however, we will use the term "biopathy" only where it is definite that the disease process begins with a disturbance of pulsation, no matter what secondary disease pattern results. Consequently, we can distinguish a schizophrenic biopathy from a cardiovascular biopathy, and these from an epileptic or carcinomatous biopathy, etc.

This addition to medical terminology is justified by the fact that we cannot understand any of the many specific diseases of the autonomic life apparatus unless:

1. We distinguish them from typical infectious and traumatic surgical diseases.
2. We look for and discover their common mechanism, the disturbance of biological pulsation.
3. We learn to understand their differentiations into the various disease patterns.

Cancer is particularly well suited to a study of the fundamental mechanisms of biopathies, because it manifests many of the disturbances treated in everyday general medical practice. It reveals pathological cell growth; it has as one of its essential characteristics bacterial intoxication and putrefaction; it develops from chemical as well as bio-electric disturbances of the organism; it is related to emotional and sexual disturbances; it generates a number of secondary processes, such as anemia, which otherwise develop as independent diseases; it is a disease decisively influenced by our "civilized" mode of living; it is of as much concern to the nutritionist as to the endocrinologist or the virus researcher.

The many manifestations of cancer, like the multiplicities of neuroses and psychoses, conceal a single common denominator: *sexual stasis*. This leads us directly to our thesis: *Sexual stasis represents a fundamental disturbance of biological pulsation*. Sexual excitation is a primal function of the living plasma system. *The sexual function is demonstrably the productive life function per se*.[1] A *chronic* disturbance of this function must of necessity coincide with a biopathy.

The stasis of biosexual excitation is manifested in two ways principally: *indirectly*, as emotional disturbance of the psychic apparatus, i.e., as a neurosis or psychosis; or *directly*, as a functional disturbance of the organs, in which case it appears as an organic disease. According to our present knowledge, it cannot actually generate infectious diseases.

The central mechanism of a biopathy is a disturbance in the discharge of biosexual excitation. This statement requires the most detailed substantiation. But it should come as no surprise that physical and chemical processes as well as emotional factors are at work in biopathies. The psychosomatic harmony of the total biological system is most clearly evident in biosexual emotion. It is only logical, therefore, that disturbances in the discharge of biosexual energy, wherever they appear, form the basis for disturbances of biological functioning, that is, a biopathy.

[1] *Cf*. Wilhelm Reich, *The Function of the Orgasm*.

2. BIOPATHIC SHRINKING

The living process in man is fundamentally the same as in the amoeba.[2] Its main characteristic is *biological* pulsation, the alternation of *contraction* and *expansion*. This process can be observed in single-celled organisms in the rhythmical contractions of the vacuoles or the contractions and serpentine movements of the plasma. In metazoa, its most obvious manifestation is in the cardiovascular system, where the pulse beat is clear evidence of pulsation. Its manifestation in the organism as a whole varies according to the structure of the individual organs. In the intestines, for example, it appears as "peristalsis," waves of alternating expansion and contraction. In the urinary bladder, the biological pulsation functions in response to the stimulus of mechanical expansion caused by the filling of the bladder with urine. The process also manifests itself in the muscular functions, namely as contraction in the striated muscles and as undulating peristalsis in the smooth muscles. It permeates the entire organism in the orgastic convulsion (the orgasm reflex).

Neither the pulsatory movements of the body organs, nor their disturbances, such as blocking, shrinking, etc., are compatible with the prevailing notion that the nerves act merely as conductors of impulses, while they themselves remain rigid and immobile. *Autonomic movements can be comprehended only if the autonomic nervous system is itself mobile.* This can be proven by direct observations. We place a small, sufficiently transparent worm (e.g., a meal worm) under a good microscope, so arranged that both the ganglion and its *fibers* are in focus. Since the worm is constantly in motion and reacts sharply to the stimulus of light, focusing requires repeated movement of the fine adjustment screws. This experiment will provide convincing evidence that *the autonomic nervous system is not rigid but actually contracts and expands.* The movements of

[2] *Cf.* Wilhelm Reich, "Der Urgegensatz des vegetativen Lebens" (1934).

the nerves are serpentine, slowly undulating, and occasionally jerky. They consistently precede the corresponding movements of the total organism by a fraction of a second: first the nerve and its rami contract, followed by the contraction of the musculature. Expansion proceeds in the same fashion. As the worm dies, the nervous system gradually shrinks, and there occurs a bending of the organism. This process of gradual shrinking is interrupted by occasional contractions. After a period of complete immobility, the rigid contraction (rigor mortis) abates, the organism grows slack, together with the nerves, and movement fails to return.

Biopathic shrinking begins with a chronic preponderance of contraction and an inhibition of expansion in the plasma system. This manifests itself most clearly in the respiratory disturbances of neurotic and psychotic patients in whom pulmonary and thoracic pulsation (the alternation of expansion and contraction) is restricted, and in whom an inspiratory attitude predominates. The general contraction (sympatheticotonia) is not confined to individual organs. It encompasses entire organ systems, their tissues, the blood system, the endocrine system, as well as the character structure. It is manifested in a variety of forms, according to its locality, e.g., as high blood pressure and tachycardia in the cardiovascular system, as shrinking of the red blood corpuscles (formation of T-bacilli, poikilocytosis, anemia) in the blood system, as affect block and character armoring in the realm of emotions, as spastic constipation in the alimentary canal, as pallor in the skin, as orgastic impotence in the sexual function, etc.

Here the attentive reader will raise an objection: Can one speak of "shrinking," he will ask, if the autonomic life apparatus is merely in a state of chronic contraction? Is it not possible that the contraction will yield and the function of complete pulsation be reestablished? Should a distinction not be made between "chronic contraction" and "shrinking" of the autonomic nervous system? Could not the shrinking very well be a *result* of the chronic contraction of the autonomic nerves, that is, a gradual withering of the life apparatus, a gradual, premature dying?

The objection is correct. *Biopathic shrinking in cancer is in fact the consequence of a gradual, chronic contraction of the autonomic life apparatus.*

3. SEX-ECONOMIC PREMISES

The following facts, familiar to us from our sex-economic clinical practice, connect the sexual function to cancer:

1. Poor external respiration which results in a disturbance in internal respiration in the tissues.
2. Disturbances in the orgonotic charge-discharge functions of the autonomic organs, especially the sexual organs.
3. Chronic spasms of the musculature.
4. Chronic orgastic impotence.

The connection between disturbances in the discharge of sexual energy and cancer has not been carefully examined. However, experienced gynecologists are aware of the existence of such a connection. Respiratory disturbances and muscular spasms are direct consequences of an acquired fear of sexual excitation (orgastic impotence). Poorly charged, spastic organs or organs with insufficient respiration develop a biological weakness that renders them highly vulnerable to cancer-producing stimuli of all kinds. Organs that function in a biologically natural manner resist the same stimuli. This is an obvious and necessary assumption.

The clinically established findings of deficient biological charge, muscular spasm, and reduced external and internal respiration give the concept of "cancer disposition" a tangible content. I now want to show how discoveries in sex-economic clinical practice prepare the way to cancer research.

The sex-economic examination of character neuroses revealed

again and again the crucial role of *muscular spasms and their devitalizing effect upon the organism.* Muscular spasm and deficiency in orgonotic charge are felt subjectively as "deadness." Muscular hypertension, resulting from chronic sexual stasis, regularly causes a decrease of organ sensations, to the point where the individual feels dead. This process corresponds to a block of bioenergetic activity in the affected organ. The blocking of biosexual excitation in the genitals, for instance, is accompanied by spasm of the pelvic musculature, as in the uterine spasms of frigid and neurotic women which frequently lead to menstrual disturbances and pain, polypous tumors, and myomata. Spasm in the uterus has no other function than to prevent the biosexual energy from being felt in the vagina. Spasms inhibiting the free flow of plasmatic currents affect particularly the *annular* musculature, e.g., in the throat, at the entrance and exit of the stomach, in the anus, etc. These are areas in the organism where cancer occurs with particular frequency. Disturbance in the biological charge in a gland, mucous membrane, or a particular area of the skin is caused by a muscular block close to the affected point which cuts off the plasmatic current. A woman I treated orgone-therapeutically had an incipient, carcinomatous lesion, confirmed by X-ray, of the fourth costal cartilage on the right side. This condition was the result of spastic contraction, occurring over several decades, of the right pectoralis muscle due to a strong holding-back in the shoulders, brought about by repressed beating impulses. She had never experienced orgasm and suffered from compulsive flirting.

In the practice of orgone therapy, we see not only characterneurotic disturbances but also, quite routinely, schizophrenia, epilepsy, Parkinson-like disease, rheumatic and cancerous manifestations. An organic disease may emerge during treatment or develop later, recalling early evidence that foreshadowed it: for example, the spasms of the pelvic musculature that occur so frequently in women, usually resulting in the development of benign tumors in the genital organs.

In our clinical practice, we have been faced with the important question of what happens to the *somatic* sexual excitation when it is not regularly discharged. We know only that biosexual excitation can be restricted and bound up in chronic muscular tension. In female patients this tension manifests itself in knot-like inspissations in the uterus and can be felt as lumps above the pubis. The muscular spasm of the uterus usually spreads to the anal sphincter and the vagina, then to the adductors of the thigh. The pelvis is regularly retracted and the sacral spine is often stiff and ankylosed. Lumbago and lordosis are typical of this condition. No organ sensations are felt in the pelvis. During exhalation, the wave of vegetative excitation is blocked by the rigidly elevated chest or the tense abdomen. The excitation of the large abdominal ganglia does not penetrate through to the genital organs. Consequently there is a disturbance of biological functioning. The genitals are no longer susceptible to biological excitation.

Many women suffering from genital tension and vaginal anesthesia complain of feeling that "something is not right down there." They report having experienced during puberty the familiar signs of biosexual excitation, itching and prickling, and having learned to combat these excitations by holding their breath, with the consequence that they no longer felt anything. Later, they typically relate, they began to feel a sensation of "deadness" or "numbness" in the genitals, which worried them. Since the biological state of the organs is mirrored in organ sensations, we must impute serious significance to such descriptions for the evaluation of somatic processes.[3]

The sexual inhibition commonly found in women is responsible for the prevalence of breast and genital cancer. In countless cases, this inhibition may be present for decades before it takes the form of cancer.

The following case illustrates in a particularly simple manner the direct connection between character armoring, muscular spasm, and the appearance of a cancer tumor.

[3] Women are usually unable to understand their own organ sensations. Character-analytical exploration is needed to enable them to do so.

A forty-five-year-old man came to my laboratory for treatment of a total obstruction of the esophagus caused by a carcinomatous growth. The intake of solid foods had become impossible for him, and he would immediately vomit liquids. X-rays showed a shadowy area the size of a small fist and a complete obstruction in the middle of the esophagus. Emaciation and weakness had already appeared, as had severe anemia and T-bacilli intoxication. The patient's history revealed the following facts: Several months before the first occurrence of the cancer symptoms, his son, whom he especially loved, had been drafted into military service. This worried him and he became deeply depressed. (Characterologically, he tended to be depressive.) In a few days, he developed a spasm of the esophagus. He experienced difficulties in swallowing, which, however, disappeared when he drank water. These complaints, accompanied by a feeling of pressure in the chest, came and went for some time, until one day they became irreversible. The difficulties in swallowing increased rapidly. He visited a physician, who established the existence of the constriction and a small growth. X-ray treatment proved ineffective, and after a few months the man was on the verge of death from starvation. It should be noted that from childhood this patient had suffered severe rigidity of the jaw musculature; his face bore a stiff, grim expression. Passive movement of the jaws was markedly curtailed. His speech was correspondingly restricted; he spoke through his teeth.

It is not yet possible to gauge the full extent of the somatic devastation resulting from an inhibition of the natural biological rhythm manifest in respiration, and in sexual tension and gratification. Poor breathing must do severe damage to the internal respiration of the organs, i.e., to the supply of oxygen and the elimination of carbon dioxide. Several years ago, when I recognized the significant part played by respiratory deficiencies in emotional disturbances, I remembered that *in cancerous tissue there is a marked oxygen deficiency.*

The Viennese scientist Warburg discovered that the various cancer stimuli have one common feature, namely the production of a local oxygen deficiency, which in turn causes a *respiratory disturbance* in the affected cells.[4] According to his hypothesis the cancer cell is a poorly breathing cell, deficient in tissue oxidation. Warburg sees this oxygen deficiency which leads to respiratory disturbance of the cells as one cause of cancer. He reasoned that in certain affected, localized areas the only cells capable of survival and further development will be those which overcome the respiratory disturbance caused by the oxygen deficiency, thereby assuming the metabolism of the cancer cells. The process is, basically, a disturbance of the energy metabolism. The respiratory disturbance is a property of all known malignant tumors, including the Rous sarcoma. *Cancer metabolism, is, therefore, to be viewed as the metabolism of normally growing cells in a condition of anoxia.*

However, we cannot conclude from Warburg's correct findings that the cancer cell is just a normal cell assuming a different kind of growth because of oxygen deficiency. Biologically, the cancer cell is basically different from the normal cell; it is nothing but a protozoal formation.

These findings provide the factual link between the autonomic life functions and cancer.

4. FROM THE CASE HISTORY OF A CANCER PATIENT: AN EXPERIMENT IN ORGONE THERAPY

I would now like to submit the case history of a cancer patient that is particularly revealing of the nature of the shrinking biopathy.

The patient's brother stated that the illness had set in three years before, in the form of excruciating pain in the right hip bone. The pain was incessant and "pulling." At this time, the patient weighed 125 lbs. She could not raise herself from a supine position. Her physician diagnosed a sacroiliac spasm and gave her injections

[4] *Cf.* Otto Warburg in *Biochemische Zeitschrift,* Bd. 317, a.o.

of morphine and atropine, but without success. The pain remained acute and the patient could not leave her bed. According to reports from her relatives, she lay flat on her back, immobile. Three months later, the patient began to have episodes of vomiting. About this time, pain spread from the ilio-sacral region to the fifth cervical vertebra. X-rays showed a collapsed vertebra. An orthopedist had the patient placed in a plaster cast. This physician was the first to discover an atrophy of the tenth dorsal vertebra, traceable to a cancerous tumor in the left breast. The diagnosis of cancer was then confirmed by biopsy. The patient underwent X-ray treatment of the pelvis and spine. She remained bedridden. Another physician then made her sterile, using X-ray. When she left the clinic, her weight was down to 90 lbs.

The patient's hospital file provided the following information: Four months prior to her admission, she had begun to feel pains in her right hip, especially when she walked. It was also difficult for her to sit down. We were struck by the fact that *the pains which kept the patient bedridden for more than two years were not originally felt in the area of the cancer tumor.* The pains were in the right hip, whereas the primary tumor was located in the left breast, with metastases in the spine.

The patient also suffered from vomiting. The hospital record stated that she lay flat in bed and could move only with great pain. Her lymph glands were not enlarged. Her breast tumor measured roughly $3 \times 2 \times 6$ cm. Even at this time, her leg movements were restricted. The sacrum was rigid and the spine was painfully sensitive over most of its length. The hospital diagnosis was *carcinoma of the left breast, with bone metastases,* and her physician at the hospital concluded that the case was hopeless.

Twenty-six months after the discovery of the breast tumor, the patient was brought to my experimental cancer laboratory. She was barely able to stand on her own, and had to be helped along by two relatives. Her skin, especially on her face, was ashen, and shrunken around the nose. The pains in her back, sharply localized at the twelfth dorsal vertebra, were extraordinarily severe. The left breast displayed a tumor the size of a small apple, barely movable. A blood test undertaken the same day yielded the following results: hemoglobin content 35%, T-bacilli culture in bouillon strongly positive after twenty-four hours. Elongated, serpentine rot bacteria were seen, and the red blood corpuscles for the most part were in a state of bionous disintegration, with large numbers of T-spikes. Small nucleated round cells and heaps of T-bacilli were also visible. The autoclavation test yielded predominately blue bions, but the vesicles were small and radiated only weakly. Inoculation of the bouillon culture on agar produced a distinct margin of T-bacilli.[5] These findings in the blood indicated extreme biological weakness of the blood system. Radiographic examination revealed the following:

X-RAY EXAMINATION OF ENTIRE SPINE

The fifth cervical vertebra is collapsed. No significant findings at the other cervical vertebrae. The dorsal spine shows collapse of the tenth and twelfth vertebrae and a narrowing of the joint space between the third and fourth vertebrae. There is also strong suggestion of a metastatic lesion at the medial third of the right ninth rib.

No lesions are present at the lumbar spine but there are three round areas of lesser density at the right ilium near the sacroiliac joint which are very suggestive of metastatic lesions, although they might be gas shadows of the cecum.

Conclusion: *multiple metastatic bone lesions.*

The physician to whom I sent the patient for a general examination declared the case hopeless on the basis of the X-rays. However, it was the biological weakness of the blood, and not the X-ray photographs, that made the greatest impression on me.

Two physicians who were friends of the patient's family declared that she would not survive more than two weeks. Another

[5] *Cf.* Wilhelm Reich, *Bion Experiments on the Cancer Problem* (Sexpolverlag, 1939).

physician felt, on the basis of the information received from physicians at the hospital, that the patient could live a maximum of two months.

THE MUSCULAR ARMOR

The biophysical habitus of the patient when I first saw her was as follows: Her jaw was clamped tight; she spoke through her teeth as if hissing; the masseters reacted with strong spasm to any attempt to pull down the jaw. The superficial and deep musculature of the neck, especially in the supraclavicular region, was extraordinarily rigid. The patient held her head somewhat pulled in and tilted forward, as if she were afraid something terrible would happen to her neck if she moved her head. At first, this manner of holding the head and neck seemed to be attributable to the fact that her fifth cervicular vertebra was collapsed. The patient had been wearing a collar brace for some time, and a fracture of the cervical spine as a consequence of too rapid or extreme movement was a possibility. As later became clear, the patient made good use of this fact as a neurotic defense. *Her fear of moving her neck existed long before the collapse of the vertebra. Indeed, her manner of holding her head and neck was only part of a general biophysical attitude which we had to understand not as the result but as the biopathic cause of her cancer.*

All reflexes of the head, trunk, and legs were normal. Respiration was severely disturbed. The lips were drawn in, the nostrils somewhat distended, as she labored to inhale air through the nose. The thorax was immobile. It failed to contract and expand with the rhythm of respiration and remained chronically fixed in the inspiratory position. When directed to breathe out fully, the patient was unable to; in fact, she did not seem to understand what was being asked of her. The attempt to push the thorax manually into the expiratory position, i.e., to push it down, was thwarted by marked muscular resistance. Head, neck, and shoulders formed a unified, solid mass, as if independent movement in the individual joints was impossible. The patient was able to raise her arms only very slowly and with great difficulty. The handclasp in both hands was exceptionally feeble. The scapular muscles were extremely taut and knotted. The muscles between the shoulder blades, on both sides of the cervical spine, were painfully sensitive to the touch.

The abdominal wall also was tense, and reacted with strong resistance to the slightest pressure. The musculature of her legs seemed thin, relative to the rest of the body, as though atrophied. The pelvis was sharply retracted and immobile.

Superficial psychiatric examination yielded the following information. The patient had suffered from insomnia for many years before the discovery of the cancer tumor. She had been widowed for twelve years. The marriage, which had lasted two years, had been to all outward appearances stable but in reality had been unhappy. In contrast to so many other cases of marital unhappiness, where there is no consciousness of suffering, the patient had always been fully aware that her marriage was a bad one. Her husband was impotent. When coitus finally succeeded, the husband suffered from premature ejaculation and the patient remained unsatisfied. In the first months of the marriage, her sexual dissatisfaction caused her much suffering. She later "got used to it." She had always been conscious of the need for sexual gratification but had been unable to find the means. When her husband died, she devoted herself to the upbringing of her child, rejecting any approaches from men and avoiding social contact. In time, her sexual excitation subsided. It was replaced by anxiety states, which she combated with various phobias. When she came to me, she showed no anxiety; she seemed emotionally well balanced and reconciled to her fate. To the character analyst, she presented the familiar picture of neurotic resignation; she no longer had any impulse to change her life. I avoided any attempt to probe deeper into the latent conflict of the patient and focused my attention on the organic changes that soon appeared.

THE RESULTS OF THE ORGONE THERAPY
EXPERIMENT

A precise account of the technique of orgone therapy will be presented later.* Here, I shall only convey the essentials.

Our orgone therapy experiments with cancer patients consist in having them sit in an orgone accumulator. The orgone energy "accumulated" in the interior of this enclosure penetrates the naked body and, moreover, is breathed in. The length of time the patients are exposed to the radiation in the accumulator is determined by the atmospheric energy tension, which is measured in minute-orgs by comparing the speed of electroscopic discharge inside the accumulator with the speed of discharge in the air outside the accumulator.[6]

During the initial sessions of the experiment, I exposed the patient to 30 minute-org of radiation, i.e., the patient remained inside the accumulator for thirty minutes, exposed to radiation in which the electroscopic discharge occurs at a rate of sixty minutes per unit.

In the following account, I wish to mention only those reactions of the patient that are typical of all cancer patients undergoing orgone therapy. Individual reactions will be designated as such.

During the patient's first exposure to orgone radiation, the skin between her shoulder blades reddened at a spot that two months later would play a significant role in her functional disease. From the second exposure on, the reactions became intenser and more distinct. The pain in the region of the tenth dorsal vertebra regularly decreased during the radiation. The subsidence of the pain

---

* *Cf.* Chapter VII.

[6] The concentration of orgone energy inside the accumulator is about three to five times greater than in the open air. One unit of electroscopic charge discharges inside the accumulator two, three, or five times more slowly than in the atmosphere. The more minutes it takes for a single unit to discharge, the higher the orgone energy tension.

generally lasted until the next treatment. The pains intensified acutely in bad weather, especially with humidity or rain. During the patient's second exposure, the reddening of the skin spread to the upper part of the back and the chest. When the irradiation was interrupted for five minutes, the reddening disappeared, returning as soon as the patient reentered the accumulator. From the third irradiation on, the patient felt the air in the accumulator to be "closer and heavier." "I feel as though I'm filling up"; "I have a buzzing around the ears from the inside"; "something makes me strong"; "something clears up in my body." During the third exposure the patient also began to perspire, especially under the arms. When asked about this, she reported that during the past years she had never perspired.

These reactions of the organism to the effects of orgone radiation are typical of all cancer patients. In some, one particular reaction may be most prominent; in others, a different one may predominate. Reddening of the skin, lowering of the pulse rate, the outbreak of warm perspiration, and the subjective sensations of something in the body "loosening up," "filling up," or "swelling," etc., represent a pattern of reactions for which there can be only one interpretation: the cancer habitus is determined by general sympatheticotonia, i.e., by vegetative contraction. That is why the symptoms of most cancer patients include accelerated pulse, pallor, blotchy cyanosis and dryness of skin, sunken cheeks, sluggish functioning of the organs, constipation, and the inability to perspire. *The effect of the orgone energy radiation is vagotonic.* In other words, it acts as a counter-force resisting the general sympatheticotonic shrinking of the organism. The pulse of a patient exposed to orgone radiation in the accumulator may drop within twenty minutes from ˙120 to 90, or from 150 to 110. This is accomplished without any medication. The reddening of the skin and the outbreak of perspiration are corresponding phenomena; the peripheral blood vessels dilate and the blood pressure decreases. In terms of biological pulsation, *the chronic contraction of the plasma system subsides and gives way to vagotonic expansion.* This "plasmatic expansion" is accompanied by a reduction of the typical cancer pain.

The pain suffered by cancer patients is usually attributed to local mechanical tissue damage caused by the tumor. In some cases, pain undoubtedly is caused that way, e.g., if there is pressure on a nerve or if a sensitive organ is damaged. However, the typical cancer pain to which I am referring here should be clearly distinguished from local, mechanically produced pains. I will refer to it specifically as "shrinking pain." To understand it, we have to review a few facts generally overlooked until now.

Sex-economy has to relinquish the view dominating contemporary medicine that the autonomic nerves of multicellular organisms merely transmit impulses and are themselves rigid. "Tearing" and "pulling" pains are incomprehensible without the realization that the autonomic nervous system itself expands and contracts, i.e., is mobile. This fact can be confirmed, as I demonstrated earlier, by microscopic examination of the autonomic nervous system in, for instance, meal worms. We observed that the nerve fibers of the autonomic ganglion expanded and contracted and indeed moved independently of the movements of the total organism. These movements actually preceded those of the total body. The impulses manifested themselves first in the movements of the autonomic nervous system and were transmitted secondarily to the mechanical locomotor organs of the organism. This finding sounds revolutionary and strange, but in actual fact it represents a banal conclusion, later confirmed by direct observation, that I had to draw from the pulsatory functions of the organism. *The contracting and expanding of the amoeba continues to exist in the multicellular organism in the form of the contractile and expansile autonomic nervous system. This autonomic nervous system is nothing other than organized contractile plasma. The emotional, vegetative, autonomic movement is therefore a direct expression of the plasma current.* The prevailing notion of the rigidity of the autonomic nerves does not accommodate any of the phenomena observed in biophysical functioning, such as pleasure, fear, tension, relaxation, sensations of pressure, pulling, pain, etc. On the other hand, the contractility of the autonomic nervous system, which forms a functional and histological unity (*syncytium*), explains in a simple way our subjective plasmatic sensations. What we feel as pleasure is an expansion of our organism. In pleasure corresponding to vagotonic expansion, the autonomic nerves actually stretch out toward the world. In anxiety, on the other hand, we feel a crawling back into the self: a shrinking, a hiding, a constriction (*angustiae, Angst*). In these sensations, we are experiencing the real process of contraction of the autonomic nervous system.

We feel the orgasm as an involuntary convulsion; this again reflects the objective process of expansion and contraction of the entire plasma system. The pain felt by cancer patients mirrors the retraction of the autonomic nerves from the diseased area and the "pull" on the tissues. The expression "pulling pain" or "tearing pain" conforms completely to the objective process. The unequivocal and simple fact of the identity of our organ sensations with the actual processes within the autonomic nervous system can be denied only if one assumes a mechanistically inflexible, unalive, unbiological, and unpsychological attitude. Such a perspective exiles our organ sensations to the realm of metaphysics and thereby fails to apply to a single fact of the cancer syndrome.

We now understand the seemingly remarkable phenomenon of cancer pain generally decreasing or disappearing in the orgone accumulator. If cancer pain is not the expression of a local mechanical lesion but of a general contraction of the autonomic nerves, a "pulling at the tissues," then it becomes understandable that the vagotonic expansion of the nerves reduces the "pulling" and, thereby, the pain.

This finding reveals an essential effect of orgone energy: *it charges living tissues and brings about an expansion of the plasmatic system* (*vagotonia*).

The general revitalization of the organism's functions by orgone radiation is manifest also in the blood picture of cancer patients.

When the patient came to us, the hemoglobin content was 35%. Two days later, it was 40%; after four days, 51%; after seven days, 55%; after nine days, 63%; after fourteen days, 75%; and after three weeks it had risen to the normal level, 85%. The patient was able to leave her sickbed, take her child back into her own care, and after years of inactivity and confinement in bed, begin again to work. But she did too much; she went shopping, spending hours in different department stores. Her pains had gone; she slept well and felt completely healthy. She did her housework without any help. I had to warn her that she had an extremely serious illness to overcome and should not overtax herself. My warning was justified. After about six weeks, the patient felt tired and the hemoglobin content dropped to 63%. The pains in her back did not return, but for the first time she complained of difficulty in breathing, and about a "wandering" pain in the region of the diaphragm. I ordered bed rest, and the blood picture improved again. The hemoglobin soon rose to 70% and eight days later was back to normal at 85%. Her weight remained constant at around 124 lbs. After another four weeks, the hemoglobin was still 85%.

The patient no longer had to be brought to me in an automobile. She came for her daily treatment alone, by subway. Her relatives and the doctors who had treated her were amazed. However, the subsequent behavior of the physicians, from any rational standpoint, is incomprehensible. Here was an apparent *reversal* of a carcinoma, yet the doctors never once asked how the improvement had been brought about. At the beginning, I had sent the patient to a doctor who predicted that she would not live more than a few days. Now the patient was walking around and X-rays showed complete ossification in the previously cancerous spine; also, the shadows in the pelvic bones had disappeared, only two weeks after the beginning of the treatment. Yet I neither saw nor heard from any of those doctors.

The X-rays clearly showed the healing process. They confirmed what I had frequently observed in the cancer experiments with mice, namely that orgone energy arrests the growth of the tumor and replaces it by a hematoma which, under favorable conditions, is reabsorbed and eliminated by connective tissue, or, if the tumor is in bones, by calcification.

ORGONE-BIOPHYSICAL BLOOD TESTS

I would like to summarize what is to be presented more fully elsewhere.

Orgone energy charges the erythrocytes biologically. Each individual erythrocyte is an independent, self-contained orgonotic energy vesicle. It is subject to the same biological function of tension and charge and pulsation as the total organism and every one of its autonomous organs. The expansion and contraction of erythrocytes can be observed easily at a magnification of about 3000x. The erythrocytes shrink with the admixture of adrenalin, whereas potassium chloride makes them swell. They are, therefore, subject to the antithesis of the pleasure-anxiety function.

Our blood tests on cancer patients are done as follows:

1. *Culture test.* A blood sample is tested for bacterial growth in bouillon or in a mixture of 50% bouillon plus 50% KCl (0.ln). *In cases of advanced cancer, the blood consistently shows a strong growth of T-bacilli.*[7]

2. *Biological resistance test.* A few drops of blood are autoclaved for half an hour in bouillon and KCl at a steam pressure of 15 lbs. per sq. in. Healthy blood withstands the process of autoclavation better than the biologically weakened blood of cancer patients. Biologically healthy blood corpuscles disintegrate into large blue bion vesicles. Carcinomatously devitalized blood disintegrates into T-bodies. The T-body content increases and that of the blue bions decreases, in proportion to the degree of devitalization.

Orgone treatment charges the erythrocytes. The effect is demon-

[7] *Cf. Bion Experiments on the Cancer Problem.*

strated by the transformation of the T-reaction into a B-reaction; i.e., the blood becomes more resistant to high temperatures.

3. *Disintegration in physiological salt solution.* A small drop of blood is placed on a hanging drop slide in 0.9% sodium chloride solution. The blood corpuscles disintegrate slowly or quickly according to their biological resistance. The more rapid their disintegration, the shrinking of their membrane, and the formation of bion vesicles inside the cells, the lower their biological resistance. Erythrocytes that are biologically vigorous retain their shape for twenty minutes and longer. Disintegration within one to three minutes indicates extreme biological weakness. In cases of severe anemia, the erythrocytes display the typical T-spikes, i.e., shrunken membranes.

4. *Blue orgone margin.* Biologically vigorous erythrocytes reveal a broad, intensely blue or blue-green margin when viewed at 300–600x, using apochromatic lenses. Devitalized erythrocytes, tending toward rapid disintegration, have an extremely narrow margin, with weak blue coloration.

Blood tests conducted on our patient showed a general biological strengthening of the blood. Initially, the patient's blood cultures were strongly positive; i.e., they showed an extensive growth of T-bacilli. Three weeks later, the blood cultures yielded negative results and continued to do so. The erythrocytes were no longer shrunken. They were full and taut, with wide, dark-blue margins. The autoclavation test showed 100% bionous disintegration and no further T-reaction. Bionous disintegration in the sodium chloride solution took place very slowly and without the formation of T-spikes.

The patient no longer suffered from any pain and was cheerful, but she felt unwell in rainy weather. She came every day for the orgone irradiation. Her blood pressure remained constant at 130/80. Her pulse rate never exceeded the norm, around 80. There was just one symptom that would not subside, but grew even worse. She was having unexplainable difficulty in breathing.

THE EMERGENCE OF THE CARCINOMATOUS BIOPATHY

I will now proceed to the description of the carcinomatous biopathy, which emerged only after elimination of the tumors and the restoration of the normal blood picture. I did not have the slightest presentiment of what I am about to describe, and I experienced it, at first, with amazement and incomprehension. It was difficult to understand the connections between these phenomena. After the local cancer tumors had disappeared, there developed a general biopathic disease picture that formed the essential background of the cancer: biopathic shrinking.

The patient seemed to have recovered her physical health completely. This lasted about six weeks and was confirmed objectively by the results of the blood tests and X-rays. The tumors had vanished. Her blood remained vigorous; the anemia did not reappear. The tumor in the right breast was no longer palpable after the eighth exposure to orgone radiation. Those with a mechanistic view of pathology would have considered this a triumph and proclaimed the "cure" of the case. However, the simultaneous emergence of emotional symptoms, which became more and more prominent, restrained me from drawing premature conclusions.

When the patient first came to me, she was totally devoid of sexual feelings. Roughly four weeks after starting orgone therapy, I observed signs in her of severe sexual stasis. She had been cheerful and gay and full of hope for the future. Now a depression gradually began to set in and she developed symptoms of stasis anxiety. Once again, she withdrew from people. I learned from her that attempts to rectify her sexual situation had failed.

I succeeded in breaking through the patient's shyness and learned that she had recently been suffering from intense sexual excitations, which, as she said, were incomparably stronger than those she had experienced and combated fourteen years before, at the beginning of her marriage. Judging by her descriptions, the sensations she was feeling were quite normal vaginal excitations.

During the first two weeks after her recovery, the patient had made several attempts to approach men sexually, but she was unsuccessful and relapsed into despair and a state of physical exhaustion. These attempts, which had continued for several weeks, were healthy and indicative of a positive turning toward life. One day she asked me whether sexual intercourse with a man "once a month" could be harmful to her. The question seemed to be tinged with fright, in contradiction to her sexual knowledge. It indicated the presence of an irrational fear, which turned out to be that some terrible disaster might befall her during sexual intercourse, "since her spine was collapsed in two places." She feared the effects of the violent movement in sexual excitation. It should be noted that this idea appeared suddenly after the failure of her attempts to find a sexual partner. She had met a man who proved to be impotent. She was enraged, but fought down her hate and disappointment. Whenever she felt rage, she "swallowed it." Now the patient displayed the picture of a complete stasis neurosis: the depression increased, she suffered from uncontrollable fits of crying and complained of oppression in the region of the heart. "There is a dreadful pressure in my chest," she complained. "It goes through and through."

It would seem possible to attribute this "pressure in the chest" to the collapsed twelfth dorsal vertebra. But there was one consideration that clearly conflicted with this possibility. The patient had been free from pain for six weeks, had felt no oppression in the chest, and had worked hard. It was inconceivable that the mechanical pressure of the collapsed vertebra on a nerve should now suddenly become active after an absence of weeks. The events that followed confirmed the idea that the patient had developed an anxiety hysteria for which the spinal lesion served as a rationalization. Any physician untrained in psychiatry would have tended to attribute all the manifestations of the disease to the collapsed vertebra, without regard for the fact that the same vertebra had been no less collapsed during the weeks when the patient was moving around without pain.

After about ten orgone irradiations, the patient felt sexual excitations. She had been biophysically charged by the orgone energy, but she was unable to handle the resultant sexual excitation. The anxiety neurosis that now appeared was only a reactivation of the conflicts she had suffered in puberty. Now the patient was in the tragic situation of awakening to new life only to find herself facing a void. As long as she was ill, the cancer tumor and the suffering it caused absorbed all her interests. In the fight against the cancerous growth, her organism had indeed used up great amounts of biological energy. But now these energy resources were free and intensified by the orgonotic charge. During a period of extremely severe depression, the patient admitted to me that she felt herself to be ugly, ruined as a woman, and she did not know how she could go on with her life. She asked me if orgone energy could cure her anxiety neurosis too. I had to give a negative answer, and she understood why.

Let us now summarize the sequence of events.

1. At the beginning of her marriage, a severe stasis neurosis occurred as a consequence of her husband's impotence.

2. Repression of sexual excitation, resignation, depression, and a decade of abstinence followed.

3. Then, as the cancer developed, the sexual excitations disappeared. As will be shown later, *the localization of the cancer metastases occurred in precisely those organs affected by the muscular armor that blocked the sexual excitations.*

4. With the destruction of the tumors by orgone energy came the physical recovery of the patient, and sexual excitability reappeared.

5. Intense sexual excitation ended in disappointment, and the old stasis neurosis returned.

This overall disease pattern resulted eventually in a general shrinking of the organism.

Then one day an unfortunate accident occurred. The patient

stepped out of the orgone accumulator and began to dress. She bent over to pick up a stocking that had fallen to the floor. We heard a scream and rushed to her. She was as pale as a corpse, had a thready pulse, and seemed about to faint. It frightened us because we did not know what had happened and also because we regarded the collapsed vertebra as the sword of Damocles. Nobody could be sure when the patient might suffer a fracture of the spine. It was precisely because this possibility was so strong that it so easily became a rationalization of the patient's neurosis. Once she had calmed down, it became apparent that she had only experienced a severe fright. For a moment she had believed that, in bending down too quickly, she had actually fractured her spine. In fact, she had merely incurred a muscle strain in the shoulder, having moved a hypertonic muscle too swiftly. The muscle strain quickly subsided. During the first few days that followed, the patient felt well. On the fourth day, however, she complained of severe "pressure in the chest" and "weakness in the legs." Examination of the reflexes showed no damage to the nervous system. For the next few days her legs felt stronger, but the pressure in her chest persisted. Then, one day, during a conversation in the examination room, the patient suddenly let out a scream and doubled up, giving everyone present the impression that she had broken her spine. An immediate examination showed all reflexes to be functioning perfectly. On the other hand, there was now a new symptom which kept the patient bedridden for many months and baffled a number of physicians. She began to have trouble breathing and had to gasp for air. The impression I had was of a spastic contraction of the diaphragm—a diaphragmatic block.

The pain in the lower ribs about which she now complained could be ascribed just as well to this spasm as to a mechanical pressure of the collapsed vertebra on a sensory nerve: *the collapsed twelfth thoracic vertebra corresponded to the costal insertion of the diaphragm.* The events of the following months represented essentially a conflict of opinions about the validity of these two explanations. I advised the patient's relatives to take her to the orthopedist who had earlier prescribed a collar brace for her. The orthopedist stated that the spine and pelvis were free of shadows and metastases, and diagnosed the patient's condition as being due to a mechanical lesion at the twelfth thoracic vertebra. He did not ask how the metastases had disappeared. He prescribed bed rest in a plaster cast. However, her brother rejected this advice, since he had followed the course of his sister's disease with understanding and was convinced that I was correct. During this period I realized for the first time the connection between the lesion at the twelfth vertebra and the biopathic contraction of the diaphragm. There had to be a reason why the diaphragmatic spasm, so familiar to the orgonomist, happened when it did. There also had to be a reason why one of the most significant cancer metastases had occurred exactly at the costal insertion of the diaphragm. The clinical diagnosis of the patient's condition was rendered extraordinarily difficult by this concurrence of diaphragmatic spasm and lesion of the vertebra; yet it opened the way to an understanding of the crucial *connection between emotionally induced muscle spasm and the localization of metastases.* One of the tasks of this chapter will be to establish that *the localization of a cancer tumor is determined by the biological inactivity of the tissues in its immediate vicinity.*

Orgone treatment of the patient had to be interrupted, since she was again confined to bed. Reexamination at a cancer hospital and by private physicians showed total absence of cancerous growths and calcification of the defects in the spinal column. The original tumor in the breast did not reappear. Still, no one could foresee whether or not new cancer growths might appear. I visited the patient several times at her home. She complained of violent pain in the lower ribs. The pain was neither constant nor confined to any specific areas; it appeared here and there along the lower margin of the thorax and could be regularly eliminated by correcting the breathing. The overall picture was that of a neuralgia with strong hysterical overtones. The patient lay flat in bed, giving the impression that the pain made it impossible for her to move at all. My attempts to move her arms or legs made her cry out, become pale, and break out in a cold sweat. A few times I managed to get her out of bed and into an armchair by having her breathe deeply for ten minutes. Her relatives were astonished that I was able to alleviate her pain with such ease. They had witnessed the disappearance of the tumors and had had it confirmed by outside physicians. Since I worked without chemicals and injections, my orgone therapy seemed mysterious. To counteract this impression, I tried to explain the mechanism of the disease to them. They understood very quickly that the pain could not originate in the lesion of the vertebra, since it then would be sharply localized and not susceptible to correction by improved breathing. As yet, I had no presentiment that the patient did not actually have any pain, only a panic-stricken fear that pain might start.

An intercostal injection of an anesthetic was tried at the precise point where the pain was most violent. The anesthetic had no effect, and shortly after the injection, the pain appeared at another rib. The attending physician, who in the beginning had been convinced that the pain originated in the vertebral lesion, finally had to admit that the problem was essentially "functional." But none of us had any idea what "meaning" the "functional" symptom had. Moreover, to many doctors "functional" means "not organic," which is to say, "not real but imaginary."

One day I again found the patient suffering from violent "pain." She was gasping for air and uttering peculiar moaning sounds. Her condition seemed serious, but improved considerably as soon as her breathing was corrected and the spasm in her jaw muscles was dissolved. I then delegated the work on her respiration to a colleague, since I had to be away for two months. His subsequent reports to me confirmed that the establishment of full expiration consistently relieved the pain.

The patient was once again admitted to the hospital. The attending physician there confirmed the absence of metastases in the bones and stated his belief that X-ray treatment would not eliminate the pain. He doubted also whether neurosurgery at the twelfth spinal segment would serve any purpose. It was now five months since the beginning of orgone therapy, and three and a half months after its interruption. When told by the patient's brother about the successful results obtained through orgone therapy the physician became very reserved. He would have nothing to say on that subject, he declared, until it was "accepted by the medical world." He conveniently overlooked the fact that he himself was part of this "medical world" upon which he was pushing the responsibility to acknowledge the significant results achieved in the treatment of a cancer case by orgone therapy.

The patient soon returned home, where, as before, she lay flat on her back in bed, motionless. Her musculature continued to atrophy from disuse and there was great danger of a recurrence of the tumors. I saw the patient again one month later. Once more I succeeded in eliminating the pain by correcting her respiration. She was able to leave her bed, but felt extremely weak. During one of the attempts to extend her stay out of bed, the patient developed severe anxiety. She begged to be allowed to go back to bed. At that particular moment, she had no pain. I convinced her to stay on her feet for a while longer. All at once, she began to tremble violently, became frightened, broke out in a cold sweat, and went pale. What she was experiencing, in fact, was a severe shock-like reaction of the autonomic system to the act of standing up. I did not let the patient return to bed, because I noticed that there was some fear driving her to do so. A few moments later, there were visible convulsions in the upper abdomen. She gasped for air and I could see the diaphragmatic spasm dissolving into clonic convulsions of the abdominal musculature. She then felt relieved and was able to move freely.

Now I understood for the first time an essential element of the biopathy. She had reacted to the biological charging of her organism by the orgone and to the ensuing sexual excitations with a contraction of the diaphragm.[8] This diaphragmatic contraction evidently caused the "pressure in the chest" and the sensation of pain

[8] The repression of sexual excitation by means of a chronic attitude of inspiration is a phenomenon familiar to the orgone therapist.

that the patient attributed to the lesion of the vertebra. The "painful" pressure in the chest disappeared each time I succeeded in overcoming the inspiratory spasm by extending her exhalation, thereby restoring the pulsatory movement of the diaphragm. But it was precisely these contractions and expansions of the diaphragm that aroused in the patient a severe anxiety, which she counteracted by reverting to the inspiratory spasm. It was now clear that the "danger" of a clonic dissolution of the contraction was too great for the patient when she was standing or walking. The danger lay in the violent convulsions that threatened to dissolve the diaphragmatic spasm. She did not dare get out of bed because of her deepseated fear of these convulsions. It was mainly—though not exclusively—this fear that kept her confined to her bed.

There can be no question that the diaphragmatic spasms did generate neuralgic pain in the ribs and at the insertion of the diaphragm. But these spasms constituted only one part of her enormous fear of moving. More important was her fear that movement would cause her to "collapse" or "break her back." The involuntary convulsions of the diaphragm that threatened to overwhelm her whenever she stood up seemed to confirm this danger. Thus, she was not really suffering from acute pain but rather from a deadly fear of the onset of such pain. Her experience of a few months before, that "something snapped inside when she moved too swiftly," intensified her fear. She was suffering, therefore, from a misinterpretation of the normal orgonotic sensations that accompany movements of the diaphragm. Confining herself to bed was a tremendous defense mechanism designed to protect her against this fear of "falling apart." The danger of "falling apart" made itself felt when the diaphragmatic spasm was on the point of dissolving into clonic contractions. She counteracted this danger with intensification of the spastic diaphragmatic contraction. Understandably, this emotional state had harmful physical effects, producing a generalized muscular rigidity that impeded every movement. In time, this lack of movement resulted in an atrophy of the tensed musculature. For instance, she was hardly able to raise her arms; she could raise her left arm only with the help of her right. She could not raise her legs at all, and was barely able to bend her knees. The head was held rigid, as if locked by the tension of the deep neck musculature. Passive movement of the head met with automatic resistance. The patient was clearly afraid that her neck "might break." Every physician she had consulted had impressed upon her the need to guard against rapid movements since the fifth cervical vertebra was collapsed.

On one of the following days, I found the patient in very poor condition. Although she had a strong urge to defecate, she had not gone to the toilet for several days, in order to avoid having to leave her bed. As always, however, when she was made to breathe deeply her "pain" vanished and she was able to get up. Her subsequent bowel movement was copious and without difficulty.

I told her brother that I wanted to try to treat her for two weeks with psychiatric orgone therapy, but that I would have to stop if there were no results. She moved nearby and during the next few weeks I worked with her every day for roughly two hours (without honorarium). During this treatment, the phobic background of her biopathic condition revealed itself.

THE CHARACTEROLOGICAL EXPRESSION
OF THE SHRINKING BIOPATHY

Six months after her collapse in my laboratory, a flaccid paralysis of the rectum and the bladder appeared. Now the most important determination to be made was whether the manifestations of paralysis were traceable to a localized mehanical lesion or, as I surmised, to a *functional shrinking of the autonomic system.* In the first instance, an emotional basis would be absent; the disturbance would be sharply localized and would point to a specific focal lesion. In the second, however, one would expect emotional and characterological disturbances to be paramount and the manifestations of paralysis to be inconstant.

As again and again I pointed out her fear of imminent pain, the patient was able to move around in bed independently and totally free of pain. However, before she could accomplish this movement, she always had to improve her breathing and relax the spasms in her jaw muscles. As she expressed it, she always had first to rid herself of her "fear of moving." This would have been impossible in the case of a mechanical lesion of the twelfth dorsal segment.

The effort to lie on her side or her stomach left her in a state of apparent exhaustion. Together we tried to trace the cause of this exhaustion, finding it finally in an extraordinarily severe tension of the deep and surface musculature of the neck. The patient's head had the appearance of being pulled down into the thorax. It was the same position involuntarily assumed by a person defending himself against a blow on the head. This attitude was completely automatic. The patient could not consciously relax it. When the musculature of her neck contracted, respiration ceased and she made rattling sounds as if through a constricted throat, similar to the rattle that occurs in dying or in severe shock. To relieve the spasm, I had her stick two fingers deep into her throat. She reacted to this immediately with severe choking and reflex gagging. The reaction was so violent that she became blue in the face. After a while she felt "much freer in the throat."

In connection with these throat reflexes, she told me spontaneously of her anxiety dreams. Every night she dreamed, with extreme anxiety, of falling into an abyss, of sinking to the ground, of choking, of being annihilated by something falling on her. Falling dreams of this kind are familiar to the orgone therapist. They appear in a typical manner in the concluding phases of character-analytical treatment, during the period when preorgastic sensations begin to emerge in the abdomen and genitals, and are suppressed before they become conscious. These sensations, when charged with anxiety, are experienced as falling. The following mechanism is at work:

Preorgastic excitation is the onset of an involuntary convulsion of the plasma system. If this convulsion is feared, then in the midst

*of the expansion that should end in the convulsion, the organism
develops a counteracting contraction, i.e., an inhibition of the
expansion.* The resulting sensation is similar to the feeling experienced in a rapidly descending elevator or in an airplane dropping
suddenly. *The falling sensation is, thus, the perception of a contraction of the autonomic system just as it is about to expand.* The
typical falling dreams are often accompanied by a sudden contraction of the entire body.

The significance of these considerations for the case of our
patient is as follows. Her usual reaction to vagic (expansion)
excitations of the organism consisted in spastic contractions; her
organism locked itself into muscular spasms in the throat and the
diaphragm, as though trying somehow to "hang on." Fear of the
convulsions diminished considerably when I succeeded in eliminating the spasms by eliciting the gag reflex. The movements she then
accomplished in bed no longer ended in spasms but in a feeling of
well-being; she began to enjoy moving.

Every plasmatic current originates in a central tension contraction, which dissolves into a vagic expansion;[9] this vagic expansion is
connected with the sensation of pleasure. In the case of orgastic
pleasure anxiety, it results in muscular spasms. It is now clear that
the patient was suffering from a spastic reaction to vagic expansion,
as a consequence of orgasm anxiety. *Biopathic shrinking thus begins
with a spastic restriction of plasmatic pulsation.* It is differentiated
from simple sympatheticotonic stasis neurosis in that the impulses to
stretch out, i.e., to expand, cease gradually, whereas in stasis neurosis they retain their intensity. It is not possible, however, to draw
a sharp distinction.

This mechanism of spastic reaction of the musculature to
vagotonic expansion impulses functioned differently in each muscle
system. For instance, whenever I tried to move the patient's arms,
she always reacted with a contraction of the shoulder muscles and
the flexors of the arms. The reaction resembled the muscular nega-

[9] This phenomenon in the amoeba limax can be directly observed microscopically at a magnification of 2000x.

tivism and rigidity of catatonics. The patient gave the impression that she had a flaccid paralysis of the arms. When I asked her to hit my arm, she was at first unable to do so; but when I suggested that she imagine she was venting her rage, she was able, after only five minutes, to overcome her paralysis and strike out freely. After a while, the movement and the action felt pleasurable. The paralysis seemed considerably reduced. It was therefore possible for her to overcome temporarily her fear of expansion and plasmatic pulsation. This regularly improved her general condition.

The same process could be observed when I sat her up in bed. Her first reaction was always fear: she gasped for breath, paled, and repeated several times, in great anxiety, "You shouldn't have done that." However, after I had gone through the procedure several times until the patient had become convinced that nothing would happen to her, she was able to sit up by herself. She was astonished and told me, "It's a miracle I've been able to do that."

Thereafter, I had the patient repeatedly elicit the gag reflex, bite the pillow, hit my arm, in order to release clonic contractions in the shoulder and throat musculature. Experience had taught me that biological energy can be released from tonically contracted muscles only in the form of clonisms. This finding was again confirmed in the patient. After about half an hour of voluntary movements, involuntary contractions began in the arm and shoulder muscles. The patient's legs also started to tremble involuntarily. Gentle bending and straightening of the legs regularly intensified this trembling.

The first time the clonic contractions occurred, the patient was very frightened. She did not know what was happening to her. It was the same fear of the involuntary clonisms of her musculature that she had avoided by her tonic contractions. But, after a few minutes, the clonic movements felt pleasurable to her. Gradually the deep throat musculature was drawn into the clonus and the patient was afraid she would have to vomit. At one point she seemed on the verge of fainting. I urged her not to resist the involuntary contractions, to give in to them. After a time, they became less violent; the dammed-up biological energy had been discharged. She sank back exhausted, her face flushed, her breathing calm, deep, and full. The gag reflex could not be elicited any more and she told me, "My throat is strangely free, as if a pressure had been removed." The pressure in her chest was also gone.

The next day her respiration was normal and I attempted to relieve the paralysis in the legs by inducing a clonus in the musculature of the legs. I succeeded to a certain extent by moving her legs, which were bent at the knees, slowly apart, then together again. I had not forewarned the patient about the preorgastic sensations in the genitals that usually appear when the contractions in the leg musculature are relaxed. All at once, the patient inhibited her breathing, locked her jaw, paled, and assumed an expression in her face that I can only describe with one word: "dying." The reaction was so violent that it frightened me. But since I had moved the legs quite slowly, there could be no question of mechanical damage having occurred. The patient expelled sounds similar to those resulting from severe pains in the chest; they were a mixture of groaning and rattling. From my clinical experiences, I knew that all this was the patient's reaction to plasmatic currents in the genitals. Vegetotherapy has taught us that under the pressure of orgasm anxiety, *orgastic sensations manifest themselves as a fear of dying*—"dying" in the sense of total disintegration, dissolving, losing consciousness, "not being."

The patient groaned loudly, became pale and blue, rolled her eyes, and seemed in a state of utter exhaustion. I had never witnessed the neurotic attitude of dying so realistically expressed. In spite of having worked for twenty years on orgasm dysfunctions, I had still underestimated the deep significance of disturbances of biological pulsation. To be sure, I had always maintained that the orgasm is *a function basic to all living activity* and that "the orgasm formula is identical with the life formula per se." But I had never before seen an organism "die" so realistically as a consequence of orgasm anxiety. I told her relatives that the patient might well not live more than another few days. It was clear to me that the shrinking of her life apparatus could lead to actual death. Had the patient not been dying at the time she came to me seven months before, I would have stopped the treatment in such a situation. In this case, however, there was nothing to lose by continuing, and much insight to be gained about the nature of the shrinking biopathy.

The following day, I received a telephone call from the relatives: the patient was in fact dying; her respiration was poor, there was a severe rattle in the throat, and she was unable to defecate. I went to her at once. At first glance, she seemed actually on the point of death. Her face had a blue color and was sunken; rattling sounds came from her throat, and there was a forlorn look in her eyes as she whispered to me, "This is the beginning of the end." Her pulse was rapid but strong.

In the space of fifteen minutes I was able to establish good contact with the patient. I asked whether, before she had become ill and developed tumors, she had ever felt that she was about to die. She told me, without hesitation, that as a child she had often rolled up her eyes and played "dying." The groaning and rattling sounds were also familiar to her from childhood. She had been in the habit of making them whenever she felt a constriction in her throat or, as she put it, when she felt "something tightening in her throat." *The appearance of one of the cancer metastases at the fifth cervical vertebra I now knew was attributable to a decades-old spasm of the deep throat musculature.* The patient went on to report that the constricted sensation in the throat was accompanied by a drawing-in of the shoulders and a tightening "between the shoulder blades" at precisely the same spot where the pain later started.

Now that the patient was talking to me in a completely wide-awake and lively manner, I had her "play dying." It took her only a few seconds to reproduce consciously the very "condition" that so recently had overwhelmed her involuntarily. She rolled her eyes upward, closing the lids except for a small slit that left just a sliver of white visible, clamped her chest into the inspiratory position, and started to utter groaning and rattling sounds. It was by no means easy to bring her out of this dying pose; but the more frequently she adopted it consciously, the easier it became for her to come out of it. This was completely in accord with my experiences in orgone therapy: *an autonomic function can be objectivized by practice and in the end be made subject to conscious control.*

I asked the patient whether she believed she was unconsciously attempting to commit suicide. The patient broke into tears and declared that she no longer felt any reason for living. Her illness had destroyed her sexual charms; she would never again be happy, and she could not imagine living without happiness.

I had the patient elicit the gag reflex. The clonic trembling in the upper extremities and the throat musculature immediately set in, though not so strongly as on the day before. She even succeeded in sitting up in bed without help, but as she did so, her legs gave out. My impression was that the upper part of her body was functioning whereas the lower part, from the hips down, was not

For a few days the patient enjoyed a hearty appetite, felt well, and was cheerful. Then, suddenly, she relapsed into the dying attitude. It was clear to me that she was not acting but had been completely overcome by her own biopathic reaction. Her breathing was labored and shallow, she became weak and pale, her nostrils were pinched, her cheeks sunken, and her throat rattled severely. I did not understand why her relapse had occurred at precisely this moment. She complained of extremely violent pains and was unable to move at all. Once again I succeeded in restoring normal respiration, and she fought bravely. Violent clonisms appeared in her neck and trunk, but the lower extremities remained "dead." I had the patient stick her fingers down her throat once more; the reaction was intensification of the spasms.

I noticed that the pelvis began to be included in the spasms, but the patient clearly held back. The spasms lasted approximately ten minutes, then subsided. Previously, she had given the impression that she was suffocating; this time, distinct vagotonic reactions were noticeable. The patient's face flushed, the pallor of her skin disappeared. The pains caused by the diaphragmatic spasm subsided. After a while the patient began to talk. She was afraid that something could "happen" to her "down there." She told me that up to the time when she entered into treatment with me she had occasionally masturbated. This statement was an extremely belated qualification of her original contention that she had lived in total abstinence for the past decade. Within the first week of the orgone treatment, she had suppressed impulses to masturbate in response to fantasies of having sexual intercourse with me. Since that time, she had not dared to touch her genitals. The inhibition of masturbation, together with the fantasy, had resulted in a stasis of excitation which was intensified by the biological charge received in the orgone accumulator. The increase of her sexual needs intensified her fears. In this way, the phobia that her spine might break developed. Straining her shoulder muscle by suddenly bending over seemed only to confirm her fear, as though she were saying to herself, "See, I said it would happen."

The day after she had told me about her masturbation fantasies, I found her in good spirits, free of complaints, and full of hope. Her confessions of the previous day had enabled her to masturbate again for the first time in several months. She claimed to have experienced great satisfaction. On this particular day, she was able to control the diaphragmatic spasm very easily. She was constipated but had the urge to defecate. However, her fear of movement prevented her from making the trip to the bathroom. Turning over in bed had become much easier for her. She even succeeded in sitting upright in bed without any help, an achievement that amazed and pleased her. And for the first time she was conscious of the chain of causes: fear of spinal fracture → inordinate fear of pain → inhibition of respiration by diaphragmatic block → actual pain in the chest → fear of spinal fracture. But this time the inhibition of movement by the fear of pain did not occur so quickly. The fear only appeared when the movement required great effort. The connection between her fear of spinal fracture and her fear of moving now became understandable.

The following day the patient was again breathing poorly, complaining, groaning, and displaying the dying attitude. She was

unable to say what had happened. Her relatives told me that she
had felt well until late in the evening, when her condition deteriorated rapidly after the following occurrence. Her boy was in the
bathroom next to her room. She heard a noise and became very
frightened. Suddenly she had the idea that her son was closed into a
very small space, could not breathe, and was going to suffocate.
During the night she slept very little and suffered from severe anxiety dreams, some of them concerned with falling. There was nothing I could do for her on this particular day except correct her
respiration once again, which did have the effect of reducing her
complaints about her "pains."

Subsequently, the patient improved considerably. She was able
to move around in bed without pain, and to lift her legs. The
weakness in her arms had subsided, her appetite was good, and she
was optimistic. Then, during one of my visits, a movement she
made happened to bring her near the edge of the bed. She paled,
gasped, and then screamed. She was afraid of falling out of bed. Her
reaction was unquestionably excessive and did not correspond to
the reality of the situation. She now told me quite spontaneously
that while in the hospital during the summer, she had asked to have
beds placed on either side of her bed because of her fear of falling
out of it. I lifted her toward the edge of the bed. Even though I was
holding her firmly, she still cried out in fright. Her fear of falling,
which was at the root of her fear of moving, was now obvious.

The next day, I sat her up in bed. She felt no pains but was
mortally afraid and broke into a sweat and a hysterical fit of crying.
She had to die now, she proclaimed. She had kept up the fight
against dying for a long time, but now she would certainly die. She
cried for her child. She asked me to give her a fatal injection to put
her out of her misery. "I don't want to leave this bed, I want to
remain lying here." After a while she calmed down and realized, to
her astonishment, that she was able to sit up without any effort.
Gradually, however, violent clonic spasms set in throughout her
whole body; they were especially severe in the shoulders. She was
deathly afraid of these spasms and, therefore, would not get out of

bed. Each time she was forced to sit up she felt the clonisms setting in. Her fear of falling had subsided, but the connection was clear. The intense clonic convulsions of her musculature formed the physiological basis of her neurotic fear of falling. As I have mentioned, the patient regularly suffered from nightmares: she fell into cavernous depths, heavy objects tumbled down upon her, and men attacked her and wanted to choke her. She now remembered having suffered from exactly the same kind of anxiety for a long time during adolescence. She also remembered a phobia: whenever she was walking along a street and heard footsteps behind her, she used to run, for fear that "someone was after her." Usually her fear was so strong that "her legs failed her," and she had the constant feeling that she was about to collapse. She now recognized in this the identical physical sensation that overcame her whenever she had to sit herself up in bed. Her legs would fail and she would feel on the verge of collapse. With it, she would experience a spasm of the diaphragm and become afraid that she was about to die.

It is thus clear that the motor weakness of the legs was caused by a phobia that had dominated her since adolescence, long before the cancer appeared. The paresis she now developed was nothing other than the intensification of the old weakness in the legs, which was associated with her falling phobia. By this time she was able to associate this fear of falling with the idea of fracturing her spine.

The previous day she had had to go to the bathroom repeatedly. The movements of her intestines and bladder were "extraordinarily vigorous." That night she had been restless. Then, during the late morning she was unable to urinate. Her legs were without sensation. I examined her and found sensitivity to pinpricks reduced up to about the tenth dorsal segment. The patellar, Achilles, and the abdominal reflexes were all normal. Over the telephone I had been told that she was unable to move her legs. It turned out, however, that she could in fact move her legs, although their movement was restricted. Deep sensitivity in the toe joints was reduced. The picture was that of a functional paresis. From the symptoms, it was not possible to diagnose either spastic or flaccid paralysis. There was just one basis for conjecture that the lesion at the twelfth vertebra was playing some part: the sensory disturbance in the upper abdomen had a relatively sharp upper line of demarcation.

On the next day the patient was able to urinate, but three days later the anal sphincter weakened and she could no longer control her bowels. Her reflexes were all normal, but she again became extremely fearful of sitting up in bed.

She was once more admitted to a hospital for a general examination. *The X-rays showed the spine, pelvis, and upper thighs to be free of metastases,* but new metastases had appeared in the cranium and in the right humerus. The new tumors had therefore appeared at a considerable distance from the regions of the body that showed evidence of paresis. The functional biopathy and carcinomatous growth were separated from each other; they had nothing to do with each other.

The patient remained in the hospital for fourteen days. She was not given a neurological examination. The paresis of the legs was presumably regarded as a logical consequence of the mechanical vertebral lesions. The functional character of the paralysis escaped the attention of the physicians, who informed the relatives that the patient at most had two weeks to live.

The relatives took the patient home again, since she was receiving nothing at the hospital except morphine injections. I saw the patient on the day she returned. In a decidedly apprehensive manner, she emphasized that she would have to be especially careful in her movements, since the physicians in the hospital had impressed upon her that "her spinal column was pressing on a nerve and might break." This warning from the hospital physicians naturally confirmed and strengthened the patient's phobia. Her relatives wanted me to undertake a new experiment with orgone radiation in order to eliminate the tumors in the cranium. But on that particular day I was unable to feel any swellings on the cranium.

I continued to see the patient at her home for another four

weeks. *Her leg reflexes were entirely normal, and bowel and bladder functions were again in order.*

However, the atrophy of the musculature and the bones progressed rapidly. In addition, she had developed a putrid bedsore on the buttocks. The legs moved in response to painful stimuli, but seldom spontaneously. Her nightmares continued: men threw themselves into deep ravines and broke their necks; an elephant charged at her while she remained "as if paralyzed," unable to move. During the day, there was a look of terror in her eyes and she felt constricted in her chest. The pain had disappeared completely, but the fear of moving, and of spinal fracture, was as strong as ever.

We had a special accumulator built for her bed. The effect of the orgone was manifested in reddening of the skin and reduction of the pulse rate from 130 to between 90 and 84. While in the orgone accumulator, she had a feeling of well-being, often developed rosy cheeks, and was free of anxiety.

Her blood picture, which had deteriorated over the past months (50% T on autoclavation), improved demonstrably, and spontaneous impulses to move her legs increased in frequency and intensity. Then an unforeseen catastrophe occurred which sealed the fate of the patient. One evening, turning over in bed, she fractured her left femur. She had to be taken immediately to a hospital, where the doctors were astonished at the thinness of the femur. The absence of a tumor in the region of the fracture and the disappearance of the breast tumor were incomprehensible to them. The patient received morphine, deteriorated during the following four weeks, and finally died.

The orgone therapy had prolonged her life for approximately ten months, had kept her free from tumors and pains for months, and had restored her blood function to normal. The interruption of the orgone treatment by the biopathic paralysis eliminated the possibility of a favorable outcome in the case. It is certain, however, that the cause of death was the biopathic shrinking, and not the local tumors.

This case provided us with important insights into the vegetative-emotional background of cancer. The important question that confronts us now is, *What happens in the tissues and the blood as a consequence of biopathic shrinking?* In other words, *in what way does the general shrinking of the autonomic system produce the local growth?* I venture to anticipate: *The general consequence of biopathic shrinking is putrefaction of the tissues and the blood. The growth of cancer tumors is only one of its symptoms.* This finding needs detailed clinical and experimental documentation, which will be provided elsewhere.

5. THE NATURE OF FUNCTIONAL DISEASE: SUMMARY

Let us now review our findings. The "dying" of the patient in the biopathic attack did not convey the slightest impression of hysteria or simulation. The autonomic system reacted in such a way that death could in fact easily have followed: the sunken cheeks, pinched nostrils, the rattling sounds, the cyanotic coloration of the skin, the accelerated feeble pulse, the spasm of the throat musculature, the marked limitation in movement, and the general physical weakness were dangerous realities.

I would hazard the opinion that every one of these attacks represented the beginning of a real cessation of the vital functions. The act of dying, set in motion by extreme intensification of the shrinking of the life apparatus, could be interrupted again and again by the dissolution of the spasms and correction of the respiratory-diaphragmatic block. The vagotonic expansion again and again counteracted the dying process. This counteraction could not have been a matter of suggestion. Suggestion, in the usual sense, could not affect the biological apparatus at such a deep level. However, the release of biological expansion impulses in various body systems did arrest the shrinking process repeatedly for months. Good emotional contact with the patient was also, of course, an indispensable part of the orgone-therapeutic process; only in this respect might suggestion be said to have played a role.

Let us use our familiar schema of psychosomatic functioning to clarify which part of the vital apparatus is affected by the biopathy—in contrast to anxiety neurosis or a mechanical lesion—and by the orgone-therapeutic experiment.

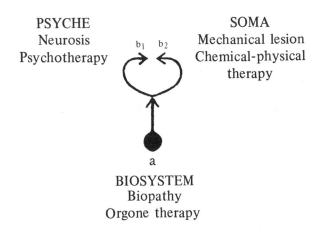

PSYCHE   SOMA
Neurosis b_1 b_2 Mechanical lesion
Psychotherapy   Chemical-physical
                               therapy

a
BIOSYSTEM
Biopathy
Orgone therapy

Every prolonged energy stasis in the biological plasma system (autonomic system, a) inevitably manifests itself in somatic as well as psychic symptoms (b_1 and b_2). Psychotherapy is directed at the psychic symptoms, chemical-physical therapy at the somatic symptoms. Orgone therapy proceeds from the fact that soma and psyche are both rooted bio-energetically in the pulsating plasma system (blood and autonomic system). Thus orgone therapy influences not the psychophysical function itself but rather the common root of psychic and somatic functions. It accomplishes this by relieving the respiratory block, the inhibition of the orgasm reflex, and other inhibitions of biological functioning. *Orgone therapy is, therefore, neither a psychic nor a physiological-chemical therapy but rather a biological therapy dealing with disturbances of pulsation in the autonomic system.* Since these disturbances reveal themselves in the superficial layer of the psychosomatic apparatus, e.g., as hypertension and cardiac neurosis in the somatic realm and as phobia in the psychic realm, orgone therapy necessarily affects the symptoms arising from the superficial biological layers. Therefore, we can claim orgone therapy to be the most advanced method for the influencing of biopathic disturbances. At present, it remains limited to biopathies. In the carcinomatous biopathy, treatment of the respiratory and orgasm disturbances is combined with physical orgone therapy, which is directed against anemias, T-bacilli in the blood, and local tumors. As will become evident later, we, in the laboratory of our institute, are fully conscious of the complexity and of the still predominantly experimental nature of this new cancer therapy.

The prevailing view knows only the antithesis of mechanical-chemical lesions of the somatic system and functional disturbances of the psychic system. *The orgone-biophysical investigation of the carcinomatous shrinking biopathy reveals a third, deeper factor: the disturbance of plasmatic pulsation operating at the common biological basis of soma and psyche.* What is basically new here is the fact, experimentally established, that an *inhibition of the autonomic sexual function can induce a biopathic shrinking of the autonomic nervous system.* What remains problematic is the question whether this etiology is valid for all forms of cancer.

There is a tendency to accept the misconception that the organism is divided into two independent parts: the somatic, physical-chemical system, which is destroyed by cancer tumors and cachexia; and the psyche, which produces hysterical phenomena (the so-called conversion symptoms) and "wants" or "fears" this or that, but has nothing to do with cancer. This artificial cleavage of the organism is deceiving. The notion that a psychic apparatus "makes use of somatic phenomena" is incorrect, and it is equally incorrect to think that the somatic apparatus responds only to chemical and physical reactions but neither "wants" nor "fears." *In reality, the expansion and contraction functions of the autonomic plasma system represent the unitary apparatus responsible for "wishes" and "fears" in the psyche and "life" and "death" in the soma.* Our patient clearly showed *the functional unity of psychic resignation and biopathic shrinking.* The life process in the patient gradually declined; the expansion function failed. Expressed in psychological terms, movement, action, resolve, and struggle were devoid of impulse. The vital apparatus was locked in an anxiety reaction that manifested itself psychically in the patient's fixed idea that movement could cause something in her body to break. Movement, action, pleasure, and expansion now seemed dangerous to life. The characterological resignation *preceded* the shrinking of the vital apparatus.

The motility of the biological plasma system is itself damaged by the biopathic shrinking. The real basis of the fear of movement is to be found precisely in this vegetative shrinking. The plasma system contracts, and the organism loses its autonomic stability and the self-regulation of its locomotor function. The final stage of the process is a gradual wasting away of the body substance.

The inhibition of plasma motility, by the process of shrinking, satisfactorily accounts for all aspects of the disease picture. It explains neurotic anxiety as well as functional paralysis, the falling anxiety as well as the atrophy of the muscles, the spasms as well as the biological disturbance that breaks through as "cancer" and ends in general cachexia. I was repeatedly able to help the patient develop new living impulses by correcting the diaphragmatic spasm, which is central to the biopathic disturbance of motility, to the defense against sexuality, and, indeed, to the defense against the expansive life function. The respiration of the patient was actually poor; the ventilation of the tissues was in fact insufficient; the plasmatic locomotor impulses in the limbs were, in fact, insufficient for coordinated movement; her fear of falling and of ensuing injury had a basis in fact and was not merely neurotic fantasy; indeed, *her "fantasy" of a disaster caused by falling had a very real basis in the restriction of biological motility.* The hysterical, functional character of the paralysis acquired a real, biopathological basis. Only differences of degree separate paralysis of motility and paralysis caused by biopathic shrinking.

In medical circles, functional paralyses tend to be regarded somewhat skeptically. The predominant view, even today, is that a functional paralysis must be more or less "simulated." My contention is that functional disturbances of motility attributable to biopathic disturbances of the plasmatic pulsation are much more serious, and can affect wider areas, than a paralysis resulting from a mechanical segmental lesion. Biological functioning of the total organism is not impaired by a local mechanical lesion. But *a functional paralysis is a manifestation of a total biological disturbance. The function of plasmatic impulse formation in the biological core of the organism is itself disturbed* and may cause an extensive loss of substance in the tissues (muscular atrophy, general cachexia, anemia, etc.). It is not relevant to argue that a mechanical disturbance cannot be influenced by suggestion, whereas the functional disturbance can. The "suggestion" capable of bringing about an improvement of functional paralysis is in reality a pleasure stimulus for the biological plasma system impelling it toward new living possibilities and renewed biological functioning.

The fundamental disturbance in the functioning of the body plasma, represented and caused by chronic sexual stasis, by character rigidity and resignation, and by chronic sympatheticotonia, should be taken much more seriously than local mechanical lesions. The functional standpoint must partially supplement and partly prevail over the mechanistic and purely materialistic viewpoints of medicine today. It was this functional perspective which opened a breach in the wall that had kept the cancer problem inaccessible. In the following discussion, it will be shown how far this is in fact already practicable. We now turn our attention to the changes in the blood and tissues that are brought about by biopathic shrinking.

6. SEXUAL STARVATION OF THE ORGANISM IN CHRONIC ABSTINENCE, ILLUSTRATED BY A CASE OF CARCINOMATOUS SHRINKING WITHOUT TUMORS

In the foregoing, I tried to show that the local tumor is not itself the cancer. Behind the tumor, a shrinking of the autonomic system is actually taking place. In the cancer patient whose illness I described, the local cancer tumors were eliminated by orgone therapy, but she then perished because of a deep-seated sexual disturbance that caused the continued shrinking of the vital apparatus. By chance, I encountered a second case that confirmed and amplified the conclusions I had drawn from the first case. Like the first one, this case clearly reveals the social and sexual background of the shrinking biopathy. At the same time, it demonstrates the potential of orgone therapy for treatment of the cancer biopathy. The responsibility that the sex-economist and psychiatrist must face in the struggle against the sexual biopathies is immeasurable. There is no way to accumulate insights into the nature of biopathies except bit by bit through the study of many cases. One case will raise questions that the next case will answer, though not without introducing new questions. These questions are evident only to the psychiatrist whose orientation is sex-economic. For the mechanistic pathologist they remain unasked.

A sex-economist who was a distinguished colleague at the Institute had succeeded within a few months in effecting a remarkable change in the condition of a woman suffering from a severe character neurosis. One of the woman's acquaintances noticed the change. She, in turn, knew of a thirty-year-old woman who, for two years, had appeared to be succumbing to a malady that no physician was able to explain. That is how the patient happened to come to my laboratory.

My immediate, superficial impression of the patient was that her face called to mind a death mask. The skin of her face was pale and somewhat bluish. Her cheeks were sunken, so that the jaw-bones protruded sharply. Her eyes looked tired and veiled, hope-less. Her mouth was drawn down at the corners, expressing deep resignation and depression. Her body was thin; ribs and vertebrae were abnormally prominent. The musculature in the entire body was so thin that an atrophic process could hardly be doubted. Her movements were lethargic, somewhat shuffling. The patient spoke slowly, as if with great effort, and without changes of facial expression. It seemed that all activity was arrested and that there was insufficient energy behind the impulses. The pelvic bones were extremely prominent. Feet and hands were clammy, cold, and pale. Her voice was monotonous and feeble. The patient seemed to want to make contact with me, but was unable to do so.

She weighed 90 lbs., having lost 10 lbs. in the last four weeks. Two years before, she had weighed 120 lbs. From the age of five on, she grew rapidly and became thin; since then, she had always been underweight for her age. As a child she had had measles and whooping cough. She frequently suffered from colds, and had undergone a tonsillectomy. Menstruation had begun at the age of fourteen and was regular every four weeks. However, it always lasted a week or more and was extremely painful.

Five years before, she had consulted a psychiatrist in an effort to deal with her sexual difficulties. Ever since puberty she had been convinced that she was not in order sexually. She often had to stay out of school to "build up her health," as she put it. On closer questioning, she admitted that she had often felt tired and weak and had been unable to keep up with the schoolwork. Even the simplest tasks represented major undertakings to her. She suffered from severe depressions and felt totally unable to cope with life. Gradually her resignation turned into complete inactivity.

Her mother had undergone a total hysterectomy for cancer, but died later from metastases to the bones. The patient described her mother as a very quiet person, devoted to her children. She had died as uncomplainingly as she had lived.

The patient's education in sexual matters had been very strict and ascetic. She had never experienced sexual intercourse. She had rarely been permitted to attend dances. For a time, during puberty, the desire for companionship with men had stirred in her, but her attempts failed. Her strict religious family tolerated no situation that could have become "dangerous." She failed miserably in her attempts to break through these external inhibitions and realized that she had become *inwardly* incapable of an intimate friendship with a man. This condition had taken hold of her during late puberty and persisted until the present time. It was a major contributory element in her depressions and her secluded way of life. She was pretty, but men nevertheless seemed to shy away from her. Several times, a friendship had begun to develop. But it always failed because at the mere thought of physical intimacy a *spasm of the genitals* would inevitably set in. In time, fear of these painful spasms developed and she avoided every occasion that might lead to sexual involvement. Though aware that her behavior was pathological, she did not know what to do about it. She was afraid of asking doctors for advice or consulting with friends about her problem. In short, she gave up. She had never masturbated, despite the suffering that sexual excitation caused her, but she tended to hold her hands over her genitals at night. In contrast to other patients suffering similarly from sexual abstinence, she had a clear insight into the nature of her disturbance. She made no attempt to disguise it with ascetic ideals; her suffering was, consequently, all the more intense. During our very first conversations, she talked about it almost uninhibitedly. Here, however, I would like to interrupt the description of her abstinence, and return to it later.

The seriousness of the patient's condition necessitated a complete physical examination. The outcome was surprising. The doctor who examined her prescribed a diet but found no physical disturbances. His report was worded as follows: "This is to certify that I have given Miss —— a complete physical examination, including blood and urine tests, and find her to be in good health." This finding was in such sharp contradiction to the impression I had received of the patient that, at first, I did not understand it. As noted, she had recently lost 10 lbs. For two years she had been incapable of working and had been lying around at home, feeling weak and unable to make any social contact. It is not surprising that the physician failed to recognize a biopathy caused by abstinence, but the loss of weight should have made a strong impression. Also, the general appearance of the patient could not easily have been overlooked. I reflected that the medical profession is trained for mechanical and chemical examinations only. It happens frequently, therefore, that a severe biopathic habitus is overlooked simply because the physician has not learned to take into consideration the patient's bodily expression and the *character of his sexual life.*

The patient had a small tumor, approximately the size of a bean, on the outer margin of her right breast. I asked whether the examining physician had seen it. She affirmed that he had. But since this small tumor grew alternately larger and smaller, the doctor had diagnosed a harmless glandular swelling, apparently in the belief that a malignant tumor could not become smaller spontaneously and would grow steadily. The small tumor had existed for about a year without becoming larger. Not wishing to alarm the patient unnecessarily, I did not have a biopsy performed. Since the patient wanted to undergo the experiment with orgone therapy, I could wait to ascertain whether the tumor would vanish after a few irradiations. Rapid disappearance would be an indication that the tumor had been malignant; whereas if the growth took many weeks or months to disappear, or else would not go away at all, or showed no signs of growing larger, then the diagnosis of a harmless glandular swelling could be correct. In addition, we had our cancer tests to confirm our findings.

The tests were all positive; the diagnosis was certain to be cancer. Examination of the rate of disintegration of the erythrocytes in physiological salt solution showed bionous disintegration and T-spike formation in about one minute. The orgone margins of the erythrocytes were narrow with only faint blue coloration. Hemoglobin content was normal at 80%. In the culture test, bouillon became cloudy after twenty-four hours. Inoculation on agar showed the typical growth of T-bacilli, which was confirmed by Gram stain. Autoclavation of the blood in bouillon and KCl yielded a strong T-reaction of the red blood corpuscles (about 60%).

These results, together with the biophysical condition of the patient, made the diagnosis of an *advanced* carcinomatous shrinking biopathy almost inevitable. It was unimportant whether or not the small tumor on the right breast was, itself, carcinomatous. My impression was that the patient had no more than a year to live.

I notified a close relative of the patient and had him confirm in writing that I had diagnosed cancer but had offered no promise of a cure. I warned him that the patient must be expected to die within a very short period if the experiment with the orgone irradiation did not succeed. I knew that no physician, on the basis of the present disease picture, could arrive at a diagnosis of cancer. Furthermore, even if another physician had suspected cancer because of the patient's general condition, there would still have been no alternative treatment to orgone therapy available, since there were no local tumors that were considered to be cancerous.

The patient began daily orgone irradiations in my laboratory. Later she acquired an orgone accumulator and took two daily irradiations in her own home, one in the morning after her bath and one in the evening before going to bed, for half an hour on each occasion. In the first twelve weeks this treatment produced the following results:

Weight: After one week still 90 lbs., no increase but also no further weight loss; after two weeks, 91 lbs.; after three weeks, 91.75 lbs.; after four weeks, 92.25 lbs.; after six weeks, 95.75 lbs.; after twelve weeks, 100 lbs. Thus, not only had the process of shrinking been stopped, but the patient was gaining weight at an accelerating rate.

Growth of T-bacilli in blood culture: After five weeks, bouillon, as well as the agar culture, was *negative,* and remained so during the following weeks.

Autoclavation test: After three weeks no improvement;
T-reaction still approximately 60%. The blood bion solution did not have the character of a pure colloid but
showed the blue-green discoloration typical in advanced
cancer.

Breast tumor: After ten days of orgone treatment, the small
tumor in the right breast was no longer palpable. Two to
three weeks is the usual time span needed for the elimination of medium-sized breast tumors by orgone therapy.

These findings had the greatest significance for the orgone
therapy experiment. They showed that symptoms of an advanced
cancerous state can exist in the organism without conspicuous local
manifestation. This confirmed my earlier view that cancer consists
essentially in a general shrinking of the life apparatus; the local
tumor is therefore only one of the symptoms of the disease and not
the disease itself. These findings also proved that standard medical
training does not enable the practicing physician to diagnose cancer
prior to the appearance of conspicuous local phenomena. Finally,
they proved the usefulness of our laboratory's biological blood bion
tests in cases where traditional methods cannot verify the diagnosis
of cancer. Even if a surgeon had suspected that the small tumor on
the breast was cancerous and had removed it surgically, the general
shrinking biopathy would have remained untouched and the patient
would have died. It is absolutely inconceivable that this small
tumor, without metastases in the axillary glands, was the cause of
the patient's poor general condition. The tumor was a much later
development than the general shrinking condition. Thus, there is
ample justification for speaking of a "carcinomatous shrinking biopathy, without tumors." It is important to establish how frequently
such cases occur. In any event, the availability of orgone therapy
greatly reduces the fear of the disease, even if many questions still
remain unanswered. In this particular case, the orgone therapy
experiment was successful, and this success validates its claim to be

tested and developed on a wider scale. I will address myself further to this problem in a later chapter.*

Before proceeding to the main theme of this discussion— namely, the principles of the orgone therapy experiment, the problem of the development of cancer cells, and the processes in the tissues—a few more points about this case should be considered. When the *International Journal of Sex Economy and Orgone Research* first appeared, a physician clearly sympathetic to our viewpoint made the comment that sex-economy was certainly important and correct, but insisted, "What does it have to do with cancer?" The discussion of cancer and orgone research would, he felt, have the effect of impeding the acceptance of sex-economy. Astonishment and incredulity were the reactions I had from many other circles whenever I referred to cancer as a sexual biopathy or a sex-starvation scourge. These reactions were a clear sign that the cardinal point of our work had not been understood, namely, that *diseases generated by sexual stasis are severe biopathic diseases of the organism. The cancer biopathy is one of the diseases in which chronic disturbances of human sexual economy are manifested. Cancer is a sexual biopathy (sex-starvation disease). Sex-economy and cancer research are, therefore, inseparable.* Character analysis, vegetotherapy, and orgone therapy may appear to be different methods of treatment, but basically they are *one and the same biotherapy* at work in a *unitary* organism. They complement each other and have a common root in the biosystem. Their superficial differentiation corresponds to the artificial differentiation of the total organism into biophysical, characterological, and physiological functions.

I had the patient examined gynecologically. The examination fully confirmed my diagnosis of plasmatic shrinking. The body of the uterus was very small in relation to the cervix, and the ovaries were not palpable rectally—an indication, in the opinion of the gynecologist, that they were extraordinarily underdeveloped. The

* *Cf.* Chapter X.

glandular tissue of the breasts seemed totally undeveloped. It was of course difficult to come to any conclusion about whether the case was one of atrophy or of *primary inhibition* of development of the sexual organs. The gynecologist was of the opinion that it was a primary underdevelopment of the ovaries. However, the assumption of such an isolated, primary ovarian disturbance would not be in accord with our theoretical position. The ovaries are not independently functioning organs but are an integral part of the total autonomic life apparatus, upon which they depend. On the basis of the sexual history of the patient, I am inclined to view the underdevelopment of her breasts and genital organs as an *atrophy of disuse* of the sexual apparatus. The question as to what extent the endocrine glands play a *primary* role, and to what extent they should be regarded as the executive organs of the general plasma function, cannot be answered conclusively at this time.

I decided to treat the patient, without remuneration, by simultaneously utilizing physical orgone therapy and the technique of psychiatric orgone therapy. It was not long before the patient began asking questions: "Does sexual intercourse hurt?" "When are you going to rape me?" (This patient, like so many others who suffer from chronic sexual starvation, was beset by severe rape fantasies. She really believed that a woman could not be alone in a room with a man without being raped.) "Does the man move his penis in the vagina? That really must hurt!" "What do you do if you get too many children?" (She knew nothing about contraception.) "Does a woman have to give in to a man if he wants satisfaction? I'm frightened of it." The patient was totally ignorant about even the most elementary questions of sexual life. As a child, she had pressed her mother with questions about it but had been rebuffed and had stopped asking those questions of anybody. She now believed that "such things" were not supposed to be known. She had developed a strong attachment to her father, an authoritarian educator and strict moralist who had immediately suppressed the girl's first pubescent impulses. Soon afterward she began to suffer from perverse fantasies, the principal content of which was brutal rape. This led to the development of a feeling of panic whenever a boy came near her. Even in puberty, this fear was accompanied by spasms of the genital apparatus. These spasms persisted as a chronic complaint. She withdrew more and more from contact with men and became increasingly lonely.

Gradually the traditional distortions of sexuality were absorbed and anchored characterologically: sex is evil, devilish, a monstrous sin against God's commandments. Sexual intercourse is an activity reserved for marriage and then only to beget children. (Everything she observed around her completely contradicted these ideas.) The man is an evil sexual animal who violates girls "to still his lust." Women have no sexuality and only bear children. They have sexual intercourse with a man only because he "needs it." Masturbation makes you a cripple or an idiot, and "makes you lose life-juice from the marrow." (As a consequence of these beliefs, she had never actually masturbated, but since childhood had kept her hands on her genitals at night, clenched and motionless.) The difference between man and animal is that man is not sexual. What is animal is base and must be fought. Everything sexual is animal. "Ideal values" are what should be cultivated, "bad thoughts" should be kept out of one's mind. Of course, she had "bad thoughts." In consequence, she felt guilty, became still more tense, and still developed "bad thoughts." Even during her childhood, she had brutal and sadistic fantasies that she fearfully suppressed. She felt the urge to bite or tear off the penis of the men around her. During her puberty, whenever she was about to dance with a boy, an impulse to choke him broke through, accompanied by intense sexual excitation. This feeling made her withdraw even more into herself. Her father warned her about venereal diseases, giving her the impression that sexual intercourse inevitably leads to them. But he did not tell her how to protect herself against such infection. And so she remained helpless, torn between longing for love and fear of it. This impelled her into situations that really *were* dangerous. Curiosity drove her to approach completely strange men and indulge in various sexual practices only to flee in fright, and then completely

isolate herself for months. Understandably, it was her very fear that
exposed her to dangerous situations. She wanted to find out if what
she had been told was actually true. The fear was an expression of
her vital urge for sexual gratification. This confirmed what sex-economy has always maintained: *Compulsive morality and asceticism
generate sexual criminality and perversion, the precise opposite of
what they intend.*

The patient was totally ignorant of the anatomy of her geni-
talia. Yet, since her genitals caused her so much suffering, she was
obsessed by the thought that she really had to know about them.
Sexual curiosity would suddenly seize her during harmless conversations with both male and female acquaintances; her instinctive
reaction was immediate flight and withdrawal. Just once, when she
was twenty, she felt she was really in love with a boy and tried to
break through. Instead, she sank back, helpless; she "went to pieces."
The sexual excitation became so intense and the genital spasm momentarily so violent that she wanted to commit suicide. It was impossible for her to conceive of the sexual act as anything but a brutal
violation.

Even during puberty her capacity to work was disturbed as a
consequence of her tremendous sexual stasis. Compulsive sexual
thoughts always intruded when her interest in work was aroused.
Clearly, the emotional stimulus provided by her work simultaneously triggered the sexual excitation that she feared so much. *Sexual
stasis is the most important cause of work disturbance in puberty.*
With the years, the patient's work capacity declined more and more;
she became dull, until finally she reached a state of complete
emotional emptiness, which she had displayed for the last two
years. During those two years, the characterological and emotional
emptiness proceeded into somatic shrinking.

In these first attempts to treat a shrinking biopathy I started
with the following assumptions: Sexual stasis, which produces "the
stasis neurosis," is at the basis of both the carcinomatous and the
cardiovascular biopathy. But there must be an essential difference

between the cancer and the cardiovascular biopathies. Cancer victims predominantly show emotional mildness and characterological resignation. People who suffer from cardiovascular hypertension, i.e., from chronic vascular contraction, are, in contrast to the cancer sufferer, for the most part easily excitable, "emotionally labile," explosive personalities. This is clearly expressed in acute anxiety attacks. On the other hand, I have never seen cancer patients with violent emotions, outbreaks of rage, etc. We are therefore justified in concluding the existence of specific differences between the two forms of biopathy, in spite of their common etiology in sexual stasis. The essential factor is *how the organism reacts to the dammed-up sexual excitation once it has occurred.*

When investigating new connections, we are compelled again and again to make assumptions suggested by the disease patterns, without being able to state with certainty that these assumptions are correct. We have no alternative but to leave the confirmation or refutation of our hypotheses to future experience. In such matters, one can never be flexible, careful, or self-critical enough. Briefly, the clinical comparison of the cancer biopathy with cardiovascular hypertension forced us to assume a basically different view of the dammed-up sexual excitation in the biosystem. *In the cardiovascular biopathy* (anxiety neuroses as a consequence of abstinence), *the sexual excitation remains lively* biologically, i.e., physiologically and emotionally. In other words, the biological core of the organism, the autonomic life apparatus, continues to generate energy to the fullest extent. When it is contracted, however, the organism reacts with outbreaks of anxiety or rage and with somatic symptoms such as hyperthyroidism, diarrhea, etc. *In cancer, on the other hand, the biological core lowers its energy production.* With this diminution of energy production, the emotions and excitations become gradually weaker and weaker. The energy metabolism is thus disturbed far more profoundly than in the more conspicuous symptom-producing disorders, such as hysteria. Seen functionally, an outbreak of anger is still an energy discharge, even though it may be pathological. *Chronic emotional calm, on the other hand, must coincide with a bio-energetic stagnation in the cell and plasma system.*

With some hesitation, I feel obliged to speak here of "suffocation of the cell energy system." It seems conceivable, although at present this contention cannot be stated with any certainty, that characterological resignation is the surface expression of an inner process of gradual cessation of the energy functions of the life apparatus. Let us illustrate it in this way:

In a flowing brook, the continuous movement of the water purifies it. Dirt is dissolved very quickly, by a process not yet completely understood. In a stagnant pond, however, not only are the processes of putrefaction not eliminated, they are accelerated. Amoebae and other protozoa grow poorly, or not at all, in moving waters but develop profusely in stagnant water. We still do not know much about this "suffocation" in stagnant water or in the stagnant energy system of the organism, but we have every reason to assume the existence of such a process and state. It cannot be mere coincidence that cancer develops so seldom in a bio-energetically alive organism and so easily in the bio-energetically stagnant organism. It is clear that the shrinking biopathy, in contrast to other biopathic forms, begins with this abnormal calm in the person's sexual and emotional life. Symptoms of stasis anxiety, which are often numerous in the previous history of cancer patients, are rare once the cancer reaches a mature stage. The impression is of a sharp reduction in the biological energy metabolism, which in healthy persons is vividly reflected in the function of the orgasm. These assumptions are, I believe, of great significance and I hope they will be thoroughly investigated.

It is not to be assumed that the cells of the organism submit to the extinction of the energy system without a struggle. When the functioning of the bio-energetic (orgonotic) excitation of the total system is reduced, the orgonotic excitation in individual cells or cell systems can still continue intensely, just as a suffocating organism resists final subsidence in clonisms. Thus, individual cells can still demonstrate orgonotic overexcitation even when the total organism has already lost the capacity for excitation and energy metabolism. However, such isolated excitations, occurring without connection with orgonotic excitations of the entire organism, can no longer be physiologically normal. They must have damaging effects on the cell structure.

Further discussion of this subject will have to be deferred. Orgone physics will provide important clarifications about the affective function of the body cells and its relationship to orgone energy metabolism. (There is, for instance, the phenomenon of orgonotic lumination in bions, which discloses important connections with cell lumination and cell excitation in the organism.) But now let us return to the patient.

Her emotional and bio-energetic behavior conformed completely to the assumptions just described. She constantly asked about sexual processes, but the questions lacked urgency and excitation. By contrast, a patient with anxiety hysteria would have asked the same questions with intense excitation, or she would have repressed them and developed severe anxiety. The emotional import of the questions would have stood out immediately. With our patient, it was different. She asked everything in a flat voice, as if without interest, even though these matters filled her life. Her fantasies were gruesome but she seemed unmoved, and only superficially interested. Very soon she began complaining about the superficial and corpse-like way she experienced things. She had suffered from this problem since puberty. It gave her the feeling of being unable to establish close contact with anything or anyone. This emotional calm of the cancer victim is in sharp contrast to the coldness and contactlessness of the affect-blocked, compulsive character. In the compulsive character, powerful energy impulses are bound in the block; in cancer, the energy is lacking.

Careful observation of the patient's behavior contradicted the assumption that there were repressed affects in the biological depths. There were no affects at all. The orgasm reflex appeared with surprising ease, yet with scarcely any affective strength. Affects are the manifestations of bio-energetic cell excitation. If we overcome the respiratory inhibition of a patient suffering from stasis neurosis with cardiac anxiety, strong excitations will be the immediate and inevitable consequence. But in the case of our patient this did not happen. The correction of her respiration over a period of two months did bring about spontaneous vegetative actions, but no lively movements. Since the orgasm reflex was weak, she had no fear of it, in contrast to a person with stasis neurosis who experiences severe anxiety in connection with it. This poverty of affect thus reached deep into the biological system.

The question confronting me was whether the spasms of the genital apparatus could be dissolved without the presence of strong excitations. It was clear that she would recover only if her sexuality began to function vigorously. After two weeks of treatment, she developed weak vegetative currents in the genitals. Thereupon the genital spasms were alleviated and the pains disappeared. But because the excitations were so weak and failed to intensify, the patient did not develop the usual anxiety. This finding was extraordinary and confirmed the assumption that in the shrinking biopathy the sources of excitation in the autonomic system slowly die out. Whether fading energy functions can be fully revived by orgone therapy remains to be established.

Resignation without open or concealed protest against the denial of joy in life must be regarded as one of the essential causes of the shrinking biopathy. *Biopathic shrinking, therefore, represents a continuation of chronic characterological resignation in the realm of cell functioning.*

Let us visualize the fundamental biological (the physiological and emotional) functions diagrammatically. Imagine a wide circle with a center ("core"). The shrinking of the circle periphery would represent the onset of characterological and emotional resignation. The core, the center of the circle, is still unaffected. The shrinking process advances toward the center, i.e., the "biological core." The biological core is nothing but the sum of all plasmatic cell functions.

Once the shrinking process has reached this core, the plasma itself shrinks. This coincides with the process of weight loss. But long before the plasma function is directly damaged, the peripheral physiological and characterological functions are disturbed: the loss of ability to establish social contact, the loss of *joie de vivre,* the loss of capacity for work, and, finally, the disturbances of pulsation and of vegetative excitation.

The vital apparatus envelops the biological core in layers of varying depth. The biosystem has superficial and deeper layers.[10] Disturbances of bodily functioning are accordingly superficial or deep. An acute respiratory disturbance will not affect the core of the biosystem. A chronic respiratory disturbance, due to a chronic inspiratory attitude, will generate chronic anxiety but will not influence the biological cell plasma function, so long as the bio-energetic functions in the cells themselves continue, that is, so long as the organism continues to produce vigorous impulses. The impairment of impulse production in the cells is an indication that peripheral characterological resignation has seized the cell plasma system. We are then dealing with the process of biopathic shrinking. We shall have to study this process also in chronic schizophrenics (especially in hebephrenia).

It now appears certain that biopathic shrinking is specific for cancer. The actual cancer process resembles, in its essentials, protozoal life in a pond, in which there is no longer any movement of water but a flourishing growth of protozoa. Unfortunately, these processes in the background of the shrinking biopathy cannot be directly observed microscopically; they can only be deduced. There remains a gap, so far as the completeness of direct observation is concerned, between characterological-biological affect-stillness and the process in the cell plasma that, in the cancer process, is microscopically visible in the form of vesicular, bionous disintegration.

[10] A comparable layering has been found in the character. [*Cf.* Wilhelm Reich, *Character Analysis* (New York: Farrar, Straus and Giroux, 1972).]

We now want to consider these cell and tissue disturbances. What is clear is that cancer cannot develop from a simple scar, a wart, a wound, or a chronic irritation unless there already exists a fundamental disturbance of the life function, in the core of the biological system, that ultimately seizes upon the local damage. The question is: In what way does this happen?

CHAPTER VI

The Cancer Cell

1. THE RIDDLE OF THE ORIGIN OF THE CANCER CELL

The cancer scourge is surrounded by a plethora of unsolved problems, of which none has fascinated physicians and laymen more than the question of the origin of the cancer cell. Healthy tissue is "at rest," i.e., the numerous individual cells of the organism live with each other in harmony and mutually fulfill the respective organ functions, such as absorption of food, excretion, respiration, sexual excitation and gratification, etc. In short, they are subordinated to the organ functions, which are responsible for the vital functions of the total organism. Cancer tissue develops from tissues that previously seemed healthy. According to the traditional viewpoint, cancer is chiefly characterized by the fact that cells that were "at rest" become "agitated." These cells divide rapidly, proliferate wildly, grow into large heaps, and so form the "cancer tumor." The cancer cells, unlike healthy cells, are mobile. By a process of rapid division, they grow into the surrounding tissues, ceaselessly penetrating and destroying everything in their path. It is accurate to describe them as infiltrating and devitalizing.

Let us concentrate for a moment on the most essential question: *How is it possible that an immobile cell, living and functioning in harmonious union with other cells, is transformed into a mobile, "wild" cell that emerges from the local tissue and destroys everything in its path?* This fact is all the *more* peculiar inasmuch as the cancer cell itself is an extremely weak structure that disintegrates easily.

The sudden transition from a healthy to a cancerous cell has not been understood until now. The properties of healthy cells are well known. The form and many characteristics of cancer cells are moderately well known. But nothing at all is known about what happens in between, i.e., how the one is transformed into the other.

Several years ago bion research successfully led—although by a strangely roundabout course—to a satisfactory explanation of this riddle. With the solution of this crucial problem, many gates were opened to the understanding and control of cancer. I will state at once the most essential finding: It was erroneous to believe that the cancer cell develops directly from healthy cells. *An immobile, healthy cell does not suddenly change into an agitated, motile, proliferating cell.* A series of pathological changes occurs in the tissue and its immediate surroundings long before the development of the first cancer cell. These local changes are themselves brought about by a general disease of the vital apparatus. The development of the cancer cell in a specific place is, in reality, only *one* phase in the development of the general disease called "cancer." We designate this systemic disease *carcinomatous shrinking biopathy.* The cancer tumor is not even the most important part of the disease; it is only the most apparent and was, until now, the only visible and palpable factor of the cancer biopathy. Therefore the discovery that the shrinking biopathy is the actual disease was of major significance, for it directed our attention to the essential factors. If the systemic disease, and not the local tumor, is the critical element, it follows logically that the treatment of cancer must be a general one; it can no longer be restricted to the small spot in the body where a tumor suddenly develops. Ignorance of the systemic disease "cancer," in conjunction with the traditional belief that the local tumor is the actual disease, has been responsible for the lack of progress in the fight against cancer.

Let us now return to the question of what happens in the tissue *before* the appearance of the first fully developed cancer cell. To answer this question, we must first eliminate certain procedures that hinder cancer research:

1. Neither healthy tissue nor tissue suspected of being cancerous should be examined, as is customary, in the dead state, fixed and stained. We must accustom ourselves to the practice of examining them in the living state. The fixed, stained preparation can be used as a control, but living preparations yield findings that are not revealed in dead preparations.
2. Microscopic observations cannot be reliably made using a magnification of less than 2000x. At less than 2000x, it is not possible to follow the development of the cancer cell.
3. We must make repeated observations, at high magnification, of *all* available cells in the organism: excreta (sputum, feces, urine), viable blood, skin and mucous membrane cells, etc.

UNUSUAL FORMS IN CANCER TISSUE AND THE BLOOD OF CANCER PATIENTS

Healthy living tissues and blood, examined at 2000x, show the cells and formations that are described in any good biology or physiology textbook as constituents of the organism. Let us now observe blood, excreta, and tissues from a cancer patient, from one suffering, say, with lung cancer. We discover formed cells and unformed shapes that are never found in healthy mice or in the tissues and excreta of healthy humans. Most striking is the presence of *striated, vesicular structures showing an intense blue color,* which resemble neither cells nor bacteria. Some have irregular, formless contours, while others have an elongated, *club-like, or caudate, shape.* The presence of caudate, rapidly moving, pulsating amoebae in lung sputum is an unexpected finding. *How do amoeba-like formations get into the lung?* It cannot be through "air infection," for there are no amoebae in the air. *Therefore they must have*

developed in the lung itself. From what? Certainly not from germs
that had accidentally strayed into the lungs. We have learned that
amoebae develop in infusions from vesicularly disintegrating moss,
which passes through many intermediate phases. We have also
learned that there are no "germs" in the sense of traditional protozoology. Is it possible that the amoebae and the other formations in
the lung sputum have developed from *disintegrating lung tissue* in
precisely the same way that amoebae in moss infusions develop
from disintegrating moss tissue? This sudden idea gives us much to
think about, since at one stroke it explains the origin of cancer cells.
However, such ideas should, for the moment, be held in reserve and
translated into definite statements only after the necessary objective
proofs of their accuracy have been assembled.

We are somewhat unsure of our undertaking. After all, why did
it never occur to anyone before that one could simply examine the
sputum of suspected or confirmed cancer patients to establish the
presence of unusual formations? Without question, amoebae from
the lungs would have been found. If it is that simple, we must be
doubly careful and try first to understand the reason for such negligence in cancer research. An examination of cancer literature reveals
that in not a single work is there so much as a mention of the form,
variety, or even the existence of living, mobile, cancer cells in
excreta and living tissues. Nevertheless, without further evidence,
we cannot automatically assume that several generations of cancer
researchers have so seriously erred. Either our idea is nonsense and
the amoebae in the lung sputum have nothing to do with cancer, or
generations of cancer researchers actually have made a stupendous
error. We do not want to exult in this and intend rather to seriously
consider all aspects of the problem. To begin with, it is obvious that
such errors and omissions do occur in science. Moreover, they always occur immediately prior to the birth of important new knowledge. Countless women died of puerperal fever in the days before
Pasteur and Lister, when nothing was known about infection and
sterilization. Yet it would have been very simple to refine the old

discovery of Leeuwenhoek and look into microscopes. Nothing but chronic, deeply rooted prejudice kept the physicians of Pasteur's time from making use of the microscope and it cost an incalculable number of lives. Before Sigmund Freud discovered infantile sexual activity, which is now familiar to every physician and educator, it did not exist in the eyes of science. Yet, today, how simple it is to see that the foremost interest of small children is their own sexuality.

We begin, therefore, to feel more confidence in the belief that a similar catastrophic error has been committed by the cancer researchers. But we must identify the error, understand its nature, and prove positively that our view is correct. Once we have acknowledged the possibility of a gigantic error, there is no turning back. If our concept is erroneous, we must admit it; if traditional cancer research has proceeded from false premises and is now on the wrong track, we must prove it. But let me anticipate my conclusion: Traditional cancer research does start with incorrect premises and is, indeed, on the wrong track. This accounts for its negligence in failing to examine microscopically the sputum of lung cancer patients.

The consistent study of excreta and blood from cancer patients eventually will give us reliable methods for making an early diagnosis of cancer. Someday, it will no longer be necessary to wait until the cancer tumor has become so large it can be diagnosed by X-ray or biopsy. We will ultimately gain a firm foothold regarding the origin of cancer and the way to its cure will be opened.

The demonstration of the basic error of traditional cancer research goes together with the proof of the accuracy of our own concept of the origin of the cancer cell. Once we understand how the cancer cell develops from healthy tissue, we will also understand where traditional cancer research went wrong.

First, let us subject the lung sputum of our cancer patient to even closer examination by increasing the magnification from 2000x to 3000x, and even 4000x. We discover a profuse number of very small, *lancet-shaped bodies* which were overlooked at magnifications below 2000x. Their shape and motility are identical with that of *T-bacilli,* which we can cultivate from degenerating tissue, disintegrating blood, or from putrescent protein. They are the same minute bodies we see in charcoal bion preparations, and can be obtained from any kind of cancer tissue by simple culture inoculation.

Since T-bacilli result from tissue degeneration and putrid disintegration (cf. Fig. 32, Appendix), we must conclude that a process of disintegration and putrefaction is taking place in the lung tissue. What we do not yet know, but must determine, is whether the T-bacilli are a *result* or a *cause* of the tissue disintegration. The point is certain, however, that the T-bacilli did not enter the lungs as infection from the air. This can easily be proved. It has not been possible to cultivate T-bacilli directly from the air no matter what culture media are used (cf. Fig. 33, Appendix). T-bacilli can be obtained only when cultivated air bacteria (rot bacteria, B-subtilis, staphylococci, etc.) degenerate. The T-bacilli growth on the culture can be recognized by the fine, green-blue shimmering margin that forms around every kind of degenerating culture. It gives off a strong, acrid, ammonia-like odor. From this margin, pure T-bacilli cultures can be grown. The question as to whether the T-bacilli precede the formation of cancer, or result from it (perhaps both), can be answered experimentally. We shall say more on this matter later.

We also find, in the sputum of our lung cancer patient, blue, contractile forms of varying shapes, which are not present in healthy lung tissue. They are the familiar *PA bions.* Since we did not put them into the lung, they must have developed there. Like the T-bacilli, they cannot be cultivated directly from the air. We know they are PA bions because they exercise the identical paralyzing effect on the T-bacilli as do the PA bions produced experimentally from earth and coal. The question now arises: What connection exists between these large blue bions and cancer? The problem becomes all the more complicated the longer we continue our observations. We shall find, however, that the solution is a simple one.

AUTOINFECTION OF THE ORGANISM DUE TO TISSUE DISINTEGRATION

The structures found in the lung sputum are not present in the air. They must therefore have their origin within the organism. Our task is to establish how they develop. We conjecture that they are products of tissue degeneration and act as an *autoinfection* of the organism. For confirmation, we examine excretions and secretions from the cancer patient's other organs: the vaginal and uterine secretions, urine, feces. We also examine skin cancer epithelium, or tissue from spontaneous cancer tumors in physiological saline. The more cancer tissue of various origins we examine, the more secure our conclusions become:

1. The fully developed cancer cell is merely the final product in a long sequence of pathological processes in the affected tissues. These processes have never been investigated.
2. There are a number of typical phases of tissue disintegration and certain cell forms that are found only in unhealthy tissue.
3. The first phase of cancerous tissue degeneration is the loss of normal structure through the formation of vesicles.
4. The vesicularly disintegrating tissue yields two basic types of bions: blue PA bions and the small, black, lancet-shaped T-bacilli.
5. *Cancer cells are organized from these bionous energy vesicles, developing through a number of intermediate phases to the motile, amoeboid protozoan.*

In every type of cancer tissue examined we find the same initial and transitional forms (*cf.* Fig. 20, p. 260).

Healthy muscle tissue shows a regular, striated structure without vesicles (*cf.* Fig. 51, Appendix). Cancerous muscle tissue regularly shows vesicular disintegration (*cf.* Fig. 52, Appendix). Healthy living cells show a bluish, finely striated or unstructured protoplasm. The same cells in cancer tissue show deep-blue bionous vesicles or extremely small black bodies. Healthy cells (muscle, skin epithelium, tongue epithelium, etc.) disintegrate into large blue bions when boiled in KCl solution. Cancer cells, however, disintegrate into T-bodies when boiled. Therefore, the fully developed cancer cell can be distinguished from the normal tissue cell by the fact that it disintegrates not into blue PA bions but into T-bacilli.

The type of cancer tissue (sarcoma, adenocarcinoma, epithelioma) and its location in the body are a matter of indifference. What characterizes cancer is the *vesicular structure of the surrounding tissue* and the various formations that either evolve into the fully developed cancer cell or result from its disintegration. The first phase in the development of a cancer tumor is always vesicular disintegration of the tissue. The assumption can therefore be made that the proliferation of cancer cells into the surrounding areas is to be ascribed not only to the advance of already formed cancer tissue but also, and perhaps even more, to the disintegration of the softened surrounding tissue. The surrounding healthy tissue must itself undergo vesicular disintegration before it can allow infiltration of the tumor into the surroundings. It is a question of reciprocal action between formed cancer tissue and the healthy tissue that surrounds it. The first vesicularly disintegrated cell group organizes into cancer cell tissue. This formed cancer cell tissue damages the healthy tissue surrounding it and brings about its vesicular disintegration. This surrounding tissue, which is itself now disintegrating, offers no resistance to the infiltration, increasingly recedes, and progressively develops into cancer cells. In this way we are able to explain the typical destructive, infiltrating growth of the cancer tumor. The microphotos of living, unstained cancer tissue (*cf.* Fig.

53, Appendix) show that parts of the tissue are gradually transformed into darkly colored cancer formations.

The shape of fully developed cancer cells is the same for all cancer, wherever localized (bone, gland, muscle, etc.) (*cf.* Figs. 49 and 54, Appendix). To the trained eye, it is instantly recognizable by its caudate form. The cell takes on this shape long before it acquires motility. Therefore, if elongated, vesicular (bionous) formations shaped like a club and having an intense blue glimmer were found in vaginal secretion, a diagnosis of incipient cancer would be confirmed. However, it would not be possible at this point to predict the progress of the disease. That depends on a number of other circumstances which will be discussed shortly.

The club-shaped forms cannot be mistaken for any healthy cell. There are cylindrical cells in the gastric mucosa that could conceivably be confused with cancer cells, but the experienced observer will not fail to recognize the difference.

Alongside the typical club-shaped formations, there are masses of large round cells that have a smooth, structureless plasm or contain bions of an intense dark blue. (The question of whether this structure has anything to do with typical chromatolysis and nuclear chromatin—a problem most familiar to the cancer specialist working with *dead* tissue—is of interest only to the specialist and will therefore be discussed later in its particular context.)

The typical stages in the development of cancer cells in mice and in humans are the following:

1. Swelling and vesicular disintegration of the tissue. This disintegration originates in local spasms and chronic systemic energy stasis.
2. Organization of the bionous vesicles into heaps of energy vesicles or bions ("bion heaps").
3. Formation of a membrane around the bion heap.
4. Dissolution of the bions into structureless or striated blue plasma. (Note, however, that bions sometimes retain their original form.)

5. Formation of club-shaped bodies.
6. Appearance of motility in the fully developed club-shaped bodies. This cannot be observed at magnifications of less than 3000–4000x. The movements are slow and jerky, and from place to place.
7. Liquefaction of the plasm and with it the development of flowing amoeboid protozoa. This stage is rarely reached in human cancer, since the organism generally succumbs much earlier to the tissue disintegration and the process of putrefaction. (More later about the process of putrefaction.) These amoeboid formations occur much more frequently in mice, especially mice that have been injected with T-bacilli and, as a consequence, have developed an artificial cancer. The cancer cells move by means of rhythmic contractions or by flowing from place to place. Many of them are caudate and move like fish in water (this is recorded on film). Of fully developed cancer cells there is a great variety. There are both small-celled and large-celled formations. For reasons not yet understood, the small-celled ones are much more malignant than the large-celled ones; i.e., they lead more rapidly to death. The most virulent form is the small-celled sarcoma in young people.

The development of a cancer tumor simply corresponds to *protozoal self-disintegration and autoinfection of the organism.* Or, in other words, *individual tissues of the metazoal organism are transformed into single-celled organisms of varying size and shape.* If this process were not interrupted by death, the affected person or the cancer mouse would eventually be completely transformed into protozoa. The most destructive concomitant phenomenon of this transformation is the typical cancerous process of putrefaction. For bion research, it is irrelevant whether the cancer cells develop from epithelial tissue, glandular tissue, connective tissue, or bone; the basic process is always the same. The traditional differentiation between various forms of cancer (epithelioma, adenocarcinoma, glioma, etc.) thus loses in importance. For the patient, the significant factor is not the histological type of the tumor, but its location.

THE FUNCTION OF THE ORGASM IN THE ORGONE ENERGY METABOLISM OF THE CELL: NUCLEAR SUFFOCATION IN THE PRECANCEROUS CELL

Conclusions drawn from observations in orgone therapy indicate that *local spasms* and *disturbances of tissue charge* are the basic causes of tumor formation. On the other hand, *respiratory inhibition* is the primary cause of the systemic shrinking and therefore it influences tumor formation as well. These processes explain the disturbances in the organism and in the individual organ. But they do not make comprehensible the disturbance of the *cell* functions in the affected organs. In a roundabout way, this problem leads back to the old questions: *What is the function of the sexual orgasm in the energy metabolism of the cell? Why has this cardinal function been developed, and on what biophysical processes in the cells is it based?* Scientists often tend to ask questions that appear to the layman superfluous or naïve. They are nevertheless of crucial importance.

Until now, no answer has ever been provided to this question, neither by the sexological research that preceded sex-economy nor by sex-economic research. Nor is it possible to withdraw to the comfortable position of the mystic that *man in contrast to the beast can exist without the orgastic function*. The damages inflicted on mankind by orgastic impotence have been too devastating to be denied any longer. The significance of the orgasm for the bioenergetic equilibrium of the organism was accepted as a *fact* in sex-economy, but not understood. We knew only that the orgasm regulates the energy household and that its absence causes biopathies. What we did not know was *how* the orgasm fulfills its function, *what causes the orgastic (orgonotic) discharge in the cells.* Unexpectedly, sex-economic cancer research led to the solution of this crucial question in the following way:

The local cancer tumor develops in spastic and poorly charged, i.e., in *suffocating,* organs. The individual cells are severely affected by this process. We must assume that the development of a cancer cell from a normal resting cell corresponds to a change in the "bioenergetic," i.e., orgone-physical, cell function. Chemical investigations have revealed many important factors, for instance, the production of lactic acid in the cancer tissue, or the excess of carbon dioxide, which indicates a suffocating metabolism in the cells, etc. Bion research now adds the orgone-physical, i.e., the energetic, viewpoint to the chemical one. It maintains that an energy stasis leads to bionous disintegration of the cell substance and that the cancer cell develops from these bions. But we must learn more about it: *How does the energy stasis in a tissue lead to bionous disintegration of the cells?*

In the organism, every cell, with its nucleus, its plasm, and its orgone energy field, forms a complete "orgonotic system." Since every cell contains orgone energy, its structure must be connected to its orgone charge. It is not difficult to guess what this connection is: The *nucleus* is the most important component of the cell and contains the most energy. Cell plasm without a nucleus is not capable of life; but cells can live very well with only minimal cell plasm, as do sperm cells, for example. The nucleus must therefore be regarded as the "vegetative center" of the individual cell, just as the autonomic nervous system forms the "biological core," or the "vegetative center," of the total organism. The cell nucleus, and the autonomic nervous system, represent the most concentrated and substantial energy apparatus in their respective orgonotic systems, the cell and the total organism.

The nucleus is *energetically stronger* than the cell plasm. All essential biological processes and functions begin in the nucleus and then spread to the plasm. For instance, cell division begins with the division of the nucleus, which is followed by division of the plasm. Amoebae, in the process of division, often live for several hours with a divided nucleus, i.e., with two nuclei, before the body divides into two amoebae.

Great credit must be given to the German biologist Richard Hertwig for having been the first scientist to investigate and formulate the relation of the nucleus to plasm in his famous "nucleus-plasma relation."[1] It had been known for some time that most cells are a certain size when they divide, varying only within narrow limits. Following division, the daughter cell grows to the same size as the parent cell just before it divides. The relation of the nucleus to the plasm immediately after division is regarded in classical biology as the normal nucleus-plasma relation. According to Popoff, a young cell just produced by division grows at a fixed rate, the nucleus growing less rapidly than the plasm. Then suddenly, immediately before division, the growth of the nucleus accelerates rapidly ("growth of division") until, like the plasm, it has nearly doubled its original size. The retardation in the speed of growth of the nucleus after division of a cell results in a shift in the nucleus-plasm relation in favor of the plasm: there is more plasm than nucleus. This disproportion creates a tension in the cell that causes the nucleus to grow and overcome the gap created by the growth of the plasm, thus restoring the normal nucleus-plasma relation. Hertwig assumed that this tension in the cell not only initiates the growth of the nucleus but also stimulates the cell division. On the basis of our orgasm formula we can say further that *immediately preceding division, the cell is under more mechanical tension and is more charged energetically than immediately after division, when it is smaller.*[2] Before division, the nucleus-plasm relation shifts in favor of the more highly charged nucleus because the nucleus is stronger orgonotically than the plasm. Because the relation of the

[1] *Cf*. Hartmann, *Allgemeine Biologie* (2nd ed., Jena, 1933), pp. 364 ff.
[2] *Cf*. Wilhelm Reich, *The Function of the Orgasm*, p. 251 ff.

mass of the nucleus to the mass of the plasm remains the same, *orgonotic* nucleus-plasma relation must shift considerably in favor of the nucleus. The relatively high tension and charge of the nucleus at the peak of its size now induces division. As we know, division itself follows the tension-charge formula and leads to the *discharge* by way of division, and *relaxation* in the form of the daughter cells. What has this process to do with the problem of the cancer cell? A great deal.

Cancer cells are usually recognized in the dead, stained section by the following characteristics: The nuclei are grouped irregularly. There are numerous divisions of these nuclei (mitoses); they are large, extraordinarily rich in chromatin, and bunched together, as if the nuclear mass were greater than the plasm mass. One is impressed with the rich nucleation of the degenerating tissue. If we now fit this finding into our orgone-physical description of the process of cancer cell formation, the next question is: *Can Hertwig's nucleus-plasma relation be expressed in terms of orgone biophysics?*

It is possible. The nucleus is the strongest, i.e., the most orgonerich, system in the cell. The cell plasm is orgonotically the weaker system. This means that there is a difference between the orgone charge of the nucleus and that of the plasm, a fact that can be confirmed microscopically. The nucleus shows all the orgonotic characteristics more intensely than does the plasm. It radiates more strongly than the plasm and has an intense blue color. Surrounding the cell is an *orgone energy field* which may be designated as the orgone-weakest part in the *total orgonotic system* of the cell. It is a basic law of orgone physics (in contrast to electrophysics and mechanics) that *the stronger orgone system draws off energy from the weaker system and attracts it.* This finding is crucial; it illuminates at once important questions that have been hitherto unsolved:

1. *What holds the cell together?*
2. *How is it possible that the nucleus-plasma relation always remains approximately the same* (except during

the period of division), i.e., *that the nucleus is always orgonotically stronger than the plasm?* Every organism continually radiates orgone and thus, in time, should lose its orgone charge completely.

The answer is that the nucleus is functionally the energy center and the energy source of the cell, its "autonomic nervous system," so to speak. The cell plasm is the storehouse for foodstuffs and the executory organ of the impulses from the nucleus, just as the digestive and locomotor organs of the metazoan are the executory organs of the autonomic system. *The nucleus constantly draws orgone energy from the cell plasm which has assimilated it by way of nutritional absorption and respiration.* In this way, the nucleus maintains its orgone energy preponderance in relation to the plasm. The nucleus-plasma relation has to be determined not only in terms of material, i.e., according to *mass,* but also, and more importantly, in terms of energy, according to the difference in orgone charge. If the plasm grows in the period between two cell divisions, orgone energy is accumulated in the plasm. At a certain point, the nucleus grows rapidly; i.e., it corrects the relation in orgone charge. It follows that during the phase *between two divisions* (two orgonotic convulsions), *the absorption of orgone energy into the cell exceeds by far the discharge of orgone energy into the surroundings.* This (and not chemical-material processes) explains the growth of the total cell up to the time of its division. The preponderance of the energy flow from the outside into the nucleus leads inevitably to an *excess of orgone energy* and with it to the reversal of the energy flow from the nucleus toward the outside. *The discharge of the excess of biological energy occurs in the entire living realm—in plants as well as animals, in metazoa as well as protozoa—by the convulsion of the total plasma, in other words, through the orgasm.* Thus it is not a matter of speculation but an orgone-physical fact when we say that the orgasm, either in a single cell or in a mass of cells (the organism), is a basic "cell function," the "regulator of the energy household of the organism." The four-beat *tension → charge → discharge → relaxation* characterizes the sexual orgasm of the metazoan as well as individual cell division. The "orgasm formula" must therefore be regarded as identical with the "life formula," and cell division as an orgastic process in the strict sense of *equalization of excessive biological energy.* The orgasm is not a luxury of life, not a caprice of nature, not the troublesome function that it seems to those individuals who suffer from sexual dissatisfaction and biological rigidity (orgastic impotence), but *the regulator of the household of biological energy. The orgasm discharges the surplus of orgone energy that periodically accumulates in the cell nuclei.*

Our orgasm theory is thus strongly supported by this penetration of the secrets of cell function, and is now capable of explaining cell functions hitherto not understood: The orgasm (orgone energy discharge through convulsions) releases the excess accumulation of orgone energy that occurs in every growth process. Once the growth process stops—in other words, when the production of *excess* orgone energy in the biological nucleus gradually diminishes—the orgasm function also begins to lose its significance. It occurs less often, and finally ceases. This phase, i.e., the involution of the organism, is the most essential characteristic of normal aging. On this basis, life in its ascending phase is sexually vigorous; in its descending phase it becomes progressively weakened sexually. This principle is just as true for individuals as for cell generations. There are periods of flourishing and periods of dying in cell generations, e.g., the "generation death" of protozoa. Here, much is still obscure. To clarify matters we will return to our discussion of the energy process of cancer cell formation.

I would like to offer an analogy in order to illustrate precancerous cell suffocation. Imagine a group of people working together under favorable conditions. They all have enough space to move in; they support each other, are at ease, and function to capacity. Now imagine the same group squeezed into a small room. Fire breaks out; peace and order vanish; wild disorder reigns; people are trampled. This reaction is nothing other than a revolt of the life impulses against the threatening danger. The fear has not only brought an end to orderly functioning but, in addition, has created a new kind of functioning—panic, which is deadly. The sequence is comparable to what must be imagined to occur when wild cancer cells develop in suffocating tissue.

The chronic contraction of the organism prevents orderly respiration and charge and discharge of orgone energy in the cell plasm, which first contracts and then begins to shrink. The chemical processes of metabolism are disturbed. The excess of carbon dioxide causes a condition similar to suffocation in animals. The autonomic system reacts to suffocation, i.e., threatened extinction, with violent convulsions, i.e., completely uncontrolled hyperactivity.

The conclusion can logically be drawn that the cell nuclei develop this overexcitation and wild activity when plasm functioning is reduced and the plasm begins to shrink. Specific basic laws govern the total organism as well as the individual cell, a fact that must be emphasized repeatedly. Here the principle of functional unity and antithesis is confirmed. The nucleus and the plasm normally form a functional unity. In the suffocation of the plasm, however, the nucleus reacts in sharp opposition to the disease process in the plasm. The nucleus, as the stronger orgonotic system, can still "defend" itself when the orgonotically weaker plasm begins to succumb. In respect to energy functions, the Hertwig nucleus-plasma relation thereby shifts rapidly and dangerously in favor of the nucleus. The energy excess in the nucleus becomes too great in relation to the suffocating plasm. In a condition of excessive charge, the nucleus is capable of functioning in only *one* way, through *lumination and division.* Whereas the biological orgone radiation declines during the process of the shrinking of the plasm and blood systems, the *mitogenetic radiation* of the suffocating cell nuclei intensifies greatly. This was confirmed by Klenitzky, in the case of carcinoma of the uterus. Gurwitsch established the presence of heightened radiation in tumor pulp. *The affected cell nuclei attempt to compensate for the failure of the total organism* by taking over the function of orgone energy *discharge,* which the total organism is no longer able to carry out due to orgastic impotence and contraction of the plasm system. *At the deepest biological level, energy discharge, in the form of lumination and division of the nuclei, replaces the natural orgastic convulsions of the total plasm system.*

The profusion of cell divisions (mitoses) in cancer tissue thus becomes easily understandable. Since these divisions can no longer proceed in a normal, physiological manner, the nuclei vary in size. And since the plasm is severely disturbed, the formation of the nucleus must also ultimately suffer. It disintegrates into individual, strongly radiating bions. This bionous disintegration affects the total cell, and even extends to neighboring cells, reducing them to a formless mass of bionous vesicles which, in the dead stain preparation, appear "richly nucleated," "dense" and "chromophilic." It is from this bion mass, which is spurred by the orgone energy that no longer functions harmoniously within the organism, that the protozoa called "cancer cells" now develop. The metazoan ceases to function, while the protozoan flourishes, as in a stagnant pond where energy metabolism no longer exists. Life sinks back and functions at the *lowest biological level,* for, where a metazoal organism can no longer survive, a protozoan and certainly a bion can still function.

The cancer tumor thus is merely a late, palpable manifestation of a severe disturbance of the orgonotic equilibrium and unitary function of the organism. It is the result of a rebellion of the affected cell nuclei against the processes of suffocation and shrinking in the plasm. It is this rebellion that generates the "wild cell growth." This process in the cell nuclei corresponds to the disturbance in the autonomic system in an acute anxiety attack, as for example in anxiety neurosis. It would be perfectly appropriate to speak of *an anxiety attack among the nuclei of the cells in the suffocating tissue.* In anxiety neurosis, the anxiety attack affects both the biological core and the biological periphery; the anxiety attack in cancer affects only the nuclei, while the periphery of the orgonotic system and its cells remains "emotionally" calm. In anxiety neurosis, the anxiety seizes the total organism; in local tumor formation, the anxiety attack is confined to a tissue, and, even there, only to the cell nuclei. In anxiety neurosis, the total organism retains its full capacity to function; in local tumor formation, the whole organism is in the process of dying and only the nuclei are still strong and capable of developing "anxiety." The mechanism of biopathies that result from sexual stasis is therefore, in the final analysis, a pathological cell mechanism.

The local process is concomitant with and a result of the systemic shrinking biopathy of the organism. The shrinking process itself passes through three typical phases:

1. *Phase of Contraction:* It begins with chronic incapacity for vagotonic expansion and manifests itself characterologically in resignation. Its physiological characteristics are muscular spasm, pallor of the skin, weakened biological charge of the tissues, orgastic impotence, and anemia. This first phase occurs in all biopathies and is not unique to cancer.

2. *Phase of Shrinking:* It is characterized by loss of body substance, shrinking of the erythrocytes, physical weakness, loss of biological resistance in the total organism, loss of weight, and finally general cachexia.

3. *Phase of Putrefaction:* It is characterized by loss of orgone energy in the tissue cells, transformation of the cancer material into putrid matter, rapid formation of rot bacteria (putrid disintegration), disintegration of the rot bacteria into T-bacilli, general T-bacilli intoxication, putrid bedsores, putrid body odor, death.

The manifestations of the shrinking biopathy coincide with the regression phenomena of old age, i.e., with the gradual, natural dying of the organism ("involution"). In old age, the organism shrinks slowly and putrifies after death. *In the cancer biopathy, this general process of dying occurs prematurely and in accelerated form.* Death from cancer is *a premature but regular death.* The pathological element in it lies in its prematurity and acceleration, and also in the fact that putrefaction occurs while the organism is still alive. The processes of death begin in an organ that has been in a state of contraction for years and that exhibits poor respiration and deficient bio-energetic (orgonotic) functioning: loss of orgone energy in the tissues and their cells, vesicular disintegration, formation of rot bacteria and T-bacilli. This disturbance primarily affects the blood system and with it the organism as a whole. As a result, the autonomic apparatus gradually shrinks. This process is a consequence of a disturbance in the sex-economy of the organism.

The disturbance starts in the organism long before it manifests itself in *tangible symptoms* that would be comprehensible to mechanistic pathology. The diagnosis of the local tumor is therefore invariably *too late.* On the same basis, the usual *local* treatment of the tumor by means of surgery, X-ray, or radium does not influence the disease itself. No matter how thoroughly a cancerous breast tumor is surgically extirpated, the process of putrefaction would not be affected. These facts are of supreme importance if the prophylaxis of cancer by the use of concentrated orgone energy is to be undertaken. The term "cancer therapy" will only be justifiably applicable when we are in a position to combat the systemic process of shrinking and putrefaction. This principle derives from bion experiments in cancer mice and guides the orgone therapy experiments in relation to cancer at our Institute.

It is a known fact that, biologically, cancer cells are extraordinarily weak formations and disintegrate easily. The cancer tumor itself is harmless unless it appears in the vital organs (brain, liver, etc.). That is the reason why cancer patients with small, solid tumors frequently continue to lead a normal life without feeling ill. Many older people have cancer tumors that cause no difficulty and are not even discovered until the post-mortem examination. The typical cancer pains and the general weakness set in only after the total organism has been extensively affected. Then the organism declines rapidly.

Disintegrating cancer tissue is always putrid and smells of putrefaction. The end product of this disintegration is vast quantities of T-bacilli. Since the T-intoxication spreads in proportion to the number of decaying cancer cells, the greatest danger for the patient is the biological weakness of the cancer tumor cells. This fact is a great advantage in orgone therapy wherein the tumor may be readily destroyed. The difficulties of orgone therapy today are not with the destruction of the tumor but rather with the *elimination of the products of disintegration from the body.* To overcome this particular problem, we must clearly understand the nature of those products. Let us undertake an experiment that should help to clarify this matter. We boil cancer cells from a surgically removed tumor and examine the results. There are no more formed cancer cells. Instead, we find masses of the T-bacilli that are so familiar to us (*cf.* Fig. 32, Appendix). *When healthy cell tissue is boiled it disintegrates into blue bions. Cancer tissue disintegrates into T-bacilli.* Blue bions are beneficial to the organism, T-bacilli are damaging. *Orgone therapy for cancer therefore shifts the emphasis from the destruction of the tumor to the neutralization and elimination of the products of the disintegration.*

Of course, the organs themselves cannot be examined directly for evidence of the putrefaction of the organism. It can be established and evaluated only by examination of the blood and excreta. Since shrinking and bionous disintegration always precede putrefaction, it is essential to observe the form and function of the erythrocytes in particular. Healthy erythrocytes are full and taut, and at 2000x can be seen to pulsate. Erythrocytes in the process of shrinking are smaller, often not oval but round, and their pulsation is either restricted or lacking altogether. Healthy blood corpuscles have a wide, strongly glowing blue orgone margin. In contrast, shrinking erythrocytes have a narrow, faint orgone margin. Instead of being taut, they often have a shriveled membrane. If the process

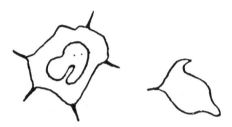

FIGURE 19. Deformed erythrocytes as seen in the blood
of advanced cancer patients. Bion formation in the center,
T-spike formation at the membrane ("sympatheticotonia" of
the erythrocytes)

of shrinking has not advanced far enough for the shrunken membranes to be immediately visible (T-spike formation: "poikilocytosis"), we observe *how rapidly the red blood cells decay, i.e., shrink
in physiological salt solution.* Healthy erythrocytes retain their
normal form for up to a half hour and even longer. Shrinking
erythrocytes, or those with a tendency to shrink, often disintegrate
in seconds or after just a few minutes, showing a serrated membrane and forming the so-called T-spikes (*cf.* Fig. 19). The T-spikes
are an indication of an advanced cancerous degeneration. The term
"cancerous" is here synonymous with *shrinking* (the "sympatheticotonia" of the erythrocytes). Healthy erythrocytes disintegrate into
blue bions—slowly in salt solution, rapidly on autoclavation—
whereas cancerous erythrocytes disintegrate almost completely into
T-bodies (the cancerous "T-reaction" in contrast to the normal "B-
reaction").

Healthy blood yields no cultures of bacteria in bouillon. *Cancerous blood on the other hand yields cultures of rot bacteria and T-
bacilli.* Rot bacteria and T-bacilli can also be observed microscopi-

cally in the blood of cancer patients (though not at magnifications less than 2000x).

Examination of the blood is therefore particularly useful for the early detection of cancer. In fact, I would like to venture the assumption that the blood is the first system to be affected by systemic contraction and subsequent shrinking of the organism. Blood is, after all, the "sap of life" which binds all the organs into *one whole* and provides them with nourishment. Blood therefore plays the major role in orgone therapy for cancer. For that reason the orgonotic function of the blood must be fully understood.

At this point I would like to call attention to the accepted theory concerning the spread of cancer tumors. According to this theory, cancer cells from the primary tumor enter the bloodstream and are then carried to distant organs, where they settle and grow into new tumors, the so-called "metastases." This process has never been directly observed, however, and the question remains: Is this hypothesis correct? Our interpretation suggests another and more plausible explanation: It is not necessary to assume that cancer cells are transported in the blood. Since the processes of shrinking and putrefaction are *general,* local tumors can form here or there, sooner or later, at any place in the organism. The case I described earlier, in Chapter V, disclosed the fact that the location of metastases is determined by local spasms and disturbances of biological functioning. A cancer tumor may first appear in the breast as a result of a chronic spasm of the pectoralis muscle, and be followed somewhat later by a second tumor in the ribs or the spine as a result of local spasms in the diaphragm. Muscle contractions are evidence of a biopathic dysfunction and represent the general tendency of the organism toward contraction and shrinking. The formation of metastases in parts of the body or organs distant from the primary tumor must of course be distinguished from the growth of the tumor into the surrounding tissue, e.g., when a cancer of the rectum grows through the bladder wall.

We might now make an assumption about the nature of cancer

of the blood system, so-called *leukemia,* though more extensive observations are required for its confirmation. If the shrinking and disintegrating of the erythrocytes represent the earliest and most general phase in the cancer disease, then the rampant proliferation of leucocytes becomes easy to comprehend. The function of the white blood cells is not, like that of the erythrocytes, to provide for tissue respiration and the supply of orgone energy. Instead, they defend the organism against bacteria or other "foreign bodies." White blood corpuscles, leucocytes, lymphocytes, and phagocytes always accumulate where foreign bodies (bacteria, dirt, etc.) enter the body substance. The formation of abscesses is the result of such an accumulation of white blood corpuscles, as is purulent secretion in wounds. When the erythrocytes begin to disintegrate, they are transformed into substances alien to the organism. The defensive power of the white corpuscles must increase enormously in order to cope with the disintegrating erythrocytes. Accordingly, leukemia— the most prominent symptom of blood cancer—is nothing but a reaction of the organism to the shrinking and T-disintegration of the erythrocytes. Therefore, leucocytosis is also found in other diseases involving shrinking of the blood system. Once white corpuscles predominate over red corpuscles and the organism has become too weak to supply fully developed red cells, death must follow inevitably.

The question that remains in relation to orgone therapy for cancer is therefore: *Is it possible to arrest or impede the process of disintegration of the erythrocytes?* A positive, practicable answer to this question would open the gates to the prevention of cancer.

In another context, we will find that the cells of a cancer tumor themselves originate not as symptoms of the disease but as a *defense* against the pathological processes. Although this statement may sound very revolutionary, it is not.

Before discussing the healing functions of the blood, I would like to answer two questions that must be uppermost in the reader's mind:

1. *How is it possible to know that the cancer cell develops in the way I have described here?* After all, one cannot repeatedly cut up the human organism in order to follow the development of cancer cells from vesicularly disintegrating tissue! The question is justified and important, and there is an answer. (See the detailed discussion of this subject, p. 259 ff.)
2. *What is the fundamental error of traditional cancer research?* How is it possible that the processes I have described were overlooked so completely? This question is equally justified.

Both questions are answered by one and the same fact: *The very omission that constitutes the basic error of traditional cancer research is also responsible for the overlooking of the developmental stages of the cancer cell.* We will now address ourselves to this.

THE DEVELOPMENT OF PROTOZOA IN GRASS INFUSIONS: THE KEY TO THE UNDERSTANDING OF CANCER

Mechanistic natural science, including mechanistic biology, is fraught with mysticism. As I have often said before, mysticism is supposed to fill the gaps that exist in the mechanistic's understanding of living functioning. For example, mechanistic natural science is trapped by the erroneous notion that "cell comes only from cell" and "egg only from egg." The *pertinent* question as to where the *first* cell and the *first* egg originated is eliminated a priori. However, the exclusion of this basic question of biology simultaneously bars the mechanist from the perception of certain facts. He assumes that for every single one of the billions of different forms of single-celled organisms there exists a "ready-made" germ "in the air." Such germs have never been seen by anyone. Nevertheless, they were taken to explain everything: tuberculosis, syphilis, pneumonia, etc. But then diseases were encountered that were not so simply explained by "air germs," diseases that must be attributed to tiny invisible particles on the borderline between living and non-living matter. Infantile paralysis (poliomyelitis), foot-and-mouth disease, etc., are not understood even today. For viruses cannot be cultivated from the air. The origin of bacteria and protozoa from the bionous disintegration of living and dead matter was unknown. The presence of living organisms in moss infusions was simply taken for granted, as was the presence of cancer cells in the body. Certainly questions have been asked about the origin of the cancer cells. However, in spite of the fact that they are not found in the air and their origin in the body cannot be doubted, it nevertheless has been strictly forbidden to assume that the organization of cells could develop from disintegrating tissues. Consequently the following steps have been neglected: 1) careful examination of human excretions in their natural state; 2) careful observation of the changes of grass tissues in infusions.

The assertion that there is an endogenous infection or even an organization of protozoa in the body sounds *absurd* to every mechanistic pathologist. He will not even listen to such a thing. And yet *the processes at work in the development of bacteria and protozoa from disintegrating moss and grass are the key to the understanding of the development of cancer cells and rot bacteria from disintegrating animal tissues.*

The question of how it is possible to describe the development of cancer cells in the organism can now be answered. We follow, in actuality, the many stages of the development of protozoa and bacteria in disintegrating grass tissue. Our assumption is that the amoebae in the grass infusion are nothing other than the "cancer cells" of the grass; if correct, then the corresponding processes in animal tissue can be inferred. This procedure would not be sufficient in itself to justify any definitive conclusions. For that reason many other observations conducted on the excreta of seemingly healthy patients and the excreta of confirmed cancer patients, sporadic and unconnected though such observations may seem at first, are of great significance. If forms and processes are discovered in the cancer tissue and its environs that are identical with those observed in the disintegrating grass or moss, the combined observations and experiments are corroborated. They become established fact when artificial cancer is produced in healthy mice and serial examinations are made during the various phases of the disease. The following simple and conclusive picture emerges from the observations of the processes in disintegrating grass tissue, in the excreta of cancer patients, and in the tissue of mice with artificial cancer:

1. The cancer cells are the protozoa in bionously disintegrating animal tissue.
2. The amoebae and other protozoa in grass infusions are the cancer cells of the disintegrating grass.
3. The origin of cancer cells is identical with the problem of biogenesis.

These three conclusions are enough to make one hesitate. They seem too simple. But great facts are always very simple. Once these conclusions have been reached, almost every gap created by the impossibility of direct observation in cancer can be filled with the observations made of the development of protozoa in disintegrating grass.

While preparing infusions from 1936 to 1942, by the simple method of placing dried grass or moss in water at various times of the year, I observed that it is impossible or very difficult to obtain protozoa from infusions of *fresh, young spring grass*. On the other hand, *autumnal grass or moss yielded every kind of protozoan easily and abundantly*. Such a finding would not be striking to those who believe in the hypothesis of air germs. For us, however, it has great significance. It confirms the identity of the protozoan in the grass infusion and the cancer cell in the organism, for *the cancer cell never develops in fresh, young tissue, only in biologically impaired, aging, "autumnal" animal tissue.*

I would like to emphasize that I had never even thought of occupying myself with the cancer problem. I was forced into it, as it were, when I discovered, during the bion experiments, the development of protozoa from bions in moss infusions and confirmed it photographically. In addition to normal grass tissue and the fully developed protozoa, there were an infinite number of forms which, from the standpoint of mechanistic biology, were indefinable, e.g., individual blue vesicles that were not air bacteria, irregular heaps of such vesicles, heaps showing a membrane at only one place, other heaps already showing a taut form only partly encircled by a membrane. In addition, a vast quantity of structured formations at the margins of the disintegrating tissue could not be defined as either "moss" or "protozoa" (*cf.* Figs. 39, 40, 41-a, b, c, Appendix).

Here I would like to report a small but interesting event. In 1936 my laboratory was associated with the botanical laboratory of the University of Oslo. I needed a culture of amoebae. The laboratory assistant searched around in an infusion and showed me the amoebae. It was at that moment the naïve question slipped out: "Can you tell me how these protozoa got into that infusion?" I had forgotten that there was a "germ theory." The assistant looked at me in astonishment, then, after a moment, finally replied, his voice revealing a trace of contempt for my biological ignorance: "From the germs in the air, of course. They settle in the moss." I subsequently prepared hundreds of air-germ cultures on a variety of media without ever seeing the germ of an amoeba or an actual amoeba. In time, I felt less bothered by my biological ignorance.

Another occurrence may serve to convince the reader that the human organism sometimes has accurate knowledge even though authorities may deem it a misconception. I prepared the first publication on bions, the vesicular disintegration of matter, and the development of protozoa during the fall of 1937, about one and a half years after the first conclusive observations. At that time I still had no presentiment of the two basic types of energy vesicles, the blue PA bions and the black T-bacilli, nor did I know that the blue, orgone-containing energy vesicles kill the T-bacilli. In other words, I really had no idea that I would ever find myself in the position of undertaking orgone therapy experiments on cancer.

Then, in the fall of 1937, the Norwegian mechanists and mystics began their smear campaign against my bion research. In spite of my appeals that I be allowed to work in peace, the newspapers published long articles alleging to "unveil the secrets of my laboratory." I was publicly accused of claiming I "could cure cancer." The accusation perplexed me; I had never made such a claim and had never even thought of it. How could such an accusation be leveled at me, if indeed it could be called an accusation? I understood it only much later, after the discovery of the killing effect of the blue PA bions. My hostile critics had obviously sensed better than I that the verification of the biogenesis of protozoa would throw open the door to an understanding of cancer.

After decades of enormous effort, cancer research was hopelessly stuck in a dead-end, precisely because of the taboo that blocked the comprehension of the development of protozoa. Protozoa were not supposed to develop from bionous moss; they had to develop, by the will of God, from "germs" that nobody had ever seen but that were simply "there," existing in "ready-made" form from the very beginning.

When I realized the error that had been made, I gropingly resumed my observation of cancer tissue, which the cancer hospital had sent to me many months before. For some time I had been in the habit of simply letting all my preparations stand in order to observe what would become of them with the passage of time. Among my cultures there were a few old bouillon solutions to which I had added sterile cancer tissue. To my astonishment, *all these cultures showed a green-blue coloration.* They emitted a strongly acrid, ammonia-like, and putrid odor. Inoculation on agar produced a smooth growth of intense green-blue. Taking material from the margin, I inoculated a new agar plate and saw, for the first time, the T-bacilli, the discovery of which would help break down the mystery surrounding the cancer problem.

I beg the reader to understand my great fear of proceeding further into the new areas of research. I waited many years before publishing these findings. It was not simply a matter of the discovery of a hitherto unknown bacillus. This discovery had raised, at one stroke, awesome questions that had to be answered before we could proceed.

The T-bacilli have their origin in the disintegration of tissue. That means we are confronted with the question of *biogenesis*, the social ordering of the biological energy. Disintegration of tissue in the living organism is the result of chronic social impairment of vital functioning. We are also confronted with the question of the disposition of life itself in the universe, since bions revealed the existence of a specific biological energy. It seemed inevitable that the discovery of the T-bacilli would be a threat to my opposition, bringing into dispute the notion of divine procreation as well as the divine destiny of man. Behind me lay bad experiences with physicians, scientists, and people generally; still before me lay the Oslo smear campaign. I was not a citizen of the country in which I made the discoveries. I was a guest in a foreign land, an "alien," an "intruder." Malicious persons were more interested in my statelessness than my discoveries. Then, one beautiful spring morning a simple thought removed all my anxieties: *I am a citizen of this planet.* As such, I now felt proud to have come into contact with one of the greatest scientific problems of this century, indeed of the centuries. The fact that bion research had spontaneously found the common denominator of many questions, hitherto regarded as unrelated, gave me courage. It was not a disgrace but, on the contrary, a triumph that these problems were beginning to be resolved despite all kinds of difficulties and harassments from colleagues and bureaucracies and despite the fact that I was compelled to move from country to country six times. When, finally, in January 1939, biological energy radiated from SAPA bions into the atmosphere of my laboratory and when, in 1940, I began to concentrate this energy inside the orgone accumulator, my anxieties dwindled and the indecencies I had suffered paled in comparison to my discoveries. From that time forward, I felt only a sense of obligation to carry out, to the best of my ability, the responsibility I now had.

The problem of cancer seemed to touch upon the nature of life and death. The problem is not solved, but the way to its solution is now open.

I have already described the T-bacilli and can therefore limit myself here to an account of the development of the cancer research. This description is essential, for the simple statement "cancer is fundamentally a putrefaction of the tissues and the blood, a slow dying in the living body" becomes understandable only through the interrelated discoveries made in the course of experiments and observations. It will become clear in this presentation why the basically simple nature of cancer has been overlooked until now. Discovering a lump of gold in the Colorado mountains is a very simple, desirable goal, but finding the way to it is tortuous and even dangerous.

The discovery of the existence of T-bacilli in old sarcoma tissue immediately raised several questions that took many years of intensive work to answer:

1. *Can T-bacilli injected into healthy mice produce cancer?*
2. *What connection has the T-bacillus to the cancer cell? Is it its cause or the product of its degeneration?*
3. *If the T-bacilli are the cause of the cancer growth, how do they get into the healthy organism initially?*

At the time I discovered the T-bacilli, I naturally had no idea that these tiny bodies would be designated *T*-bacilli, or that they are the result of the putrid disintegration of living tissues. However, every step in the course of my experiments with T-bacilli led to new secrets of the cancer scourge. The description of this path is therefore identical with a description of the nature of cancer, so far as it has been revealed to date.

Before proceeding to this description, however, I would like to now answer the question concerning the error of traditional cancer research. Summarized, it is as follows:

1. Neither the blue energy vesicles from which the cancer cells organize nor the much smaller T-bacilli into which they disintegrate are visible in the stained tissue sections. They can be seen only in the living preparation. Traditional cancer research, however, works almost exclusively with dead tissue.

2. For the same reason, traditional cancer research was unable to discover the intermediary stages in the development of cancer.

3. Accurate observations cannot be made at magnifications less than 2000x. Traditional cancer research seldom uses magnifications greater than approximately 1000x.

4. The fundamental disavowal and rejection of the natural organization of protozoa from non-living and living matter completely blocked access to an understanding of the cancer cell.

5. The "air germ" prejudice diverted the attention of the researchers in a false direction.

6. Cancer is a general disturbance in the functioning of the biosystem and therefore can be comprehended only *functionally*. Medicine and biology have a purely mechanistic, physical-chemical orientation. They look for causes in *individual* cells, *individual* dead organs, *individual* chemical substances. Thus, the *total function*, which determines the character of every particular function, remains unnoticed. (A clear understanding of sexual function has also suffered from this orientation.) The functioning of a radio can never be understood by a description of the chemical composition of the glass or metal of the tubes or a description of the mechanical disposition of the parts. Similarly, the biopathic function of cancer cannot be understood by a description of the form and stain reaction of the cancer cells or of their position in relation to the cells of healthy tissue. Nor can the chemical composition of living pro-

tein, however sophisticated and complex, ever reveal anything about *living pulsation.*

Let us now follow the path along which the T-bacilli have led us.

2. DEATH IN THE LIVING BODY: ORGONE LOSS IN THE TISSUES AND ANTE-MORTEM PUTREFACTION

I must summarize the widely divergent findings offered so far. T-bacilli reveal a *deadly* process in the *living* organism, "death in the living body." The letter *T* is taken from the first letter of the German word *Tod,* meaning *death.* Calling them *T*-bacilli conveys two facts: T-bacilli result from the dying process in tissue and they can cause death in mice if injected in large doses.

After I had obtained the first T-bacilli culture, I injected a sample of it into healthy mice. Many of these mice died within eight days; others became ill, improved for a while, but then died a few months later. Over the course of two years (1937–1939), several hundred healthy white mice, always in groups of six, were injected in the T-bacilli experiment. Two in each group, the control mice, were injected only with PA bions; two other mice in the same group were injected with T-bacilli (the amount of the dosage varying from group to group). The last two mice were injected with T-bacilli *and* blue PA bions. (This mouse experiment is summarized in the section "The Natural Organization of Protozoa" in Chapter II.)

The combined injection of blue PA bions and T-bacilli followed logically from my microscopic observation that the PA bions paralyzed the T-bacilli and caused their agglutination. As already reported, the final result, after two years, was that all the mice injected with PA bions alone remained healthy; all the (initially healthy) mice injected with T-bacilli alone either died immediately or developed, during the next fifteen months, various phases of disintegration and cell proliferation, i.e., cancer; lastly, most of the mice injected with both PA bions and T-bacilli remained healthy. *This effect of the blue PA bions was our point of departure for the orgone therapy experiments in cancer.*

I could now confine myself to the purely empirical results and be satisfied with the practical successes obtained thus far. That would spare the reader from having to be concerned with complicated processes. I cannot do this, however, because although a major inroad has been made into the cancer problem, a great deal of intensive work remains to be done if cancer is to be completely eliminated.

The conclusion I have drawn from my orgone therapy experiments in cancer is that *it will be far easier to prevent cancer than to cure it once it is fully developed,* for the very reason that *cancer is nothing other than a premature and accelerated but "normal" dying-off of the organism.* The processes in the organism that lead to premature death from cancer are precisely the same as those that cause natural death. The cancer problem is inseparable from the whole question of the relation between life and death.

I assure the reader that I am fully aware of the implications of these statements, and that I do not make them lightly. I did not start out with the cancer problem in mind, but was led to it by my bion experiments; I then had the choice of either confronting it head-on or abandoning my bion research entirely. My decision to delay the publication of the results of the first successful bion experiments on cancer and not to report them to any responsible authority was based on the realization that *the cancer problem is identical with the life-death process itself.* On closer examination, this fact is not so surprising as it may at first seem. Even the very earliest bion experiments and the observations of the natural organization of protozoa brought us face to face, again quite unintentionally, with *biogenesis.* The bion experiments then led by way of the PA bions and T-bacilli straight to the cancer disease. Since life and death are inextricably intertwined, the question of the origin of protozoa necessarily led to the question of the *cancer death* and, with it, *death in general.*

I think that for a long time I had been unconsciously preparing myself for just these questions. I became involved with certain theoretical considerations of death as early as 1926, when I began to clinically refute Freud's hypothesis of the *death instinct,* and to affirm the existence of *an objective process of dying* that starts long before the heart ceases to function. After this successful refutation of the *death instinct*° my interest in the objective process of dying still remained. It was a process unwished for and feared by the living organism, yet to which the organism must succumb sooner or later. *The T-bacilli are tangible evidence of the death process.* I will now prove this.

Orgone biophysics reduces all manifestations of life to the basic biophysical function of *pulsation.* The life process fundamentally consists of a continuous oscillation, in the organism as a whole and in each of its individual organs, between *expansion* and *contraction.* "Health" is distinguished by a sex-economic regulation of energy and by the *completeness* of these pulsations in all the organs. If expansion constantly predominates over contraction, we speak of chronic *vagotonia.* If contraction constantly predominates over expansion, we speak of chronic *sympatheticotonia.* The chronically maintained *contraction* leads, as we have seen, to muscular spasms and chronic preponderance of the inspiratory attitude. As a consequence, there is an excess of carbon dioxide in the tissues (see Warburg), a shrinking process, and loss of body substance culminating in cachexia.

The life process is thus expressed as a constant pulsation in each organ, according to its own rhythm and, in the total organism, according to a pleasure-anxiety rhythm characteristic of each individual. In the sexual orgasm, the excess of energy is periodically equalized by extreme pulsations (convulsions). However, expansion and contraction also govern the *total life span* in *one extended pulsation.* The expansion of the biosystem sets in with the fertilization of the egg and continues (with predominance of expansion

° *Cf. The Function of the Orgasm.*

over contraction) until middle age. Growth, sexuality, happiness in life, expansive activity, intellectual development, etc., are normally predominant until well into the forties. But from then on, with the beginning of the "aging" process—so-called involution—the contraction of the autonomic system gradually takes the upper hand. Growth stops and gives way to a very slow process of shrinking which affects all the living functions and finally culminates, during old age, in an involution of the tissues. The natural involution of the aged is accompanied by cessation of the sexual function. The urge for sexual pleasure, for activity and development, likewise diminishes. The character becomes "conservative," the need for rest predominates.

In old age, this natural contraction of the autonomic system can lead to "physiological cancer death." Cancer is far less dangerous in advanced age than in youth. There are many cases of death from old age in which cancer is accidentally discovered on autopsy, the disease apparently having produced no noticeable symptoms during the person's lifetime. The death of the organism itself is accompanied by an intense muscular contraction, the so-called rigor mortis, which clearly reveals the contraction of the vital apparatus. Finally the body decomposes in putrefaction. In contrast with living tissue, dead tissue shows no gradations in bio-electric skin potential. Dying tissue registers only a negative reaction. The source of biological energy is extinguished. For example, a dead fish registers an orgonotic radiation effect at the orgone energy field meter for a short time after death, but it is weak and soon fades altogether. Dead branches, in contrast to alive ones, show no orgone energy field action. This means that the dying organism loses its biological energy. First, the orgone energy field surrounding the organism shrinks, then there is loss of orgone energy in the tissues. The popular belief that "the soul leaves the body" at death is thus not without basis. Contrary to mystical belief, of course, the "soul" is not to be understood here as some structured form which, after its departure from the body, hovers in space as a "spirit" awaiting rebirth in a new body. The orgone charge of the organism forms the basis for living perceptions and these perceptions become weaker as the orgone charge diminishes. This process of dying does not take place in the last few hours only, but extends, under normal circumstances, over decades. *Acute* dying, characterized by stoppage of the heart, is only *one* phase in this long process, though obviously the decisive phase. But even when the heart stops beating everything is not suddenly "dead"; individual life functions continue for a short time, gradually ceasing for lack of oxygen. Sudden death resulting from "shock" is nothing more than a rapid total contraction of the vital apparatus to a degree that precludes a renewal of expansion.

The putrefaction that sets in after death is the result of the bionous disintegration of the tissues. It is totally unnecessary to believe that "rot bacteria from the air" invade the organism at this point. One would have to ask why the rot bacteria present in the air do not settle in the healthy *living* organism and cause it to rot. This question is of much greater significance than might appear at first glance, because it demonstrates the necessity of a natural defense maintained by the healthy organism as long as it is alive, a defense against the putrefying process that occurs after death. Bion research succeeded in providing a conclusive answer to these questions.

At the most primitive stages of life, the expansion, energy metabolism, etc., of living substance are represented by the blue PA bions; the contraction and degeneration of living substance—its disintegration and putrefaction—are represented, on the other hand, by the T-bacilli. Is this also true for highly developed organisms? The PA bions are carriers of orgone energy, "orgone energy vesicles." T-bacilli are characterized by the lack of orgone charge. The cells of the body are made up of blue energy vesicles highly charged with orgone energy. The intake of food provides a constant source of orgone energy in the form of the PA bions contained in the food. The PA bions kill the T-bacilli with their stronger orgone charge, preventing putrefaction in the organism. Orgone energy in the radiation of the sun kills rot bacteria in the same way. The functioning of the life process can therefore be ascribed to the constant disinfecting and charging effect of the body orgone, i.e., the expansion function. It prevents the contraction function from getting the upper hand, which would result in the formation of T-bacilli and putrefaction.

If the orgonotic function of charge and expansion declines, the contraction function predominates and can lead to the processes of death. The T-bacilli are an expression of these processes, as exemplified in the cancer biopathy. The fostering of positive life functions, such as pleasure, development, activity, etc., is decisive in the prevention of premature death processes. The extension of average life expectancy in many cultures during the last decades must be ascribed to the breakthrough of natural sexual functions.

These assumptions are not only justified, they are inescapable if the various observations are to be reduced to a common denominator. This is precisely the task of natural science. The carcinomatous shrinking biopathy (it could also be called the "sex-starvation disease") can be understood only in the context of concrete life and death processes.

In 1937–1938, when I succeeded for the first time in producing cancerous growths in healthy mice by the injection of T-bacilli, I thought I had found the "specific cancer agent." The T-bacilli had been cultivated from cancer tissue; injected into healthy mice, they produced cancer; the cancer cells themselves then disintegrated into T-bacilli. These facts are easily demonstrable and traditional cancer research is aware of them. Traditional research has pursued what I call the T-bacillus for a long time, but its air-infection prejudice and its resistance to the idea of endogenous infection have created an insurmountable obstacle to progress.

3. RIDDLES IN TRADITIONAL CANCER RESEARCH

I would now like to discuss briefly those riddles in traditional cancer research that seem in some way to presage the discovery of the T-bacillus. In this summary I am indebted to the extraordinarily lucid survey of the subject by Blumenthal[3] and to the omnibus volume edited by Adam and Auler.[4] At one time I was able to study a number of articles on the subject but, unfortunately, wartime conditions made it impossible for me to read all of the literature in the original. That has not damaged my summary, however, since the surveys to which I refer were excellent.

The basic question of traditional cancer research, as well as of orgone biophysics, is this: *Is cancer essentially represented only by the tumor and its metastases or is it already present in the organism before the emergence of a tumor? If it is already present, how is this so?* In the first case, the cancer cell would be the real disease; in the second case, there would be a "something" which is not the cancer cell itself but which has a definite relationship to it. How this question is answered is of crucial importance, since the decisions concerning tumor operations depend upon it, as do the question of early diagnosis of cancer and, most important, the possibility of preventing or destroying the cause of the disease.

Experiments to produce tumors in animals by the transplantation of tumor pulp led cancer researchers to the unanimous conclusion that very substantial amounts of tumor pulp have to be transplanted if positive results are to be obtained. Experiments with centrifuged substances and filtrates were negative. *The sought-for tumor agent is always connected with the residue of the centrifuged substances.* In relation to the T-bacilli, an hypothesis by R. Kraus— based on experiments conducted by Swarzoff, who had observed the development of tumor cells from tissue particles and partial cells—is very important. Kraus concluded: "Omnis cellula ex *granula,*" and not, as had hitherto been the theory, "ex cellula." The idea that cancer cells develop from tiny "granules" corresponds splendidly with the orgonological concept that they develop from bions.

[3] *Ergebnisse der experimentellen Krebsforschung und Krebstherapie* (Leiden, 1934).
[4] *Neuere Ergebnisse auf dem Gebiete der Krebskrankheiten* (Leipzig, 1937).

Here the question shifts from the cancer cell to the *development of bions in the organism. From this perspective the cancer cell would be not so much the cause of the disease as a symptom. The disease would be the result of some third more general factor present in the organism before the tumor.*

Ernst Fränkel found that the agent of the Rous chicken sarcoma was bound up with the *erythrocytes* and the globulin. Certain experiments produced evidence of the presence of a carcinogenic principle in the *spleen,* either free or in the spleen cells. Experiments conducted on animals indicate a curious connection between spleen function and tumor function. If the spleen is removed from healthy rats, they develop severe anemia (*Lauda*). If the spleen is removed from tumorous rats, anemia does not develop except after elimination of the tumor. Thus, the tumor can assume certain functions of the spleen. *This seems very strange, but it again points to the blood and its corpuscles.* It is well known that the spleen is the reservoir for erythrocytes. It is said that *what becomes of the disintegrating erythrocytes is completely obscure.* They are known to have some connection with cancer, but the precise nature of the relationship remains a mystery. Using blood drawn from a tumor vein, Blumenthal's laboratory assistant Lindner produced tumors in animals of the same species; and, with one exception, the tumors were always of the same kind. Similar experiments with blood from the heart and axillary vein also succeeded. It was shown thereby that *the cancer agent is connected with the solid components of the blood.* The experiments were particularly successful with clotted blood and washed erythrocytes. *The T-bacillus does in fact originate in degenerating erythrocytes.* Venous blood proved to be significantly more effective than arterial blood. (Cancer tissue shows evidence of a suffocation metabolism, i.e., excess of CO_2.) Laser once produced cancer in a chicken in the following way: He injected a chicken with tar solution and then, while it was still free of tumors, cultivated macrophages from its blood. These macrophages, injected into a second chicken, produced a tumor. This experiment suggests the interpretation that the macrophages had absorbed the agent circulating in the blood and had transmitted it to the second chicken. Many researchers have conjectured that this agent is a component of the cancer cells that enters the circulation *only when the cancer cells disintegrate*. Leucocytes cultivated from the blood of sarcoma rats caused sarcoma in healthy rats after injection. We are initially confused by the fact that *the undoubted "something" that produces cancer is present in the blood prior to the existence of cancer cells and also develops through the disintegration of the cancer cells.*

This "something," so it is said, can be present in an organ without the formation of a tumor. Numerous inventive experiments have shown that *the blood cells are closely related to the malignant cells.* "The normal blood cells," writes Blumenthal,

> must contain substances indispensable for the preservation of the activity of the etiological cancer principle. Blood cells are particularly rich in coagulable albumin. . . . This fibrinogen evidently joins with the etiological factor of the cancer cell and transfers it to the cells of the organism . . . transforming normal cells of the organism into cancer cells. . . . *In all . . . cases there is proof that something emanates from the cancer cells that transforms previously normal cells into cancer cells.* [Italics mine.]

The "something" being sought is bound to the blood corpuscles as well as to the cancer cells and produces cancer cells from normal cells.

These conclusions confront classical pathology with a number of questions. The most important include the following:

Is this carcinogenic "something" an enzymatic substance, i.e., *not* a living organism? As long as there is no proof that this substance can multiply, it cannot be compared with a living organism.

Is this "something" a chemical in the body that stimulates the healthy mesenchyme cells of the animal to form the same substance and transforms them into tumor cells? Is it a chemical poison? a lytic substance? an autocatalyst?

Is it cellular? If it is, then the fundamental question arises, Can something be cellular and infectious yet not "parasitic," i.e., not "foreign to the body"? One thing to bear in mind is that in the case of the carcinogenic stimulus, it is not a question of transferred cancer cells but a disease of *previously healthy cells.*

This remarkable "something" that so many people have tried to define begins therefore to take on the following outlines:

It is present in the organism *before* the cancer cell and is bound to the blood solids. Yet it develops also from the cancer cell. It behaves simultaneously like a parasite and a poisonous chemical substance. It is "infectious" without the disease itself being infectious. It produces the cancer cell from the healthy tissue cell and itself derives from the cancer cell. It acts like a parasite, yet does not originate outside the body.

Blumenthal says correctly: *"It is clear that the cancer problem exists on the border between the living and the non-living, posing the question whether animal cells can produce something showing parasitic properties."*[5]

Our T-bacilli are the bridge between the two.

The T-bacilli experiment confirms a concept that has gained vogue in modern cancer research and which Blumenthal summarizes as follows:

> In the case of the Rous sarcoma it has been proved that something is present inside and outside the tumors with which tumors can be produced, that, in other words, the tumor agent or tumor principle need not be a tumor cell. The essential difference between the tumor cell and the tumor agent in respect to cancer formation is that while the tumor cell produces only tumor cells of the same kind, the cancer agent does not itself multiply but affects previously healthy cells so that they are transformed into cancer cells.

Our T-bacilli conform to Blumenthal's description exactly:

[5] *Experimentellen Krebsforschung und Krebstherapie,* p. 94.

1. They are present in the blood and tissues *before* the tumor.
2. They lead to the development of cancer cells and are simultaneously the product of cancer cell disintegration.
3. They are produced by the disintegration of red blood corpuscles.
4. They are *genuine* bacilli with *parasitic* properties, yet at the same time cancer is not infectious.
5. The T-bacilli actually form a bridge from the non-living to the living insofar as they arise from coal bions through early degeneration and they are able to propagate.
6. They are in fact the products of animal cells that show parasitic properties.
7. They are in fact poisonous and possess a still-obscure relation to cyanide. They exercise an effect similar to suffocation and respiratory paralysis.

If the T-bacillus is the specific cancer agent that has been sought, then the animal experiment must yield the following results:

1. The injection of T-bacilli into healthy mice must result in destructive and infiltrating cell proliferation.
2. The T-bacilli must be capable of recultivation.
3. The tumors created experimentally must contain T-bacilli.

All three conditions are fulfilled in the T-mice experiments.

THE T-BACILLI EXPERIMENT ON HEALTHY MICE
(1937–1939)

The T-mice experiments were carried out customarily in groups of six. Each type of the packet-amoeboid bions was injected into four mice as a control of the pathogenicity. Two days after this first injection with PA bions—and sometimes after a second PA bion injection—two of the four mice were injected with one of the different strains of T-bacilli. Simultaneously, a third pair was injected with T-bacilli only. The dosage of the injection was as follows: a full loop of PA bions was dissolved in 3 cc. of sterile physiological NaCl solution or in a potassium chloride solution. We injected 0.5 cc. of this solution subcutaneously into the back. In the T-bacilli experiment, one loop was dissolved in 5 cc., and of this solution 0.5 cc. or 0.25 cc. was injected subcutaneously into the back. Until the end of January 1939, a total of 178 mice were injected in series in this way. Of that total, 84 mice were injected solely with T-bacilli. Of these 84 T-bacilli–injected mice, 30 died within the first eight days following the injection and 30 more died in the next fifteen months. At the time this protocol was concluded, the surviving mice were all ill. Of the 30 mice that died over the span of fifteen months, 25 were examined for carcinomatous growths. *Seven of the mice examined contained cancer cells with amoeboid movement in the epithelium of the intestines and the stomach, the cervical glands, the genitals, etc.* Thirteen of these mice showed the characteristic spindle- and club-shaped elongated-cell formations and infiltrations in various organs, predominantly in the peritoneum, cervical glands, genitals, stomach, and duodenum. The remaining 5 mice displayed no clear findings.

Of the 45 mice that were injected first with PA bions and *subsequently* with T-bacilli, 36 remained healthy and 9 died during the following fifteen months. Among the 39 mice injected only with packet-amoeboid bions, not one showed any signs of disease in the same period of time. Of 10 mice injected first with T-bacilli and subsequently with packet-amoeboid bions, 8 died within fifteen months and 2 were killed because of abscesses.

Regardless of their origin, the T-bacilli led regularly to the development of caudate, or club-shaped, cells in various organs. Likewise, the effect of the blue PA bions was the same in all types. In two cases a packet-amoeboid type (*SAPA 1*), injected after the application of T-bacilli, produced *dry*, "clean" ulcers in the mice, resembling "X-ray ulcers," precisely where the T-bacilli had infiltrated the tissue after injection.

For this experiment the T-bacilli were obtained from the following sources: cultivated directly from sarcomatous and carcinomatous tissues (*T 1*), from the blood of cancer patients (*T Ca 10*), from the cardiac blood of mice that died after tar application experiments (*T II 6*), from the blood of healthy humans cultivated by degeneration (*T 10*), from the blood of persons suspected of having cancer but in whom the usual clinical examination was negative (*T 10*), from degenerated bion cultures (*6 d TT* and *10e 41 T*), from the cardiac blood of mice that had died from Bluko tumors (*Bluko-T*), and finally T-bacilli recultivated from the cardiac blood of the affected mice (*10 Ge Tr, 10 Ta Tr, 6 dT Tr*, etc.). Every kind of T-bacilli yielded all the phases of carcinomatous growths in healthy white mice.

SUMMARY

1. The T-bacilli behave parasitically, yet have their origin in body substance.
2. They originate through the degeneration of tissues and organisms.
3. They are formed when carbon changes into bions.
4. They show a relationship to cyanide.
5. They effect bion formation.
6. They are always an indication of sympatheticotonic contraction and shrinking of the organism.

The typical syndrome of T-bacilli intoxication is the following: A few hours after the injection of T-bacilli the mouse's movements become sluggish, its body bends, it drags its legs and loses appetite. Conjunctivitis and local abscesses appear occasionally but are not typical. If the T-mouse does not perish within about eight days, it usually gives the impression of recuperating. However, *after two to five months, a new process of contraction and shrinking begins in the organism.* The pattern of the first few days following the injection of the T-bacilli returns, but this time more slowly; the process has a chronic character. *The organism gradually shrinks until it dies.* Although I was unaware of it at the time, these animal experiments, conducted between 1937 and 1941, revealed the *"carcinomatous shrinking biopathy"* that, in 1941, I discovered in human cancer. Autopsies conducted on T-mice killed at various stages of the disease or after their spontaneous death regularly showed T-bacilli in all the organs and in the blood (cultivable in bouillon); atrophic and necrotic processes in the epithelium of the mucous membranes, especially of the alimentary tract; cancerous blood picture, anemic blood corpuscles, shrunken membranes with T-spikes; enlargement of the liver and atrophy of the cells, nuclei, and lobules; accumulation of T-bacilli in the renal glomeruli with atrophy of the renal epithelial cells.

The longer a mouse lives after its injection with T-bacilli, the more numerous and more highly developed are the spindle- and club-shaped cell formations in the various organs. The diagnosis of fully developed cancer is confirmed by the presence of amoeboid cells in the submaxillary gland, in the urinary bladder, or in the kidney. The formation of polypous growths of the intestinal mucous membrane is accompanied by total atrophy of the adjacent mucous membrane. In male mice, numerous cancer formations, including amoeboid forms, are found in the testicles.

The general conclusion regarding the autonomic life apparatus is that *the flooding of the organism with T-bacilli leads to gradual contraction and shrinking of the tissues as well as of the individual cells.* Then follows loss of weight, atrophy and degeneration of the cells, culminating in putrid degeneration, i.e., putrefaction. It is exactly the same process that occurs in human cancer. In experimental T-mice, this process of shrinking is generally caused by the injection; in the human cancer patient, biophysical shrinking, as a consequence of characterological resignation, precedes the formation of T-bacilli. As the T-bacilli develop and proliferate, they hasten the general shrinking process and provoke local defense efforts, i.e., tumor formation. Further observations will determine whether or not the local tumor always represents a defense reaction and in how many cases it is formed from local tissue damage, which leads secondarily to the general shrinking of the vital apparatus.

STAGES OF CANCER CELL DEVELOPMENT IN THE T-BACILLI–MOUSE EXPERIMENT (1937–1941)

Comparative observations of the tissues of mice that had either died or been killed in the course of four years yielded the following picture of the T-effect upon the tissues of the organism. The observations were directed principally at examining *the degree of maturation* attained by the club- and spindle-shaped cells in the tissues, forms that are never found in healthy mice or in mice with other diseases. Examined at a magnification of 3000–4000x these forms are so clearly typical that they cannot possibly be confused with another kind of cell. The one exception might be the cylindrical epithelial cell of the gastrointestinal tract which, at low magnification, can be mistaken for a maturing cancer cell. The distinction between the two is, however, so marked to anyone familiar with the forms that the risk of confusing them is minimal.

I will now describe the autopsy findings in various stages of the T-bacilli effect. It was found that cancer needs a very long time for maturation. The amoeboid cancer cells represent its most mature state. However, the mice frequently died before reaching this condition if there was advanced tissue infiltration and destruction of the physiological functioning of the organs (septicemia, nephritis, atrophy of the liver, etc.).

1. *Tissue Damage Through Swelling and Vesicular Disintegration (Ca I)*

The T-bacilli–albumin experiment showed that the damage either is caused directly by the action of the T-bacilli on the tissues, or is brought about by chemical or mechanical trauma, such as by tar or a blow, which creates secondarily a field of action for the already present T-bacilli. In the latter case, it is necessary to assume that the cancer stimulus originates in *the formation of T-bacilli from disintegrating tissue.* This could explain the formation of cancer following injuries from scars, burns, etc.

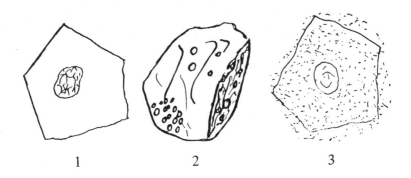

1   2   3

1. Healthy epithelial cell (no structure)
2. Epithelial cell disintegrating into blue bions;
   spindle formation with intense blue glimmer at the
   right margin: *precancerous stage* (Ca I)
3. Epithelial cell disintegrating into T-bacilli,
   which are also seen outside of the cell (Ca I)

F I G U R E   20.   Healthy and precancerous epithelial cells

The tendency toward rapid vesicular disintegration with swelling and T-bacilli formation is one of the most important signs of cancer in its initial stages. True, the organism's defenses may be able to counteract this tendency so long as its total functions are intact. However, *tissues that swell rapidly in KCl and show vesicular disintegration and T-bacilli formation must be considered cancer-suspect* (cf. Figs. 55-a and 55-b, Appendix). If this statement is correct, it opens up an exciting field of work for the diagnosis of incipient cancer long before the actual cancer cells have organized or any destructive growth and infiltration has taken place (*cf.* Fig. 56a, Appendix).

2. *Acute Inflammatory Stage* (*Ca II*)

The organism reacts to the damage caused by the T-bacilli with the familiar means: hyperemia, accumulation of leucocytes, and

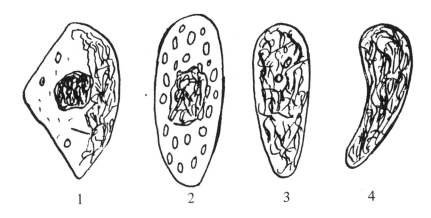

1. Part of the cell shows a blue striated structure
2. The cell assumes an oblong shape; blue bions develop
3. The blue bions flow together and form a dense, striated structure
4. The cell assumes club shape

FIGURE 21. Stages in the transformation of an epithelial cell into a cancer cell (Ca II)

formation of granulation tissue. As was often shown in the T-mice experiments, the inflammatory growth may remain localized or it can spread without yet having to be designated as carcinomatous. *Brownish* or *brownish red* granulation tissue can be observed spreading from the point of injection along the blood and lymph vessels into deeper tissues. These inflammatory growths extend with particular frequency into the glands. Microscopically, we cannot as yet detect, apart from the elements of any inflammation, any trace of carcinomatous cell forms in such tissues, whether examined in the living state or in section (*cf.* Figs. 57, 58-b, and 58-c, Appendix).

3. *Individual spindle and club-shaped cell forms in chronic inflammatory growths* (*Ca III*)

This third stage is already carcinomatous and characterized by processes not found in healthy or merely inflamed tissue. There are mostly *spindle- and club-shaped arrangements of vesicles* (*cf.* Figs. 56-c, d, and e, Appendix) and *a vesicular disintegration of the tissue surrounding the inflammation* (*cf.* Fig. 59, Appendix). Macroscopically, it can be seen that the brownish granulation tissue merges almost imperceptibly into *gray-white hard streaks*. These are in part newly formed connective tissue; but they already show a variety and multiplicity of cells (*cf.* Figs. 62-c and 62-d, Appendix). *The leucocytes become less numerous* and *formations of a new kind* are present. These cell formations, showing varying degrees of organization, are characterized by a *pronounced biological stainability* (chromophilia). Common to all of them, whatever their size, is the tendency toward a caudate shape. The same gray-white streaks that, in the eosin-hematoxylin preparation, indicate only chronic inflammation are found in the lungs, kidneys, liver, glands, and omentum. At this stage, the dead stained section shows us nothing of the carcinomatous bion formations, vesicle heaps, and spindle forms that are unmistakably seen in the living preparation at a magnification of 4000x. *A cancer diagnosis can therefore be made*

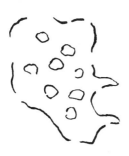

a. A typical form of
   precancerous
   epithelial cells

b. Four epithelial cells, one
   of them cancerous. From
   the renal tubule of a
   T-mouse. Drawn from life

c. Various forms of cancer cells, as found in mice with spontaneous
   tumors and with tumors produced by the injection of T-bacilli

FIGURE 22.   Cancer cells in the stage of maturing (Ca III)

from the living preparation at a time when the dead stain prepara-
tion cannot possibly yield such a result.

For instance, the living preparation from kidney tissue may present the following picture (*cf.* Fig. 22-b): Three cells surrounding a tubule are still completely normal, the plasm homogeneous, a well-defined nucleus in the center, and no vesicle formation. The fourth cell, on the other hand, is already club-shaped and shows a vesicular structure and a strong stainability over the entire cell body. The nucleus can no longer be distinguished from the structure of the plasm; nuclear material fills the entire body of the cell. Thus, *the metamorphosis from the normal cell to the cancer cell of the first stage (Ca III) takes place through vesicular disintegration of the cell and its transformation into a club-shaped structure* (*cf.* Fig. 58-c, Appendix).

In other cases, it is possible to see *two* or *three* cells lose their contiguous borders to form *one* new kind of caudate, club-shaped cell. This confluence can be reproduced experimentally. If we send electrical impulses of about 8–10 volts through a preparation of muscle or kidney tissue in KCl solution, we see the progressive appearance of vesicles in the plasm, strong light refraction, and elongation. The boundaries between the cells gradually dissolve and they flow together into *one* piece. The same experiment can be carried out with muscle tissue. Application of methylene blue stain shows that the cells that have become vesicular stain faster and more vividly than the healthy cells. The formations are identical with those which, in the eosin-hematoxylin section, gave the impression of "chromatin rich," oval-to-spindle-shaped forms. If such formations are never found in the lungs or kidneys of healthy mice but *appear regularly* in diseased mice at the stage of chronic inflammation (Ca III), it is justifiable to diagnose them as preliminary stages of the later amoeboid cancer cell. This assumption is verified by the fact that, with the continuance of the disease, these formations become more abundant and defined. The conclusion to be drawn from this series of observations on T-mice is as follows: It is true that one single healthy cell can change into one single, spindle-shaped carcinomatous cell but, as a rule, several healthy cells disintegrate vesicularly and flow together into a vesicle, from which one or several cancer cells develop.

Among these new formations in the diseased tissues are some peculiar structures formed from vesicularly disintegrated erythrocytes combined with unstructured vesicular bion heaps. The assumption can be made that in the process of vesicular tissue disintegration every conceivable combination of the disintegrated forms is possible. The *vesicular structure* is, however, the essential formation. It took considerable effort to locate these new formations, confirmed in the living preparation, in the stained section of the same tissue. Figure 60-b (Appendix) shows those transformed chromatin-rich cells that correspond to the vesicular, spindle-shaped new formations.

In the dead, stained section of the intestinal epithelium, for example, it is possible to observe, at a magnification of approximately 1600x, alongside healthy cells, deeply stained elongated cells and cell heaps that do not appear in healthy mice. If extensive growths of such cells are found outside the intestines (*cf.* Fig. 60-c, Appendix) and if heaps of spindle formations are observed in the same tissue in the living preparation, then the diagnosis of *cancer* (Ca III) is confirmed.

In many of the experimental mice, the same dark cell heaps seen inside the intestinal epithelium are found *in places far removed from the intestines*, e.g., in the epidermis of the back or neck, in the connective tissue surrounding blood vessels, in and around glands, in fat tissue, etc. (*cf.* Fig. 59, Appendix).

At a magnification of 4000x many cases reveal glandular cells that have become detached from the membrane and transformed into dark, strongly stained club-shaped formations. In other cases, the entire gland is permeated with massive heaps of such degenerated cells. To my knowledge, these cell formations are not known in classical pathology. I was unable to find any mention of them in specialized works on pathology. Several pathologists either gave varying diagnoses for these cells or admitted they were puzzled.

One pathologist thought they were pancreas cells because they were located outside the stomach. When I showed this same pathologist the identical cells in the subcutaneous tissue of the neck he conceded their novelty.

It has been known for a long time that genuine cancer tumors can result from chronic inflammatory processes (tuberculosis, syphilis, scars, burns, etc.), but interest was always directed toward the nature of the cancer cell. Our bion experiments, and in particular the new tissue formations in T-mice, shed considerable light on this question. When the histologist is still diagnosing "chronic inflammation" in the stained section, I am able to diagnose "cancer (Ca III)" on the basis of the living preparation. The sharp diagnostic distinction between genuine tumors and chronic inflammations according to the dead, stained-section picture is understandable from the pathological-histological point of view. But, in order to create common ground upon which to discuss the findings outlined here, it is absolutely necessary to consider the different results obtained by examining the *living preparation*. In bion research, *the diagnosis "malignant tumor" is made when there is evidence, no matter how sparse, in the live preparation of vesicular disintegration of the cells and the formation of new spindle-shaped structures (Ca III)*. All that then remains to be determined is the degree of maturation of the tumor cells.

In his comprehensive study *Ergebnisse der experimentellen Krebsforschung* (1934), Blumenthal writes about autonomous growth:

> While it can be observed in individual tumors, this characteristic may only *seem* to exist, for we may discover one day that they are of infectious origin. Such a discovery would, as Lubarsch says, greatly restrict the realm of autonomous tumors and extend the realm of infectious neoplasms. Fewer and fewer actual cancer tumors would then remain. But the study of all these granulomata would constitute a large part of what cancer research had previously occupied itself with. In the final analysis

autonomous growth is conceived of only as the opposite of the growth of those tumors in which the growth impulse is a parasite, the death of which terminates the growth of the tumor. A different stimulus can take the place of the parasite and would be regarded from the standpoint of the cell as exogenous. Autonomous growth means only that the growth impulse is assumed to be inside the cell. In spite of the presence of the stimulus, autonomous growth can belong only to the cell. When present in cancer, this growth is necessary only for the precancerous stage; i.e., it provides the impulse for the transformation of normal cells into cancer cells.

My bion and T-bacilli experiments lead me to agree with Blumenthal. The T-bacilli are in fact only the stimulus for the transformation of normal cells into cancer cells. *The T-bacilli are responsible only for the precancerous stage.* Once they are formed, the cancer cells' growth is completely autonomous, i.e., *independent* of the T-bacilli.

The pathologist and cancer researcher Borst came upon this problem a long time ago:

> The histological diagnosis of a carcinoma is frequently not easy. Precancerous changes are a factor as well as the atypical epithelial growths, similar to those frequently found in chronic inflammations, that precede the formation of cancer cells. It is certain that new epithelial formations of an inflammatory, regenerative, or hyperplastic nature can lead to carcinomas by way of fluid transitions. But it is impossible to predict histologically how the various atypical epithelial growths will develop. Experience has taught us only that some of these growths will change into carcinoma more frequently than others, and a few will not change at all. Our practical knowledge of the reversibility of these growths, however, is still incomplete. Consequently, it does not seem wise to speak of *precancerous transformations,* because the term implies that these atypical epithelial growths are *necessary* early stages of cancer. A better term to use in certain cases, where experience can be a

guide, would be *cancer-suspect growths,* and in such cases the physician should be alerted to keep a close watch. The histological picture of the so-called atypical epithelial growths can show a marked resemblance to incipient carcinoma. How then can the boundary be found histologically? The most essential characteristic of cancerous epithelial growths is *the autonomous penetration of the epithelium into the underlying connective tissue.* The epithelium leaves its place on the surface and penetrates deep into the tissue; the glandular epithelium breaks through the membranae propriae. The histological diagnosis of a carcinoma will therefore have to be based primarily upon the heterotopy of epithelial growth. However, it is essential to point out here that chronic inflammatory conditions also cause this borderline tug-of-war between the epithelium and the connective tissues, and that in such cases the epithelium can often penetrate far into the underlying connective tissue, especially in ulcerous and fistula-forming processes. These "inflammatory" epithelial heterotopies are not easy to distinguish from carcinoma. Epithelial heterotopy *alone* should therefore not be regarded as a sufficient histological proof of carcinoma, and careful examination must be made to establish the destructive character of cancerous epithelial growth. In carcinoma we often find in the *autonomous* penetration of the epithelial cells an *absence of accompanying connective tissue,* indicating the displacing and tissue-consuming character of this autonomous epithelial growth. Even if a histological diagnosis of carcinoma is thus possible on the basis of the *destructive heterotopy of independently growing epithelia,* it is necessary to concede that *the early stages of carcinoma, during which the growing epithelium still confines itself within its physiological boundaries,* cannot be comprehended histologically. However, although no absolutely certain and specific histological guidelines exist for so-called *potential malignancy* (Ewing), certain *nuclear transformations* take place in the surface and glandular epithelia before their destructive penetration into the tissues, allowing, with a reasonable degree of probability, for the recognition of an incipient cancerous change. When an epithelial growth gives evidence of significant variability in size, shape, chromatin content, and the general structure of its nuclei, it is always a sign of unregulated processes of cell division and probably indicative of the presence of carcinoma.[6]

The bion experiments in the living preparation, described earlier, fill the gap so clearly formulated by Blumenthal and Borst:

1. There is a series of transitional stages between the "biologically damaged but still-normal cell" and the "destructively growing cancer cell":

a) vesicular disintegration of the healthy cells;
b) organization of the bionous cell mass into spindle- and club-shaped structures;
c) maturation of these structures, at various rates, into autonomous cancer cells;
d) autonomous growth of the cancer cells into tumors.

2. The destructive "spread" of the cancer cells into the surrounding tissue is to be ascribed, for the most part, to the bionous disintegration of the latter. The surrounding healthy tissue appears to retreat before the mass of cancer cells, but, in so doing, itself undergoes carcinomatous transformation. "Carcinomatous" transformation signifies here nothing other than *bionous disintegration due to inner suffocation.* This interpretation is in accord with that of Bierisch:

We have used the finding that in cancer tissue there is aerobic glycolysis and that tumor tissue contains a relatively high concentration of lactic acid to help us form an idea of how the cancer tumor affects its immediate surroundings. It has been established by Cori, Warburg, and us that the tumor tissue gives off lactic acid. The lactic acid content of the tumor remains high, however, indicating that the lactic acid must pass directly from the tumor to the adjoining tissue. Our first in-

[6] Max Borst, *Pathologische Histologie* (1938), pp. 447–448.

vestigation concerned the effect of lactic acid concentrations, as they are found in the tumors, upon the histological structure of normal tissues when allowed to slowly infiltrate such tissues. The result was the gradual dissolution of the connective tissue. In this process there are the same structural transformations as occur in the course of experimental tar cancer development in the connective tissue bordering the tumor tissue. The dissolution process is one of proteolytic recession, which in living tissue requires the presence of lactic acid, activated kathespin, and a third factor. Once the specific structures in the connective tissue immediately adjoining the tumor are disintegrated, the physiological borderline normally separating epithelium and connective tissue is eliminated and the cancer cells can advance into the weakened vicinity. In the absence of evidence to the contrary, it must be assumed that the lactic acid is the pacemaker for the spread of the cancer cells into the epithelial tissues or the blood vessels, which leads to the conclusion that the "uninhibited growth" of the tumor *is not the direct outcome of its own cellular activity but results indirectly from the destruction of the surrounding tissues.*[7]

The cancer cell itself is therefore less significant than the tissue damage that precedes its formation. *The cancer cell results from and does not cause the cancer disease.* It becomes immediately dangerous to life only through its T-disintegration.

The question as to what specific stimulus is responsible for the transformation of the normal cell into a cancer cell may be briefly answered as follows:

T-bacilli, due to vesicular disintegration of the tissues (self-destruction), by first stimulating bion formation, constitute the specific stimulus for cancerous formations. The effect of the T-bacilli is limited to this action. The further development of the bions into cancer cell formations and the proliferation of these formations into

[7] R. Bierisch, "Uber den Stoffwechsel der Krebszellen," in *Neuere Ergebnisse auf dem Gebiete der Krebskrankheiten* (Leipzig, 1937).

a cancer tumor are autonomous, i.e., independent of the action of the T-bacilli. The cancerous bion formation and the subsequent formation of cancerous cells must be regarded as a defense of the organism against the T-bacilli stimulus. This defense, however, is pathological in character, since it makes use of the destruction of healthy cell formations and provokes, in turn, a new defense of the organism against the destruction.

4. The Mature Cancer Cell (Ca IV).

The chief characteristic of this fourth, mature stage is the presence of lively amoeboid cells. They represent the final phase in the evolution of the spindle cell formations. In the event that the organism does not perish in the early stages of chronic inflammation, i.e., the early stages of cancer (Ca II–Ca III), then the new cell formations have time to develop into genuine amoebae (*cf.* Fig. 23). Mechanistic cancer pathology regards them as "parasites"!

In Döflein's textbook on protozoology we find the following observations:

Lieberkühn had already noticed the presence of strange cells in the ascitic fluid which occurs in certain malignant tumors; he was able to confirm their motility but made no other observations about their nature. These cells have probably been observed by many researchers since then but without having received due attention.

No careful examination of these formations was undertaken until 1896 when Leyden and Schaudinn came to the surprising conclusion that the formations were a new kind of parasitic rhizipod in the ascitic fluid of living human organisms. Since this was the first time a prominent protozoologist had verified the protozoal nature of formations in a cancer-type human disease and, in so doing, had authoritatively confirmed the clinical finding, it would be useful to investigate the matter more closely.

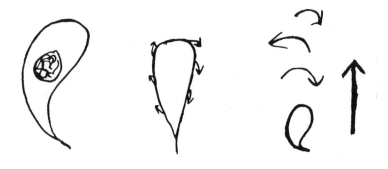

Alive. The arrows indicate the jerk-like movements of the plasm. The large arrow indicates the direction of movement of the total cell

Dead. Assumption of spherical shape and disintegration

FIGURE 23.   Forms of mature amoeboid cancer cells from T-mice (Ca IV)

According to Leyden's account, the formations were present in the ascites of a man found, on autopsy, to have been suffering from carcinoma of the stomach, and of a girl who likewise revealed tumors in the abdominal cavity. Tapped fluid contained, besides leucocytes and erythrocytes and endothelium-like cells, "large numbers of round cells with fat-like droplets and yellow pigment, usually patterned in larger groups and difficult to separate." They moved in a lively manner, with lobe- or thread-like pseudopodia, particularly during the warm days of July. In fluid kept sterile for three to seven days, they retained their motility and did not die. Some had erythrocytes inside their plasma. Schaudinn, who examined the formations closely, considered them to be amoeba-like parasites.[8]

One can see how far from reality the prejudice of parasitic infection has led even eminent scientists. Leyden had observed nothing but amoeboid cancer cells *which had developed in the organism itself*. The misinterpretation of the cancer cells as exogenous parasites is found even in 1942:

> *Miscellaneous Protozoa.* Other observers could not regard all the cancer cells as alien parasites, but certain of the tumor cells they identified as parasitic amoebae because of their bizarre forms and long pseudopodia which stretched between adjacent cells. These were the "Rhopalocephalus carcinomatosus" of Korotneff, and "Cancriamaeba macroglossia" of Eisen. L. Pfeiffer described and depicted intracellular structures which resembled the microsporidia of muscle tissue.
>
> Podwyssozki and Sawtschenko described as sporozoa a variety of free and encapsulated intracellular structures many of which resembled Soudakewitch's parasites. Ruffer and Walker improved the technical methods of demonstrating the cancer bodies and endeavored to distinguish between true and spurious parasites. Kahane thought he detected a minute protozoan in the circulating blood of cancer patients. In cancerous ascitic fluid Schaudinn observed a large amoeboid cell which he named Leydenia gemmipara. Schuller traced the complete cycle of a minute intranuclear protozoan in cancer cells which differed from nearly all other cancer parasites.[9]

[8] F. Döflein, *Generelles Lehrbuch der Protozoenkunde,* Vierte, stark vermehrte Auflage, 1916, p. 743.

[9] James Ewing, *Neoplastic Diseases,* 4th ed. (Philadelphia: W. B. Saunders, 1942), p. 116 ff.

At this point, we must assume that the malignancy of a tumor is dependent upon the degree of maturation of the cancer cells and the speed with which the cancer cells and the destroyed tissue disintegrate into T-bacilli. Metastases already exist in the maturing stage of cancer (Ca III), as the experiments on mice showed. However, spindle- or round-shaped cells with restricted motility cannot cause the same harm as amoebae with more rapid movement and consequently greater destructivity.

5. *The Final Phase of the Cancer Tumor: Putrid Disintegration (Ca V)*

Putrid disintegration may be ascribed to simple infection if the tumor is exposed to the air. But all dying cancer cells are characterized by disintegration of the tumor accompanied by the formation of rot bacteria and T-bacilli. This disintegration of newly formed cells into bacteria corresponds to the experimental decomposition of egg medium when T-bacilli are added. In both cases, the eosin-hematoxylin picture is the same (*cf.* Fig. 58-d, Appendix). It resembles the post-mortem necrosis of the tissue in which animal protein disintegrates into its chemical components. We can therefore speak of "premortem necrosis" in stage Ca V. In this final stage, the cancer displays a tendency to increasingly rapid destruction of the total organism. This is now understandable, since a systemic bacteremia and toxemia of the organism develops from the disintegration into T-bacilli of the short-lived cancer cells. When there is no gross disturbance of vital functions by the tumor itself, the cancer death is a death from general toxic putrefaction. For that reason, the disease tends to worsen rapidly at the end and lead to death.

TOWARD AN UNDERSTANDING OF EXPERIMENTAL
TAR CANCER IN MICE

In its animal experiments, classical cancer research has discovered an abundance of facts, few of which can be brought together into a comprehensible relationship. One of these inexplicable findings is the experimental induction of carcinoma in mice and rabbits by the application of tar. Yamagiwa[10] and Itschikawa were the first scientists to succeed in producing cancer by the continuous brushing of the ears of rabbits with tar. They produced carcinomatous ulcers and, in a few isolated cases, metastases in regional glands. Tsutsui, Dellman, Bloch, and Dreifuss then successfully carried out the same experiment on white mice. Naturally an effort was made to establish what components of the tar were exercising the carcinogenic effect. Dellman discovered that only tar distillates of 900–1000° C. and above were effective, while Kenneway and Russell arrived at the same result using coal tar at 900° C. which had been ineffective when unheated.

The carcinogenic effect of tar has so far remained unexplained. Two questions need to be answered: 1) *Why and how does tar substance provoke cancer?* 2) *Why is the tar substance carcinogenic only when heated to high temperatures?*

Blumenthal gives the following conclusive summary of the tar-brushing experiments:

1. Tar cancer, as Lubarsch was the first to note, eliminates many diverse cancer theories, including that of a unitary cancer agent, malformation, and embryonic germ disposition. The ear of a rabbit does not have any special disposition and, therefore, there can be no consideration of inherited disposition.
2. An *inflammatory* stage of considerable length precedes the cancer formation.

[10] All citations in this section are from Blumenthal, *op. cit.*

These two statements deal a mortal blow to the hereditary theory of cancer. They also strictly refute those pathologists who insist on maintaining a sharp distinction between the inflammatory and the carcinomatous processes. The tar-mice experiments also correspond with the fact that persons working with tar and aniline, as well as chimney sweeps in constant contact with soot, develop cancer more frequently than others.

What contribution can the bion experiment make to the solution of these problems?

First, it gives us some fundamental facts upon which to base an understanding of the problems:

1. Protozoa, which include cancer cells, develop from bion vesicles (orgone energy vesicles).
2. Animal and plant tissue can disintegrate into bions.
3. Carbon, the essential component of animal protein, plays a crucial role in the bion experiment. Heated to incandescence and combined with nutrients and substances to cause swelling, carbon yields bions and bion cultures.
4. Seen either *at a magnification of 2000–3000x* or in the dark-field, tar substances heated to high temperatures exhibit a vesicular structure similar to that of the bions produced from carbon heated to incandescence.

Unheated carbon and carbon heated to incandescence show basic differences. Unheated carbon displays only minimal vesicular structure, and viewed with the fluorescence microscope, shows its own color, black. Carbon heated to incandescence, on the other hand, if made to swell and inoculated on a culture medium, disintegrates immediately into bion vesicles which exhibit a bluish, not a black, fluorescence.

If we produce a carbon bion preparation, the following noteworthy facts are observed: The higher the temperature to which we heat the carbon, the easier and more rapid the development of bions and the more distinct their blue coloration. The carbon bion is, of course, something entirely different from the carbon from which it originates. First of all, its structure has been changed. A carbon crystal has become a conglomeration of orgone energy vesicles. These vesicles are capable of swelling, dividing, penetrating other substances, etc. Inoculated on culture media or placed in solutions that produce swelling, these vesicles absorb protein fluid and various salts. It is true that we do not yet know how to define the finished carbon bion chemically; we are certain, however, that it is no longer pure carbon. Its behavior in the culture medium experiment indicates that it bears a close relationship to living protein. Living protein is not merely a highly complicated carbon-hydrogen compound. Functionally, it is differentiated from non-living protein: *The chemical substances are merely the carriers of the orgone energy that governs the living function.*

Microscopic observation of the combination of mature carbon bions and protein substances—e.g., egg medium IV or autoclaved blood—reveals that the carbon bions permeate the protein substance and, combined with it, organize into diverse formations.

If fresh carbon bion solution is poured over egg culture medium IV, after a few weeks small "growths" about the size of a pinhead develop on the medium (Ca Experiment XIV). Microscopic examination reveals remarkably organized and structured formations, not previously found in the egg medium or the carbon bion preparation (*cf.* Fig. 61-a, b, c, d, Appendix).

The injection of fresh or twenty-four-hour-old carbon bions subcutaneously into mice causes around the point of injection the development of structures that are similar to those formed by the combination of carbon bions and protein substance. Over the course of months, cell growths develop with a pronounced chromophilic structure. They permeate, infiltrate, and, in time, destroy the tissues. In a few such cases microscopic examination revealed the typical spindle- and club-shaped formations in the organs, i.e., cells of the immature phase Ca III. Thirty-four healthy mice were subjected to the carbon bion experiment. All the mice became sick and the majority developed precancerous and mature growths (10 e Ca).

These experiments explain the effect of tar brushing. Carbon heated to high temperatures is carcinogenic because, at high temperatures, bions develop from the carbon substance and are the fundamental element in the organization of cancerous formations.

The question naturally arose during these carbon bion experiments as to whether it was simply the carbon bions that produced the growths or whether some connection with T-bacilli existed; i.e., whether the proliferation of T-bacilli effect was also operative in the tarred mice. I brushed tar on the neck of mice, in the usual way. Some of these mice died before the formation of a growth. The blood of these mice revealed T-bacilli that could be cultivated in pure culture (T 11 4). Cultures of cardiac blood from a few tarred mice that had already passed the stage of chronic inflammation and reached that of infiltrating growths also yielded T-bacilli.

How did the T-bacilli enter the blood of the tarred mice?

The question remained unanswered for some time until it occurred to me to Gram-stain a freshly produced carbon bion solution. I discovered that *T-bacilli can be detected immediately after producing a carbon bion preparation.* Unheated and untreated carbon, on the other hand, shows no reaction to Gram stain. In one case, I succeeded in cultivating the T-bacilli directly from carbon bions (10 e T XVI).

T-bacilli are therefore brought into the organism with the carbon-hydrogen substance that has been heated to a high temperature. The question of how the carbon bions act on the T-bacilli in the tissues of the animal remains unanswered. Do they complement each other in their effects or do they hamper each other? It can be established microscopically that the carbon bions attract, irritate, and paralyze the T-bacilli. Finding an answer to this question is important, both theoretically and practically, but, at this time, I can offer no experimental solution.

Protein substances are stimulated to growth by carbon bions

(PA and T). This fact explains the chimney sweep's cancer, the cancer of tar and aniline workers, and the lip cancer of pipe smokers.

4. THE CANCER CELL: PRODUCT OF A DEFENSE REACTION OF THE ORGANISM

Cancer also tends to develop readily from old scars or chronically damaged tissues, as when, for example, dental bridgework, over a period of years, damages the epithelium of the tongue. Severe injury to tissue, such as a blow, can cause a sarcoma leading to a rapid death. The results of the bion experiments make this sequence easy to understand: *Injury to tissue produces formations that degenerate into T-bacilli and stimulate cancer growth.* In tissue that is orgonotically strong, i.e., *healthy*, a scar or wound will not cause real harm. The crucial element is therefore not the local damage to the tissue, as has been the traditional belief, but rather the tissue's orgone strength, which we may refer to as its "orgonotic potency."

The discovery of T-bacilli made all these factors more understandable and strengthened my contention that they were in fact the specific cancer stimulus, occurring only in cancer patients. It is always gratifying to find the "specific" stimulus or cause of a disease and thus be able to delineate it sharply from what is healthy. We then feel more secure in establishing that there are organisms free of this particular stimulus. However, this concept is incorrect and impedes important insights into the nature of *immunity,* i.e., the natural defense functions of the living organism—in other words, its orgonotic potency. It is wrong to think that there are emotionally *healthy* people here and emotionally *sick* people there. And it is wrong to assume that there are "cancer patients" here and "cancer free" persons there. Deep within every "healthy" person are both catatonic mechanisms and T-bacilli. The boundary line is by no means clearly drawn and the problem shifts from the specific "causes" and specific "stimuli" of the diseases to *the orgonotic defense mechanisms against diseases. We must first understand health before we attempt to cure disease.* It is therefore encouraging that medicine today is giving increasing consideration to the viewpoint that the specific "stimuli" and "causes" of disease are effective only when the organism allows them to be. Tubercle bacilli, for example, can produce their pathological effect only under well-defined bio-energetic conditions within the organism. The degree to which a psychic trauma is operative depends upon the emotional state of the organism. Similarly, a general impairment of biological functioning must be present for the T-bacillus to have free rein. The crucial factor seems, once again, to be the disposition to disease, but not as the theories of heredity conceive of it. *Disposition* to disease signifies for us *the living orgonotic functioning* of the organism and does not refer either to dead substances in the blastoderm or to moralistic, empty concepts like "psychopathically degenerative constitution." Disposition to disease seems to us therefore essentially a reaction to the misery of life and not a fixed inheritance from our ancestors. It signifies *the kind and degree of the emotional (orgonotic) motility of the biosystem.*

It is assumed that the cancer cell originally initiates the disease process "cancer," in that "normal cells are transformed into cancer cells." More precise scrutiny of the development of cancer cells, however, proves this view false. The truth is exactly the reverse: *The cancer cell results from the resistance of the tissues to the effect of the T-bacilli.* This may sound strange, but examination of the facts will reveal its accuracy. The first step in the development of the cancer tumor is not the cancer cell; nor is it the disintegration of the tissue into blue bions. It is the appearance of masses of T-bacilli in the tissue or in the blood. T-bacilli are present also in *healthy* tissue and in *healthy* blood; and they are always found wherever there is degeneration of protein.

After I had completed a series of examinations of the blood of cancer patients, I proceeded to examine the blood of persons who could not be said to have cancer in the usual sense of the word. I was able to cultivate T-bacilli from the blood and excreta of completely healthy persons. This finding was at first alarming and confusing; for if, as I firmly believed by the end of 1937, the T-bacilli are specifically connected with the development of cancer, then their cultivability from the blood of healthy persons meant that basically *all humans* have "cancer." Since this supposition could not possibly be correct, the only alternative was that the T-bacillus is not connected specifically with cancer. Against this conclusion, however, was the irrefutable fact that every cancer patient and every cancer tissue contains masses of T-bacilli. Many months passed before experiment and deliberation yielded the correct answer: *The distinction between the healthy individual and the cancer patient does not lie in the absence of T-bacilli but in the orgonotic potency of the organism, i.e., in the capacity of the organism to eliminate its T-bacilli and in the degree to which the tissues and the blood cells tend toward disintegration into T-bacilli.* True, I was able to cultivate T-bacilli from the blood and excreta of healthy persons. But whereas the blood and tissues of cancer patients produced T-bacilli *easily* and *quickly,* the blood and excreta of healthy individuals had to be subjected to a more or less lengthy *process of degeneration*—in some cases several days, in others several weeks—in order to produce the T-bacilli. *The disposition to cancer is therefore determined by the biological resistance of the blood and the tissues to putrefaction. This biological resistance, in turn, is itself determined by the orgone energy content of the blood and the tissues, which is to say, by the orgonotic potency of the organism.* Every process that reduces the orgone energy content and the orgonotic functioning of the organism, or the individual organs, increases proportionately the disposition to shrinking and to cancerous disintegration. There are a number of solid observations to substantiate this.

The problem now confronting me was the difficult and decisive question of whether the T-bacillus appears only where cancer develops, or whether it is ubiquitous, meaning that cancer can appear anywhere and at any time. I proceeded to examine the blood, epithelia, and excreta of several healthy individuals. I could in fact identify local T-bacilli formations in organs and tissues where there was no suggestion of cancer. I saw T-bacilli disintegration in the vaginal and cervical epithelium of many healthy women. In some cases, the T-picture disappeared after a certain time, in others it remained constant. I found T-disintegration where a dental bridge had rubbed the epithelium on the left side of my own tongue and caused a small erosion. I was even able to produce a T-bacilli culture from it. That was years ago, and I still do not have cancer. The right side of my tongue yielded no T-bacilli and had healthy epithelial cells. I cultivated T-bacilli from the blood of one of my assistants by allowing it to degenerate, then injected them into a healthy mouse and produced a well-defined adenocarcinoma in the buttock muscle (cf. Fig. 62-a, Appendix). It was the first time I had produced a malignant tumor with T-bacilli from healthy blood. The fact that it was indeed the T-bacilli that had caused the tumor was proved by the sequence in which it developed: an inflammation extended from the place of injection along the lymph vessels on the right flank of the mouse toward the buttock muscles; there then appeared a chronic inflammation which subsequently developed into an adenocarcinoma. This diagnosis was verified at Columbia University, although I had not reported that it was a cancer of the muscle tissue (10 Ge T Ca; cf. Fig. 62-a through e, Appendix). Thus, the healthiest organism contains T-bacilli and tends toward putrid disintegration. *Cancer disposition is therefore universal.* But so long as the tissues and blood are orgonotically strong, every developing T-bacillus will be destroyed and eliminated before it can propagate, accumulate, and cause damage. What is the *first* damage the T-bacillus inflicts? The answer to this question will prove that the formation of cancer cells represents a defense reaction of the organism against T-bacilli and is not the disease itself.

When T-bacilli form anywhere in the organism and begin to accumulate, the organism reacts with a *mild* but *chronic* inflammation. Occasionally the massing of white blood cells provides sufficient resistance against the advance of the T-bacilli. In other cases, however, either the T-bacilli autoinfection is too strong or the orgonotic defense mechanism of the organism is too weak. What happens then? How does the infected tissue react?

A test-tube experiment with T-bacilli provides one possible answer. A completely sterile egg medium (E IV) is inoculated with T-bacilli, which now grow on the medium. *But we find that T-bacilli are not the only substances growing on it.* Before starting the experiment, we had examined the sterile egg medium carefully under the microscope at a magnification of 2000x and saw neither T-bacilli nor blue PA bions. However, now the inoculated medium shows not only T-bacilli, but to our great astonishment, *a mass of motile blue PA bions at the point of inoculation.* This means that the inoculated T-bacilli have not only proliferated themselves in the egg medium but, in addition, *have stimulated the protein substances that surround them (the organic protein) to form blue PA bions; i.e. they have set in motion the processes of swelling and bionous disintegration.*

The identical process occurs in the healthy tissue of a mouse that we inoculate in the neck or any other place with T-bacilli in such a dosage that, instead of immediate abscess formation and death, a mild but chronic inflammatory reaction is produced. *The tissue surrounding the place of inoculation shows bionous disintegration.* It is possible to follow the development of the cancer cell formations from the PA bions by examining dissected T-mice in series from the first day to about the tenth week.

I repeated these two experiments many times and always obtained the same results. At first I was not able to understand it. Even after things became clearer, the full implications of the findings continued to elude me for quite some time. Briefly stated: *T-bacilli, which are the product of putrid disintegration of organic or living matter, stimulate in other organic or living matter the formation of blue bions.* Corresponding to the antithetical relationship between blue PA bions and T-bacilli, this bion formation has the function of reacting against the T-bacilli. That means the blue bions stimulated by the T-bacilli are a defense reaction against T-infection.

T-bacilli would be of small interest if their only effect were this local PA bion formation, i.e., "B-reaction." Blood platelets, which are nothing other than blue PA bion bodies surrounded by dead T-bacilli adhering to them, are often seen in the blood of healthy persons. Leucocytes are also sometimes filled with T-bodies. The reaction of the PA against the T, i.e., the B-reaction, takes place constantly and everywhere, even in the healthiest organism. The weaker the orgone charge of the PA-formations, the greater the quantity of blue bions that must be produced to eliminate the T. *However, the blue bions organize into higher biological forms, protozoa, including cancer cells. We now understand that the cancer cell is in reality a product of the many blue PA bions that originated from blood cells or tissue as a defense against the local autoinfection with T-bacilli.* With this realization the problem solves itself in a very simple way. Here we might mention a seemingly far-fetched but actually quite pertinent fact, namely that humus is bionously disintegrated organic matter. The fertilization of humus results from the putrid disintegration of organic matter, essentially from simple nitrogen compounds. This "fertilization" is simply a stimulation of blue PA bion formation in the humus by putrid matter, i.e., T-bacilli. The striking fact that humus is sterile and has a sterilizing effect is to be ascribed to the presence of the blue earth PA bions. These bions can be easily reproduced and observed experimentally by autoclaving earth in KCl.

The T-bacilli experiments occasionally open up glimpses into a future chemical concept. These matters, however, remain obscure. Nevertheless, there is one finding of extreme interest that should be mentioned in this context: Methyl and nitrogen compounds (urea, scatol, indol), constituents of urine and feces, are the essential products of the putrid disintegration of protein substances. Old T-bacilli cultures have a putrid odor that is acrid and ammonia-like. The body odors of advanced cancer patients are similar and characteristic. "Putrefaction in the living body" is therefore not a simile but a very real fact.

A relationship that is still obscure also exists between the T-bacilli and cyanide (CN). According to Warburg, this poison exercises a paralyzing effect on the respiratory processes in the cells in inhibiting oxidation by combining with the iron-containing respiratory enzyme of cells. Many of our T-mice died from suffocation, due to respiratory paralysis and hypervenous blood. The connection between this property of the T-bacilli and the suffocation metabolism of the cancer tissue is obvious. A rich field is opened here for the biochemist.

Thus far, we have become acquainted with only *one* direction of the T-bacilli effect: tissue damage → T-bacilli → bionous tissue disintegration → organization of protozoa (cancer cells) from the PA bions of the tissues. This process represents a progression from the T-bacillus to *higher* biological formations. Now, the reverse process also exists, in which the cancer cells disintegrate into T-bacilli with increasing putrefaction: cancer cell → T-bacilli → general blood and tissue putrefaction and T-intoxication. The actual cause of death is not to be ascribed to the formation of cancer cells but to the *secondary T-disintegration.* Even though the tissue damage was previously confined locally and the T-bacilli were relatively few in number, the disintegration process of the cancer tumor effects an enormous acceleration and general spreading of the putrefaction in the body: *putrefaction of the blood and lymph and T-bacilli intoxication of the body fluid system.* It should be clear therefore why cancer patients can maintain themselves comparatively well for months and even years and then, quite suddenly, systemic decay, rapid cachexia, and death all follow in quick succession. The second phase, the disintegration of the cancer tumors into putrid masses, lasts only a few weeks, in sharp contrast to the length of time for tumor formation. T-bacilli formation and putrefaction are thus just as much a *cause* as an effect of the cancer biopathy.

This distinction has great therapeutic importance. Once tumors, tissue, and blood are involved in the process of secondary putrid disintegration, such enormous masses of T-bacilli are formed that any attempt at treatment is hopeless. However, in the first phase, when the cancer tissue is forming, orgone therapy can accomplish a great deal. I will return to this particular point later.

The whole problem of the treatment and prevention of cancer can now be formulated simply: *the T-reaction of the organism, the orgone weakness, is counteracted by the B-reaction, the orgone strength in the blood and tissues.* The fate of the cancer patient depends completely on the relationship of the B-reaction to the T-reaction. A practical mastery of this problem requires more knowledge of the effects of orgone energy.

5. A COMMENT ON THE PROBLEM OF HEREDITY

The reader who has some familiarity with the cancer problem will now raise a very legitimate question: *What about the hereditary factor in cancer?* Has it not been "demonstrated" that there are mice with a special tendency to cancer formation, and that in man cancer is found more frequently in certain families? I have felt obliged to stress on many occasions in my writings that we do not deny the *existence* of heredity. What we do emphasize, however, is that research on heredity has still not supplied us with any concrete account of how this hereditary factor manifests itself and how it functions biologically. Theoretically and practically the notion of genes is of no use to us. Since its earliest days, sex-economy has been prepared to debate the *mechanisms* of the heredity of characteristics and conditions, about which research on heredity has nothing to say. I refer here not to "hereditary substances" but to plasmatic *functions.* While working on the problem of cancer, we encountered the heredity question in a completely unexpected but simple way, quite different from the question of hereditary character traits. Most pathological characteristics can be traced back to the effects of early upbringing, and especially the influence of identification and early sexual stasis. This "heredity" of biopathic character traits is thus a *postnatal* phenomenon. The heredity of cancer, on the other hand, is actually a *prenatal* phenomenon, though quite different from the way the science of heredity sees it.

In our laboratory, we have had the opportunity to observe hundreds of mice, both healthy and cancerous. A striking fact was how few of the young born to our cancerous mice developed cancer themselves. At first, we satisfied ourselves with the thought that we were not dealing with a specific cancer strain. A few cases of cancer did occur in the young mice, but we had no explanation for this. I refer here only to mice who developed cancer spontaneously and not from experimental interference.

The surprise circumstance was supplied by the mice originally completely healthy and injected with T-bacilli at the age of three to eight months. *The young of these originally healthy mice* were frequently diseased and died early, often having developed cancer tumors. On the other hand, there was not one single case of a control mouse—not injected with T-bacilli—having cancerous or otherwise sick young. Autopsy and bacteriological examination of the cancerous young, who had not been given T-bacilli injections, yielded precisely the same results as they did with the mothers who had received the T-bacilli injections: T-bacilli in the blood, putrid disintegration of the tissues in the stomach, in glands, and especially in the genitals. Mice that develop cancer spontaneously are usually free of cancer manifestations in the other organs, unless there are metastases. Mice injected with T-bacilli, on the other hand, were cancerously affected in almost all organs. This is easily understood since the spontaneous tumor develops from local damage to the tissues, whereas the T-tumors in the injected mice were characterized by a general spread of the T throughout the organism. These T-mice can die of systemic carcinosis and T-intoxication without ever developing large local tumors. This seems in fact to be the general rule and the explanation for it is simply that the T-bacilli that have been injected are carried along in the blood in great numbers.

We now understand why the young of T-mice so often develop cancer prenatally when born after the injection of T-bacilli in the mother: *The injected T-bacilli are carried from the blood of the mother into the blood of the embryos, where they produce cancer.* This finding sheds light on a large area of the problem of cancer heredity: *If a mother during pregnancy has a large enough number of sufficiently virulent T-bacilli in the blood, the child must necessarily become infected with the T-bacilli.* Whether the organism of the child can cope with the T-bacilli absorbed depends on additional circumstances. It depends on the relationship of the B-reaction of the child to the T-reaction that has developed so early.

The formation of breast cancer in mice is still not understood. It must be stressed, however, that the female mice used for observation no longer lead a natural sexual existence. Either they are separated constantly from the males or breeding is regulated. Some of our observations of males injected with T-bacilli do indicate that sexual stasis increases the effect of the T-reaction and reduces the B-reaction of the organism. Males kept abstinent developed cancer more easily, especially in the testicles, than males left together with the females. I would like to stress here that these experiments have not yet been carried out comprehensively enough to permit generalizations.

In human mothers, two other "hereditary" influences must be considered, in addition to the transmission of T-bacilli through the blood: *the local effect of spasm of the uterus* and the general biopathic *respiratory inhibition.* At the moment, nothing definitive can be said about these factors. It is important, however, to note that a severe respiratory disturbance in the mother must have an adverse effect on the tissue respiration of the embryo; a chronic spasm of the uterus is also bound to have a damaging influence. But prenatal influences of this type upon the embryo are not hereditary effects in the sense of the term as understood by the "gene" theorists. They are much more *social* effects. *The organism of the mother is, strictly speaking, the first "social factor" of the unborn embryo.*

The mechanistic and metaphysical hypothesis of heredity provides us with no possibility of understanding prenatally acquired disturbances or of eliminating them practically. On the other hand, knowledge of the existence and nature of T-bacilli, of the character structure and the pulsatory functions of the parents, does enable us to clear the way toward an understanding of the problem of heredity which could very well be of great practical and theoretical importance.[11]

This excursion into the problem of heredity was not intentionally sought. It was made necessary by a number of pertinent observations closely connected to the question of orgone therapy for cancer. We will have to (and can) make ourselves increasingly familiar with the thought that *cancer is beginning to lose its dread* and that *the prevention of cancer will be easier than the cure.* For instance, it will now be possible to determine the degree to which maternal blood tends toward disintegration into T-bacilli, and whether it contains free T-bacilli, etc. Orgone treatment of the mother would in such cases protect the embryo from the effects of T-bacilli. It would also be possible to treat the infant with orgone therapy. As yet, we do not know whether the T-bacillus is specific for cancer only or whether it can also cause other diseases *when it occurs in another form* and in *a different location.* Complete obscurity reigns here, and we shall have to be prepared for great surprises. Infectious diseases, seemingly as far apart as acute ptomaine poisoning and the acute stage of poliomyelitis, may find their explanation here. This is a justifiable assumption, but *it is no more than an assumption.*

---

[11] It may be possible to answer the question of the heredity of cancer if we expose mice with a known high percentage of cancer heredity to orgone radiation. The orgone-biophysical viewpoint would be confirmed if a reduction or elimination of cancer in the succeeding generations of cancer strain could be achieved. (We tried unsuccessfully to obtain high cancer strain mice from the Jackson Memorial Laboratory in Bar Harbor, Maine.)

CHAPTER VII

Nature and Development
of the Orgone
Therapy Experiments

We are now sufficiently prepared to discuss the biophysical basis of orgone therapy. It can be reduced to a simple biological formula: *enhancement of the B-reaction of the organism; reduction or elimination of the T-reaction.* If there is a preponderant T-reaction in the blood and tissues, orgone therapy must increase the B-reaction or it will have failed. Conversely, therapy can be considered successful if the T-reactions are replaced by B-reactions. Let us now compare the B-reactions and the T-reactions schematically:

	B-Reaction	*T-Reaction*
1. *Total organism*	Erect, good tonicity. No spasms, no clonisms. Feeling of strength. Capacity for pleasure.	Bent, flaccid or hypertonic. Spasms, clonisms. Feeling of weakness. Incapacity for pleasure. Pleasure anxiety.
2. *Skin*	Warm, good tone, rosy or tanned; perspiration warm.	Cold, clammy; livid, wrinkled, pale to deathly white; sweat cold.
3. *Musculature*	Relaxed, capable of alternating tension and relaxation; strong. No muscular armor. Peristalsis good, no constipation, no hemorrhoids.	Often excessive fat. General muscular armor, particularly jaw, forehead, neck, thigh adductors, buttocks, back.
3a. *Facial expression*	Lively, changeable.	Mask-like, rigid.

	B-Reaction	T-Reaction
4. *Blood*	B-reaction on autoclavation. Erythrocytes taut, pulsating; wide, strong orgone margin; very slow bionous disintegration in physiological NaCl solution. No T-bacilli in cultures.	T-reaction on autoclavation. Erythrocytes small or shrunken; no pulsation; T-spikes; orgone margin weak and narrow; bionous disintegration in physiological NaCl very rapid. Staphylococci, streptococci, or T-bacilli in cultures.
5. *Cardiovascular system*	Blood pressure normal; pulse regular, quiet, strong.	Blood pressure too high or too low; pulse too fast or too slow, irregular or weak.
6. *Tissues* (epithelial cells, tissues from biopsy, etc.)	Turgor strong. No bion formation in KCl.	Turgor weak, shrunken. Bionous structure or rapid bionous disintegration in KCl.
7. *Eyes*	Bright. Lively pupillary reaction. Eyeballs neither protruding or sunken.	Dull, "faraway" look. Sluggish pupillary reaction; mydriasis. Eyeballs protruding or sunken.
8. *Respiration*	*Full* expiration, with pause afterward. Free pulsation of thorax. Pleasure sensation in the genital apparatus after each expiration.	Expiration shallow, incomplete. Chronic inspiratory attitude, pause after inspiration. Chronic anxiety attitude of the chest. No pleasure sensation after expiration.
9. *Orgasm*	Regular; total body convulsion. No sexual stasis.	Absent or disturbed. Chronic sexual stasis.
10. *Orgone field around organism*	Wide, "elastic."	Narrow or absent.

The symptoms of the T-reaction are identical with many symptoms of chronic sympatheticotonic contraction. However, symptoms of the B-reaction are not identical with chronic vagotonic expansion;

they simply correspond to a condition of the organism characterized by *quiet, well-ordered, full pulsation in all organs.*

The essence of orgone therapy (not only in the treatment of
cancer but in all biopathies based on contraction or shrinking of the
vital apparatus) basically is *the overcoming of chronic contraction
and the stimulating of expansion.* Once the organism is again capable of expansion, dilating its vessels, driving blood into the skin
and tissues, absorbing fluids and foods into the tissues, establishing
the wave-like peristaltic movement of the intestines, relaxing the
tensed muscles—in other words, *expanding the total autonomic
system*—normal pulsation follows spontaneously and the state of
living function that consists of *oscillation between contraction and
expansion,* i.e., *biological pulsation,* is established. The predominance of the B-reaction over the T-reaction is simply the predominance of all life-positive reactions, in every part of the organism.
Since the organism is a functioning unit, the orderly pulsation of the
total organism is the fundamental prerequisite for neutralizing the
T-reaction in the tissues and blood. And since T-bacilli develop from
the chronic contraction (T-reaction) of the organism, it is clear that
*the natural, full pulsation of the organism is the basis of cancer
prevention.* Conversely, chronic contraction is the general basis for
the carcinomatous shrinking biopathy.

It is now clear that the cancer problem cannot be restricted to
individual organs or to an individual tumor or enzyme. It is a problem of the total biological functioning of the organism. Consequently, treatment of cancer with hormones, enzymes, freezing,
surgery, or local irradiation does not really affect the core of the
problem. Cancer is not a local disease of the organs but a systemic
process of premature dying, manifested in the clinically tangible T-
reactions. The only cancer therapy that could claim to be valid
would be one that grasps this biopathy at its root. The term "cancer
therapy" is, in fact, legitimate only if the treatment is realistically
aimed at removing systemic T-reactions and reestablishing a predominance of the B-reaction, i.e., if it is designed to restore vital
functioning. If, for instance, orgone therapy succeeded in eliminat-

ing the local tumor and destroying the T-bacilli in the blood, but did not achieve any other systemic influence, then it could be regarded as a good *symptomatic* method of treatment, but not a true "cancer therapy."

We have learned from psychiatry not to consider a neurosis as "cured" just because we have eliminated a headache or a compulsion. In the practice of character-analytic vegetotherapy, we speak of a "cure" only after we have successfully removed the general characterological and biophysiological basis of the local individual symptoms, i.e., the "character neurosis." This can be accomplished only by establishing orgastic potency, the capacity for full pulsation. This requirement is exacting, but it is the only one that meets the essential medical and social hygienic demands. Our work must not be confused with those illusory methods, directed at the gullible, that claim to be able to "cure" a neurotic headache with bromides, or cancer with surgery. This requirement, i.e., that we consider a case cured only when the character neurosis has been removed, governed our clinical work even during the first years of the seminar for psychoanalytic therapy in Vienna. We want to maintain it, for it has served us well.

I would like to anticipate: *We do not yet know if orgone therapy can be regarded as the best method of treatment for cancer.* It is true that we are already in a position to change the systemic T-reaction of the organism into a systemic B-reaction and eliminate local tumors in the body. But what we still do not know is how long the systemic B-reaction can hold its own and whether, sooner or later, the T-reaction will again replace it. Nevertheless, the present publication of *The Cancer Biopathy* is justified, even though it will take many years of experience and extensive work before orgone therapy can be regarded as *the* method for treating cancer and before we know the exact limits of its capabilities. But what has been achieved until now far exceeds our expectations of a few years ago and merits a detailed discussion here.

I will now relate how today's experimental orgone therapy developed from the first groping bion experiments of 1936.

Orgone therapy for cancer can be traced, historically, to the first observation of the killing effect exerted by blue PA bions on many kinds of rot and other bacilli. It was only logical then to observe microscopically the various kinds of blue PA bions and bacilli, and to inject them into mice. Microscopic examination revealed that motile bacilli in the vicinity of vigorous blue bions— derived from iron filings, humus, earth crystals, carbon, etc.—become agitated, seem to struggle to pull away, and at closer proximities, become motionless, as if paralyzed. The same reaction occurred if rapidly moving T-bacilli were brought together with blue PA bions. The T-bacilli tended either to adhere motionlessly to the blue bions or to agglutinate into immobile heaps all around them. As previously mentioned, all mice injected with PA bions alone remained healthy. Mice injected simultaneously with PA bions and T-bacilli remained, for the most part, healthy.

These results disclosed the healing effect of the blue bions (later called "orgone energy vesicles") in T-bacilli infection. Nothing was known about the possible direct effects of PA bions upon carcinomatous tissue. At that phase of my work, there were as yet no certainties and only a few useful guidelines. No one knew what to expect from the experiments. I brought PA bions and cancer cells together and examined them under the microscope. The PA bions swarmed around the heaps of cancer cells, finally penetrating into the mass and destroying its structure (cf. Fig. 63, Appendix).

A medical colleague at the Institute persuaded a surgeon to inject sterile PA bions from the blood of a cancer patient into a patient who was dying of cancer. The surgeon gave three intravenous injections of about 10 cc. of PA bion solution. The patient reacted with a fever. She died about eight days later. Autopsy revealed a hard tumor, about the size of a fist, in the liver. *In several places, the surface area of the tumor showed a softening to a depth of about 1 cm.* The pathologist considered this unusual. To us it was an indeterminate finding that did, however, correspond with the findings in our experiments conducted under the microscope. (At the time, I knew of several experiments that had been undertaken in

Europe to test the effect that injections of streptococci had on cancer. My bions, on the other hand, were sterile formations, obtained by autoclavation.)

I was now confronted by two facts: PA bions paralyze T-baccilli, which are at the root of cancer, and they also destroy cancer tissue itself. The first fact pointed toward cancer prevention; the second toward local cancer therapy. Over the course of the years that followed, the first direction increasingly gained our attention.

It would have seemed logical to undertake further experiments with humans. One could, for example, determine the effect of injections of PA bion cultures. But certain observations of the PA bions restrained me, namely that they were nothing other than a particular kind of living organism. When brought together with the T-bacilli, they exhausted their biological energy in the ensuing struggle. Microscopically, it could be seen that many PA bions had lost their blue color, and numerous forms of blue vesicles had degenerated into round black cocci, i.e., pus-producing staphylococci. Thus the idea of injecting PA bions into humans had to be discarded.

Between the fall of 1937, when I discovered the T-bacilli in Norway, and the fall of 1939, when we started the first orgone therapy experiments on cancer mice, a number of unrelated observations were made that served as guideposts in our work. The blue PA bion cultures killed T-bacilli that had been injected into mice. When I had obtained the first SAPA bion culture, in which orgone radiation was discovered, I was confronted with an important question: *Is the energy radiated by the sand bion cultures the same as the energy in the blue PA bions that I had injected into mice to protect them against the effects of T-bacilli?* Today it is taken for granted in our work that the energy in the earth bions, the energy in the radiating SAPA bions, the energy in the blue-glimmering "red" blood corpuscles, and, finally, the energy visible in the atmosphere are all manifestations of one and the same energy. The identity of the energy in the various substances and conditions has been confirmed experimentally and has led to essential theoretical assumptions on the nature of the life function. But when I first saw the effects of orgone energy on cancer tissue, before I realized that it *was* orgone energy, everything was still uncertain. Every new hypothesis that suggested itself and was incompatible with traditional pathology made me pull back. To be sure, I clearly saw that the blue coloration of the PA bions was somehow connected to their killing effect; but I could not have suspected that this blue was the specific color of biological energy. Only after the existence of the SAPA radiation had been established in 1939, and with it, the solar origin of orgone energy, did I venture bolder assumptions.

To proceed at all, I had to hypothesize that the blue in the PA bions represented precisely the same energy contained in the radiation from SAPA bions, that is, energy *outside* the bion vesicles and outside the tube in which the cultures were contained.

I had developed a small wart on my left cheek that was found to contain T-bacilli. I applied the SAPA culture test tube to the wart a few times for periods of several minutes. Microscopic examination had previously shown live T-bacilli; now, after the tube application, they were dead. The wart itself healed. *The orgone energy of the SAPA bions was therefore effective even at a distance, through the glass of the test tube.* An erosion on the left side of my tongue showed living T-bacilli. I exposed it to orgone radiation by bringing the SAPA bion test tube close to the eroded spot. The erosion healed rapidly and the T-bacilli became immobile. In a woman suffering from leucorrhea, I found degeneration in the vaginal epithelium and masses of living T-bacilli in the secretions. In addition, there were caudate protozoa with amoeboid motility, the so-called *Trichomonas vaginalis.* Under the microscope, I observed that when a small number of SAPA bions were brought into the vicinity of the protozoa, the latter lost their motility (*cf.* Fig. 50-a and 50-b, Appendix). I had the woman introduce a sterile SAPA bion test tube into her vagina for periods of half a minute. She very soon complained of a burning sensation and had to stop. I immediately examined the vaginal secretion again and found to my amazement that it no longer contained any living T-bacilli. What surprised me was the promptness of the reaction, even though I was already familiar with the rapid reddening of the skin caused by application of a SAPA culture.

In May 1939 I was forced to interrupt my research because of the smear campaign begun in the Norwegian press the year before. I transferred my laboratory to New York, sending the SAPA cultures with one of my assistants. It was the middle of September 1939 before I had my laboratory set up again in Forest Hills and could resume my work. It had not been easy to remain patient during the waiting period. The actual experiments in orgone therapy for cancer began with the subcutaneous injection of a solution of SAPA culture into mice (obtained from Herrlein Inc., New York City, N.Y.) that had spontaneously developed rapidly growing tumors. The first mouse to be injected was from a Paris strain and suffering, according to the diagnosis, from a "mammary tumor." (I had obtained the mouse—Paris R3—from Columbia University through a student of mine who was a physician.) I can well remember the great excitement we all felt at the laboratory when this mouse received the first injection. I knew (and the thought was confirmed by the physician) that even a small reduction in the size of the tumor would be a tremendous event. For never before in the history of cancer research had anyone been successful in reducing cancer tumors in mice, let alone in eliminating them.

The tumor was on the left breast, the size of a bean, and hard. On the second day it was softer, and after a few days it had shrunk to the size of a small pea. Our sense of triumph was great, but experience had taught us not to be overly optimistic. My caution turned out to be justified. After two weeks *the tumor began to grow again,* until it was the size of a walnut. I did not know whether I should continue with the SAPA injections or stop. During this time a number of untreated cancer mice died rapidly of cachexia. However, *healthy* mice that I had injected with SAPA bions, as a control, died also, with liver enlargement and degeneration in the acini. It was some consolation that the cancer mice injected with the SAPA bions survived many untreated ones by at least several weeks and, in a few cases, several months. But in the end all the mice died, a few with reduced tumors, others with tumors that had, at first, either receded or completely disappeared, then grown large again. It was depressing. *Yet the fact that orgone energy is effective in reducing the size of tumors was established.*

I now proceeded to inject dozens of mice with the SAPA solution, using 101 mice, all told. In subsequent months the confused situation began to clear up. The puzzling factor had been the enlargement of the tumors after they had initially disappeared. (There were only a few cases where the tumor did *not* reappear.)

From the beginning of the experiment, I had examined the injected and untreated mice very carefully; yet it was not clear how the SAPA bions destroyed the tumor tissue. *Did the SAPA bions penetrate the tumor through the bloodstream and then destroy tissue the same way they destroyed the motile cancer cells on the microscope slide?* Autopsies of all injected mice disclosed a very mysterious finding: *There was no trace at all, either in the blood or in the tumor, of the injected SAPA bions.*

I did not understand, but I was struck by the fact that the tumors in the treated mice were abnormally hyperemic. After some time we began to realize why the tumors first receded and then enlarged again. *The regrowth was brought about by the hyperemia of the tumors. The blood had something to do with the destruction of the tumor.*

The mice treated with SAPA bions could be distinguished from the untreated mice by the fact that their erythrocytes were taut and biologically vigorous, whereas the untreated mice showed a typical cancer blood picture: shrunken membranes of the erythrocytes, T-spikes, and masses of T-bacilli in the blood and the blood culture. The treated mice, however, had few or no active T-bacilli in the blood. This striking difference in the form and activity of the erythrocytes led us to surmise that in reality it was the erythrocytes and not the SAPA bions that were the *direct* agents of the tumor destruction. *The SAPA bions obviously charged the erythrocytes orgonotically, and perished in the process. The charged erythrocytes carried out the healing of the tumor that we had originally ascribed to the SAPA bions.* This surmise proved to be correct, for it led to further important observations and the realization that *the actual healing factor is the orgonotically strongly charged blood. We applied this knowledge consistently in our work from that time on.* Above all, it made comprehensible the anemic and cachectic conditions of the untreated mice. The treated mice died also, but they never attained the degree of cachexia and anemia reached by the untreated ones. In the untreated mice, the available biological energy of the blood corpuscles was used up in the struggle against the disease, causing the decline of the organism: cachexia. In orgone-treated cancer mice, the organism could save its own biological energy, since it was supplied with orgone energy from the outside. The results were the same when we injected autoclaved earth bions instead of the SAPA orgone energy vesicles.

We dissected several dozen untreated cancer mice and found that here, too, the tumor sometimes contained blood-filled cavities. These cavities were free of organized or compact cancer tissue. They contained a macroscopically brownish mass which was seen microscopically to consist of detritus and T-bacilli. In the dark-field, and at a magnification of 3000x, it could be clearly seen that whenever erythrocytes came into contact with cancer cells, they not only caused the disintegration of the tissues into T-bodies, but they also disintegrated into T-bodies themselves. The untreated mice had orgone-*weak* blood. I was therefore unsure whether the T-disintegration of the erythrocytes should be ascribed to this orgone weakness or to the loss of energy in the struggle against the cancer cells. Later we discovered the same phenomenon even in the tumors of mice that had been treated (*cf.* Fig. 64-e and 64-f, Appendix). In these cases, too, erythrocytes distintegrated into T-bodies wherever they came into contact with the cancer cells. This finding can also be observed in the stained section. We now knew that the disintegration of the erythrocytes into T-bacilli was a consequence of their struggle against the cancer tissue, and not a result of orgone weakness.

Thus, we came upon the natural *autocurative mechanism of the organism,* which guided us in all further work. *The natural curative factor against cancer must be the blood.*

The reader should be reminded that at this particular time (winter 1939–1940) no one had a presentiment of the existence of atmospheric orgone energy. There was no such thing as an orgone accumulator. Orgone therapy with cancer mice consisted of injecting them with orgone-containing bions. We observed the injected mice carefully every day. We had the feeling that the orgone energy vesicles we injected, while certainly causing the destruction of the tumor, somehow also damaged the mice. Personally, I had always had an antipathy toward injecting living organisms with foreign substances, whether chemicals or exogenous sera. It could not be overlooked that so many drugs that may alleviate pain simultaneously damage the autonomic vital apparatus. For example, the anaesthetic effect of the alkaloids (morphine, etc.) is based on a depression of the organism's vegetative sensibility. Biologically, their effect is exactly opposite to that of orgone therapy: they *depress,* while orgone therapy *stimulates,* the life functions. This is a very old medical problem. *Can there be synthetic agents that can destroy disease-producing factors and alleviate pain without causing damage to the life system?* Chemical research has not been able to answer this question.

Healthy control mice also became diseased after receiving injections of SAPA bions and treated cancer mice, although rid of their tumors, failed to recuperate properly. Therefore, even in those early stages of research, I tried to develop methods other than the injection of orgone energy vesicles. At first we saw no way to apply orgone energy without bion injections. However, once it was established that the bions did not exert their effect directly, but rather *by way of the blood,* new means were found of administering orgone energy, which dispensed with the need to inject bions. I will describe these methods briefly. They represented only an instructive intermediate phase in the orgone therapy experiments and were later completely abandoned. They did, however, reveal important properties of the blood in its relation to orgone energy and to malignant tumors. The following methods of indirect administering of orgone energy were tried:

1. The blood-filled tumors of the mice that had been treated with orgone energy were tapped. The blood was drawn off under sterile conditions and then centrifuged, to separate the erythrocytes from the blood serum. A sterile SAPA bion culture was added to the serum and the solution was refrigerated for one day. Since fluids absorb orgone energy, we felt certain that the serum would be charged with orgone energy from the SAPA bions. This serum was filtered, separating it from the SAPA bions. Then the orgone-charged serum was injected into the cancer mice. It exerted a quite distinct effect, though, to be sure, not as strong as that of direct SAPA bion injections. In another series, where the serum was not treated with SAPA bions, there was not the slightest therapeutic effect. The blood of cancer-diseased organisms not exposed to SAPA bions is in itself orgonotically too weak. This experiment convinced us that no specific antibodies against cancer cells develop in the blood of cancer mice.

2. We injected SAPA bions several times into healthy rabbits, withdrew blood (again satisfying ourselves that it no longer contained any structured SAPA bions), and injected it into cancer mice in two ways: one group of cancer mice received injections of rabbit blood (0.2–0.5 cc.) diluted with potassium chloride, every day for several weeks; the other group received injections of *centrifuged* rabbit blood, i.e., pure rabbit serum, orgonotically highly charged. This method of indirectly administering orgone energy was successful. Intravenous injection of the mice proved to be more effective than subcutaneous injection, but there were a few deaths from the shock effect of introducing KCl intravenously.

3. Neither the rabbit serum nor whole blood injected *directly into the tumor* had a favorable effect.

4. Finally, we experimented with human blood. Blood was taken from an arm vein and brought together with SAPA bions in the test tube. Microscopically, it could be clearly seen that the

erythrocytes gathered greedily around the individual SAPA bions, formed orgone bridges, and absorbed orgone energy. These observations were just as instructive as they were exciting. The erythrocytes became tauter, the blue orgone margin broadened, and the radiation (seen especially well with a blue filter) became very strong. Two groups of cancer mice were again injected, one group with centrifuged serum, free of erythrocytes, the other with serum containing erythrocytes. The effect on the cancer tumors in the mice was marked. However, the whole procedure required a substantial investment of time and effort. Sterile precautions had to be carefully observed; and in addition, intravenous injections into the tail veins of mice were not easily done.

5. We also tried to produce a "T-bacilli serum." We injected healthy rabbits with very small dosages of T-bacilli, took blood samples after eight days, filtered the blood, and injected the serum into cancer mice. We could see no satisfactory effects, though we had microscopically observed the formation of blue orgone energy vesicles in the clear, filtered serum when T-bacilli were added. We soon gave up the production of a specific T-bacilli serum. Equally unsuccessful were attempts to stimulate the formation of antibodies in the blood of mice and rabbits by the injection of autoclaved T-bacilli.

Of all the methods of indirectly administering orgone energy, the one that worked best was the injection of erythrocytes that had been previously charged orgonotically with SAPA bions. This method had the same effect as the direct injection of SAPA bions: Tumor tissue disintegrated into dead T-bodies, anemia improved, and in the autoclavation test the T-reaction of the blood was found to be replaced by a B-reaction.

The table on pages 304–305 provides a summary of the results of this experiment (also cf. Fig. 64-a through g, Appendix).

Of the 27 control mice specifically examined—in actual fact, we observed a far greater number of untreated cancer mice—8 died during the first week of our experiment. (This was approximately two weeks after the mice were found to be tumorous at the animal farm. The breeder of the mice assured us that he had examined each mouse carefully once a week, so the visible tumor could not have been older than seven days, at most, at the time of its discovery.) The majority of these 8 exhibited the full cancer syndrome: cachexia, sepsis, T-reaction, tumor growth, putrid disintegration of the cancer tissue, etc. During the second week, 5 cancer mice died. Two mice died every week from the third to the seventh week, and 1 every week between the eighth and the eleventh week. In other words, with untreated cancer mice the maximum life span after the appearance of a tumor was between 10 and 12 weeks. *Average* life span of these mice was, however, much lower, namely about 3.9 weeks.

By contrast, the average life expectancy of the 101 mice that received either direct or indirect bion treatment was 9.1 weeks. The average life span figure is computed by dividing the total number of weeks of post-tumor survival of *all* the treated cancer mice by the total number of mice. The actual figure should really be set slightly higher than 9.1, since we killed 47 of the 101 treated cancer mice to study the orgone effects on the tissues.[1] Only 54 of the 101 treated cancer mice died spontaneously. *The average life span of the treated cancer mice was therefore approximately 2.5 times longer than that of the untreated mice.* Whereas the longest life span for an untreated mouse was only 11 weeks, two of the mice treated with orgone energy lived for *28 weeks,* i.e., for a total of 7 *months after the appearance of the tumor.* This result was quite unusual and represented a very successful first experiment in applying orgone therapy in the treatment of cancer mice. Since the total life expectancy of a *healthy* mouse is only about 2.5 years, and most of the cancer mice were already five to eight months old when they came to us, we had prolonged their life span by roughly a quarter of their normal life expectancy. This prolongation would be equivalent to fifteen years in

[1] From a statistical standpoint, it might be argued that it is incorrect to include the killed mice in the calculation. It should be noted, however, that they were killed when they were obviously near death; thus, including them in the calculation does not modify the result materially.

	Method of Orgone Application	Number of Mice		Life Span in Weeks																	
				1	2	3	4	5	6	7	8	9	10	11	12	13	14	15	16	17	18
Group A	Injection of orgone energy vesicles (SAPA bion cultures, earth bions, etc.)	Died	54	2	2	5	2	3	3	9	3	2	7	1		3	2	1	1	1	1
		Killed for autopsy	47		3	4	5	6	1	4	3	3	4	1	1	5		2	2	1	1
	Injection of orgone-charged blood (from rabbit, tumor, etc.)	Total dead	101	2	5	9	7	9	4	13	6	5	11	2	1	8	2	3	3	2	2
Group B	Orgone energy accumulator		36		1	3	1	5	2	3	3	2			1	2	4	3		1	1
Group C	Untreated control mice		27	8	5	2	2	2	2	2	1	1	1	1							

Total number of mice used 164

a human life. These initial results were encouraging, even though they did not come close to providing a radical cancer therapy. It seemed justified that we should anticipate even better results in applying orgone therapy to the human organism. First of all *in relation to the size of the whole body*, a human tumor is much smaller than the tumor of a mouse. Moreover, the mouse is unable to communicate any pain or other symptoms that might indicate the formation of a tumor. Man also has at his disposal a wide range of medical aids to supplement orgone therapy: vegetotherapy, forced fluids, iron colloids, diet, vitamins, etc.

After Detection of Tumor																				Average Life Span	Maximum Life Span
19	20	21	22	23	24	25	26	27	28	29	30	31	32	33	34	35	36	37	38		
		2		1	1				2												
				1																	
	2			2	1				2											9.1 weeks	28 weeks
						1							2						1	11.1 weeks	38 weeks
																				3.9 weeks	11 weeks

This was the situation, in 1940, relative to our orgone therapy experiments on mice. I am not reporting here on the many efforts we made to fill the gaps in our knowledge and achieve better results. There was just *one* major difficulty, which we encountered again during later orgone therapy experiments on humans, that should be mentioned. Although we were able to destroy tumors by the orgonotic charging of the blood, the life or death of the treated mice depended essentially on *how successfully the dead tumor material was eliminated from the organism.* Many mice died during the course of these experiments not from the cancer tumor nor from

T-intoxication but rather—and here I might appropriately quote the notorious saying "operation successful, patient dead"—from the clogging of renal and lymph passages, or from the enormous enlargement of the liver and spleen. These organs have the responsibility for the elimination of the detritus. The clogging of the renal passages was especially typical. The larger the tumor that had disintegrated, the greater this particular danger. The mice did not die from cancer cachexia, nor from the putrefaction of the tissue and the blood. At the time of death, they looked well, had smooth fur, and were not emaciated. Death resulted from attempts to eliminate the tumor detritus. This extremely critical problem is still unsolved. If large tumors are destroyed too rapidly, the excretory organs become clogged; if they are destroyed slowly, secondary tumors are likely to develop. There is only one answer here: *The tumor must not be allowed to grow too large.* Clearly then, our blood test for early diagnosis of cancer (T-reaction, culture, etc.) acquires crucial significance.

I discovered atmospheric orgone energy in July 1940. Within a few months we constructed the orgone accumulator, which was designed to concentrate this energy. From various experiments it appeared that atmospheric orgone energy displayed the same properties as the orgone energy inside the bion vesicles that we injected into cancer mice. Therefore, instead of injecting the mice with bions, we placed them in the accumulator for a half-hour each day. Positive effects were recorded in an astonishingly short time. Mice thus treated with atmospheric orgone energy improved quickly; their fur became smooth and shiny, their eyes, bright, the organism as a whole, strong; the bent, contracted posture, typical of cancer mice, became straighter and the tumors either ceased to grow or receded. At first it seemed strange that such biological effects could be obtained simply by placing the mice in a small box lined on the inside with metal. Long after these effects had become a routine occurrence for us, we continued to note the astonished reaction of people who were visiting the laboratory. They searched for electrical wiring and complex machinery and were unable to understand how such a simple metal-lined box could influence cancer.

After several months it became evident, statistically, that the results we were obtaining from the treatment of mice with atmospheric orgone energy were *better* than those obtained from the bion-injection treatment. Altogether, 36 cancer mice were treated in the orgone accumulator. The average life span of the mice injected with orgone energy vesicles had been 9.1 weeks. The average life span of the mice treated in the orgone accumulator was *11.1* weeks. In the mice treated by injection, the maximum life span had been 28 weeks, or 7 months, from date of discovery of the tumor. *The maximum life span in mice treated with atmospheric orgone energy was 38 weeks, or approximately 9.5 months after discovery of the tumor.* This finding represented an important step forward. We had increased the life span of cancer mice from about one-quarter (7 months) to one-third (9.5 months) of their total life expectancy (about 30 months). This would be equivalent to prolonging human life for 20 years, even if normal human life expectancy is set as low as 60. Of course, it has to be noted that mice probably do not suffer, as humans do, from severe emotional biopathies, which tend to complicate the cancer process enormously. We were glad that it was no longer necessary to introduce foreign bodies into the organism. In addition, the treatment was much easier to prepare and carry out. While the mice were in the accumulator, we were free to work at other tasks. The whole discovery opened up new perspectives for a future cancer therapy for humans. In the event that the orgone accumulator proved effective and not damaging to normal tissue and blood, it might be possible to let healthy people, as well as sick people, have an accumulator in their own home. The first orgone accumulator designed for human use was built in December 1940. I will now present an account of the tests we made to establish whether or not atmospheric orgone energy, concentrated in the accumulator, would be damaging to *healthy* humans.

In order to investigate orgone effects I had been spending, over the past two years, several hours a day in a Faraday cage that had iron walls and thus functioned as an orgone accumulator. Not only did I not feel pain, or any other symptom, I actually felt robust. Some of the laboratory workers used the accumulator daily for at least a half-hour. Over a period of months, we had rabbits and mice spend several hours a day in it. Apart from a certain restlessness, we could ascertain no negative effects. Too long an exposure to concentrated orgone energy at any one time can cause dizziness and nausea in humans, but these symptoms disappear quickly in the open air.

A special experiment that we undertook disclosed a peculiar fact that nevertheless fit well into the overall view. In a grass infusion, under normal circumstances, protozoa develop profusely between the second and fifth day. We now placed grass infusions in a small orgone accumulator and found that *these infusions, treated with orgone energy produced no, or only minimal, protozoal development.* However, once protozoa and bacteria were fully developed and the normal grass structure largely destroyed, the accumulator did *not* have a killing effect on the protozoa. At first we could not understand this. The blood tests on cancer mice had clearly indicated that exposure to orgone energy in the accumulator charged the blood and eliminated the T-bacilli. Yet if we placed a T-bacilli culture in the accumulator, there was no killing effect. While this finding corresponded to the result of the experiment with grass infusions, it was incomprehensible.

Careful deliberation finally led to the following analysis of the process: The SAPA bions had also not exerted a *direct* killing effect on the cancer cells and the T-bacilli but had been effective *indirectly,* by charging the erythrocytes and the healthy tissue. Accordingly, the orgone energy in the accumulator charged the fresh grass tissue in the infusion and by so doing delayed its disintegration into protozoa. If there was *no healthy tissue* to be charged, the killing effect on protozoa was also absent; in the absence of healthy tissue, the orgone energy simply charged the protozoa biologically. Clearly, the orgone experiments cannot be understood with the rigid prejudice of mechanistic thinking. *Healthy, vigorous orgone systems capable of absorbing a strong orgonotic charge must be present for the elimination of protozoal or bacterial foreign bodies, or for the prevention of their development.* It is a fundamental law in orgone physics that the *stronger orgonotic system always attracts the weaker and withdraws a charge from it* (which is the exact opposite of what happens with electrical charge, where the energy always flows from the stronger to the weaker system). The tissue or blood of a human or a mouse is a much stronger orgonotic system than that of protozoa, cancer cells, or T-bacilli: hence, its killing power. Normally, this killing effect is not dependent on any absorption of additional orgone energy from external sources. But healthy tissue and blood, in their struggle against cancer cells and T-bacilli, lose increasing amounts of orgone energy, causing anemia and loss of weight. *If the organism is supplied regularly with concentrated orgone energy from the outside, it will not need to consume its own body energy.* In this case, cachexia and anemia either do not occur or are eliminated.

The experiment with grass infusions confirmed, in an interesting and important way, the concept of the effect of orgone energy on tissues and blood. However, a whole series of important questions still need to be answered experimentally.

In the application of atmospheric orgone energy, we encountered precisely the same obstacles we found in our experiments with bion injections. Many of the mice died of a clogging of the excretory organs, *without* developing anemia or cachexia. This problem will be discussed in more detail later, in connection with the orgone therapy experiments with humans.

I shall now proceed with the description of the application of therapy in human cancer. Before doing so, I want to emphasize once again that I am not offering any *final solutions;* I am merely submitting a report of my important findings, even though they are punctuated by gaps, doubts, and uncertainties.

CHAPTER VIII

Results of Experimental Orgone Therapy in Humans with Cancer

1. ORGONOTIC CELL LUMINATION: THE EFFECT OF THE ORGONE ACCUMULATOR AND THE THERAPEUTIC FACTOR

The reader who is unfamiliar with the orgone therapy experiments may view claims for the therapeutic value of the orgone energy accumulator with disbelief. It seems implausible that one can derive any beneficial effect from sitting in an unimpressive-looking cabinet, simply constructed with outer walls of organic material and inner ones of metal, that is designed to absorb orgone energy from the air. It seems even more unbelievable when one realizes that the accumulator contains no sophisticated components, wiring, buttons, or motors. Not only that, but orgone energy, which has been found to have such significant effects upon the shrinking biopathy, does not have to be purchased. The Orgone Institute* has sought to prevent any profiteering in the application of this energy. The incredulity that can be expected in response to the simplicity of the device and its use will have to be countered by careful documentation.

The fact that atmospheric orgone energy is *concentrated* within the orgone accumulator is demonstrated by the physical and biological effects it exerts; but its therapeutic effect on the living orga-

* The Orgone Institute was not an organization but simply the name under which Reich conducted his work. It ceased to exist upon his death in 1957. [Ed.]

nism is not thereby explained. We will attempt in this chapter to obtain a clearer picture of this phenomenon.

Not much was actually known about the nature of orgone energy during our initial experiments with its therapeutic effects in early 1941. It had, of course, been made visible, and the existence of differences in temperature and in electroscopic discharge had been discovered, even if they had not yet been fully elaborated. The fact of the concentration of the energy was therefore established, but the mechanism of its therapeutic effect was still unexplained. Our working hypothesis at the time was that the concentrated orgone in the accumulator penetrated the naked body and in that way charged the blood and the tissues biologically. But over the following two years, many observations were made that provided a different and better explanation.

In scientific research, isolated facts have no importance. Consequently, there is a tendency to adorn unconnected facts with names, as in the theory of "static electricity," and then to believe, erroneously, that they are understood. People find an "interpretation" for every single one of these facts, without providing any overall context in which to see their true correlation. It is different when the congruity of many facts spontaneously yields a single concept that is inescapable, indispensable, and brings together the many diverse findings into a functioning unity. If this single concept not only elucidates the functional connection of the facts but also makes a variety of interpretations, explanations, etc. unnecessary, and if, in addition, it *discloses new facts*, then the theory can be regarded as satisfactory.

Although many so-called pragmatists regard the postulation of theories as a "philosophical luxury," it is in fact a scientific tool comparable to the ordering of the instruments to be used in a surgical operation. The arrangement of the instruments is just as germane to the outcome of the operation as is each individual instrument. The best surgeon in the world could hardly perform a successful operation if he always had to look around the operating room for every instrument he needed. Just as there is improvement in the way one arranges tools, there is, in the formation of theories, a progressive improvement in the way one arranges the facts. Theories, therefore, can never form a perfect system and will always remain incomplete and in need of improvement. This principle also applies to the following account of the therapeutic effect of accumulated orgone energy.

Our initial hypothesis that the orgone energy in the accumulator simply penetrates the organism left a few facts unexplained. Some patients reacted immediately to the orgone radiation, while others needed repeated exposure before any effects were felt. If the effect were dependent simply on a mechanical penetration of the organism, then every organism should react in the same way. Since reactions were not the same, an explanation was needed.

We made the assumption that the organism is penetrated by the orgone energy, while itself remaining passive and uninvolved, as happens during irradiation with X-rays or radium. Both of these radiation treatments involve the application of an energy that is non-biological in nature, i.e., an energy basically alien to the body, because the organism does not emit either X-rays or radium rays. Atmospheric orgone energy, however, is *an organic, specifically biological energy*. It is absorbed constantly by the organism directly from the air and sun, through the skin and by pulmonary ventilation. The organism therefore contains orgone energy in all its cells and body fluids, and constantly radiates it. When the organism is in the accumulator, two orgonotic systems come together in a functional relationship. We know this today; we did not know it in 1941. To understand the functional relationship between two orgonotic systems, it is necessary to refer to my earlier account of the observations on bions (orgone energy vesicles) (*cf.* Chapter II).

As we know, an erythrocyte and an earth bion each form a self-contained orgonotic system. The constituents of such a system, seen biophysically, are a *bio-energetic nucleus*, a *plasmatic periphery*, and an *orgone energy field* surrounding the organism. In diagram form it would look like this:

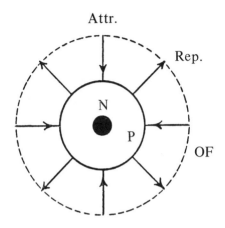

N: biological nucleus
P: plasmatic periphery
OF: orgone energy field
Attr.: orgone absorption or charge
Rep.: orgone emission or discharge

FIGURE 24.   Schematic presentation of the living "orgonotic system"

If two orgonotic systems move close to each other, contact is established between their energy fields, resulting in mutual *excitation* and *attraction*. This reaction is evidenced by their moving closer to each other. The erythrocytes group themselves around the heavier, and therefore less motile, earth bion. Once the erythrocytes are close enough, a bridge of orgone energy, strongly refractile, is formed. The biological nuclei of the two orgonotic systems now begin to radiate more strongly, a phenomenon we call "orgonotic lumination." It is the same phenomenon observed by traditional biology in cell division, referred to as "mitogenetic radiation." All the fundamental bio-energetic processes, such as sexual excitation, orgasm, cell fusion, and cell division, are accompanied by a high degree of bio-energetic excitation, that is, by *orgonotic lumination*. In living matter, substantial quantities of energy are discharged during this process. "Sexual contact" between two living organisms striving toward the sexual act represents, in orgone-physical terms, this same process of the formation of an *orgone bridge* and *orgonotic lumination* between the two bodies (orgonotic systems). Many biologists (Burr, among them) have demonstrated the existence of an energy field surrounding living cells and multicellular organisms, outside the material boundary of the organism itself. It is considered to be an electromagnetic energy field. In orgone physics, however, we contend that this field of energy surrounding the organism has nothing to do with electromagnetism and is in reality an *orgone energy field,* i.e., *a field of specific biological energy*. It functions at a distance, without the need for material contact between the body surfaces of the organisms. My own experiments with the oscillograph and the recently constructed orgone energy field meter have shown not only that such an energy field exists but also that its area of radiation varies considerably from individual to individual, from as little as a few centimeters to as much as four meters (according to observations made up to now). It also varies with any given organism; i.e., it expands and contracts. These functions of the energy field are dependent upon the emotional state of the organism. In orgonotic cell lumination, for example, there is always a considerable expansion of the energy field.

Thus, even in two such widely divergent relationships as that between an erythrocyte and an earth bion and that between the orgone accumulator and the living organism seated inside it, we are actually dealing with one and the same phenomenon. However, there is one essential difference. In the first relationship, a radiating bridge forms only where the surfaces make contact with each other, whereas *in the case of the accumulator, the orgone energy field of the non-living orgonotic system completely envelops the orgone energy field of the living orgonotic system.* The following diagram will illustrate this process:

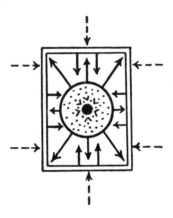

Contact between the orgone energy fields of the organism and of the orgone accumulator (solid arrows). The dotted arrows on the outside show the attraction of the atmospheric orgone energy. Effect: lumination of the organism

What facts are there to confirm this theoretical assumption?

1. The effects of the orgone accumulator are weakened and sometimes eliminated if its inner walls are more than 4–8 inches from the surface of the organism. Ignorance of this fact was the cause of a series of therapeutic failures. For example, when mice were treated in accumulators built for humans, the effects on them were poor. They improved as soon as we built small accumulators,

measuring approximately 8–12 inches. At present, we use even smaller accumulators but have increased the number of layers of organic material and metal. A four-year-old boy with bone cancer failed to react as favorably as adults suffering from bone cancer; he had been treated in an accumulator built for adults. The objection has been frequently raised that electrophysicists who work in Faraday cages would have had to experience the accumulator effect. Our answer to this objection is simply that a wire cage, many meters in width, cannot be a biologically effective orgone accumulator. For instance, I can stay much longer in my experimental accumulator, which is 3 × 2 meters, than in the therapeutic accumulator, which measures 2 × 2 1/2 *feet.*

2. In vegetative (orgonotic) terms, lively persons feel the effects of the orgone energy in the accumulator far more rapidly than do sluggish individuals. The former have a more extensive orgone energy field than the latter; thus, the contact between the orgone energy fields of their bodies and that of the metal inner walls of the accumulator is established far more rapidly and easily.

3. Orgonotically sluggish individuals begin to notice the effects of an exposure to orgone radiation in the accumulator only after several irradiations. There can be only one explanation for this phenomenon: the organism itself must be charged passively to a certain minimal degree and its own orgone radiation intensified before subjective perception of the orgone effect is possible. One physician was unable to feel the typical prickling and warmth in the palms of the hands for the first few months of his use of the accumulator. He began to feel them only after he had started to use the accumulator regularly. In other words, his organism at first remained passive, but after a while "stretched out," as it were, toward the orgone field of the metal walls.

These experiences are of immense importance for an understanding not only of the effects of accumulated orgone energy but also of the orgonotic reactions of the organism. We are still a long way from a complete comprehension.

4. The metal inner walls of the accumulator are *cold*. But if the palm of the hand is held long enough at a distance of about 4 centimeters from the walls, a delicate prickling and warmth are felt. (The objective temperature differences in the accumulator have been comprehensively reported in Chapter IV.) The assumption has to be made that the feelings of warmth and prickling are the subjective result of the impact of orgone energy particles on the skin. This fact has great significance for an understanding of the sensation of warmth with orgone irradiation.

In 1942 an important phenomenon was discovered which has a decisive connection with the body lumination in the accumulator: *Body temperature rises in the accumulator* as much as *one degree centigrade* (the rapidity and amount of increase varying from individual to individual). If the body temperature before irradiaton is close to the fever point, it will climb beyond this point in the accumulator. Thus, *orgone energy can produce mild fever.*

Temperature rise in the organism is known to be a fundamental excitation reaction of the cells and the blood. Until now it has not been understood. The temperature rise in the accumulator is indicative of lumination of the orgonotic body system. The blood and other cell systems luminate during contact with the orgone energy field of the accumulator by a process analogous to that which occurs in the contact between two bions. This contact between two orgonotic systems leads to an increase in the *orgone energy metabolism* of the organism, and it is to this metabolic increase that we must ascribe the restorative and enlivening effect of orgone therapy. In sequence, the essential stages of the process are: contact between two energy fields; interpenetration; cell lumination; increase in orgone energy metabolism. They correspond exactly to the characteristic phases of important biological processes such as copulation and conjugation. Thus, in orgone therapy we are dealing with sexual energy processes in the strictest biophysical sense of the word, and only the realization of this fact can explain why so many patients, suffering from a standstill of their biological energy metabolism, develop sexual excitations and sexual stasis while undergoing orgone therapy. More will be said on this subject during discussions of specific cases.

Our accumulator, made with organic substance on the outside and with sheet metal on the inside, is therefore not at all the unremarkable box it seems to be. It is, in fact, a biologically highly active system that will provide us with considerable material for thought in another context.

The repeated luminations of the organism brought about by the orgone accumulator manifest themselves also in the gradual intensification of biological energy in the erythrocytes, enabling them to radiate more strongly, gain in turgor, destroy cancer cells, kill T-bacilli, etc., all of which they were incapable of doing while still orgonotically weak. From one point of view, orgone therapy could also be designated as a natural *fever therapy*, if fever is understood correctly as a sign of intensified bio-energetic activity of the organism. This interpretation would create a framework within which many frequently applied but little understood curative methods in medicine would become more comprehensible. The malaria therapy against general paresis developed by my teacher Wagner-Jauregg, in Vienna, is basically the artificial stimulation of strong cellular lumination through the injection of malaria parasites. Hot tea with rum against colds and the "hot compress" for toothache are treatments that belong in this category. What confronts us now is the task of understanding the effects of many chemotherapeutic techniques from this standpoint and thereby making it possible to distinguish the drugs that are beneficial from those that are damaging. A drug that kills the bacilli but simultaneously damages the blood cells and the plasma system, rather than strengthening them, should not be permitted, even if powerful vested interests lobby against such controls. It can only be the lumination within the organism that quickly reduces or even eliminates pains of all kinds.

Observations to date suggest that the cell lumination produced in the organism by the orgone accumulator is the real and essential therapeutic factor. This cell lumination exercises an effect on the cancer cells and the T-bacilli in the organism that is as destructive as the paralyzing effect exerted by the strong orgone radiation of SAPA bions on T-bacilli and motile cancer cells, which I have observed microscopically and filmed. It is to be expected that further experiments using different arrangements of materials will considerably increase the radiation effect of the orgone accumulator. What is most important is to find ways of shortening the duration of individual irradiations while achieving greater rises in body temperatures.

The results of orgone therapy in human cancer, which I will now present, are incomplete. I would have gladly postponed their publication until more cases had been treated, but it was felt that the general effort to master cancer would receive a decided impetus if this analysis of the mechanism of the carcinomatous biopathy were explained, the fundamental question of the formation of cancer cells elucidated, and the effects of the newly discovered orgone energy made known.

The first cancer patients to submit to the orgone experiment were accepted at my Orgone and Cancer Research Laboratory in Forest Hills only under the condition that their physicians had no objection to the experiment and that their relatives signed the following statement:

> I state herewith that I came to Dr. Wilhelm Reich for possible help in the case of my _____ who suffers from cancer. I came because I was told of the experiments that Dr. Reich has made with cancer mice and human beings. Dr. Reich did not promise me any cure, did not charge any money, and told me that only during the last few months has he tried the orgone radiation on human beings who suffer from cancer . . . Death or abscesses could occur as a consequence of the disease. I told Dr. Reich that the physicians have given up the case of my _____ as hopeless. Should death or abscesses occur during the time of the experiment, it will not be because of the treatment.

I would like to describe the disappointments and failures we experienced, if for no other reason than to forestall the impression that we now have a cure-all, the means to "cure" cancer under any circumstances. Understanding of the failures is vital to any future efforts to broaden and develop the beneficial effects of orgone therapy. The following examples will demonstrate the types of difficulty and failures we encountered.

Case M. F., a fifty-seven-year-old widow came to us with numerous tumors, predominantly in the cranium and in the bones of the arms. She was compulsively religious. She also suffered from hypochondria and masochistic complaining. Seventeen years previously her uterus had been extirpated because of tumors. About two years previously pains developed in her neck, the top of her head, and her lower back. She slept poorly and lost her appetite. It was difficult to separate her hypochondriacal complaining from her genuine complaints about acute cancer pains. She was able to walk only with support; her skin was clammy and livid, feet and hands cold and sweaty. The hemoglobin content of her blood was 33%. The blood tests were all cancer-positive: T-bacilli growth, T-reaction on autoclavation, rapid shrinking of the red blood corpuscles in physiological saline. The tumors in the cranium were palpable and hard. The diagnosis of cancer had been confirmed at Memorial Hospital.

The patient came for orgone treatment daily for eight weeks. On the third day the hemoglobin content of her blood was 41%, on the sixth day, 55%, on the eighth day, 85%. The hemoglobin remained normal for four weeks, then dropped to 78% and stayed at approximately that level. The T-reactions were positive for about three weeks. After four weeks there were no more T-bacilli in the blood; but the T-disintegration of the erythrocytes, which had been almost 100% at the beginning, was 35% after seven weeks.

The palpable tumors in the cranium became distinctly smaller and softened. Nosebleeds developed. The blood was a brownish color and contained characteristic tumor material. The pains subsided, sleep and appetite improved. She began to like the accumulator and wanted to have one at home in order to spare herself the daily journey. I could not accede to her wish, however, because I still had too little experience with the effects of orgone therapy on human cancer.

After two months the patient developed tensions in the upper thighs, in the deep adductor muscles. Moreover, she seemed reluctant to use the accumulator, which I, at first, did not understand. At about the same time, the first cancer patient, whose case I described earlier, reacted to the orgone radiation with sexual stasis. I therefore thought it justified to assume that this patient too had been charged sexually and that the spasms in the deep adductor of the upper thigh were a direct reaction. Her hypochondria intensified. She had no cancer pain but became querulous. Her relatives could not tolerate her any more and the patient went into a home for the aged. The orgone treatment was interrupted. A new set of X-rays clearly showed reduction and calcification of the tumors in the upper arm and in the cranium. But the patient's neurosis complicated the cancer therapy. After a few months of distinct improvement in her condition, she died. The orgone therapy had prolonged her life for a few months and her pains had been alleviated.

Like the other cancer patients, she had also presented a picture of total emotional resignation, a factor that had been noticed also by her relatives. Her nephew once said to me, "She has nothing to live for." It seemed quite clear that the patient died because her "instinct for life" had never functioned correctly and her vital system gave up for want of joy in life.

Case C. K., thirty-three years old, was receiving medical treatment for a colostomy which had been carried out because of a cancer of the colon. The patient reported that she had always been constipated, even as a small child, and had always been anemic. In the summer of 1939 she began to suffer from a "dysentery" that coincided with every menstrual period thereafter. In 1940 she had intestinal hemorrhages. Previous to that, for many months, she suffered from unbearable pains in the rectum. Constant use of analgesic rectal suppositories and codeine by mouth provided no more than very temporary relief.

When we accepted this case at the laboratory on May 7, 1941, the patient was in a desperate state. Her cachexia was far advanced, and although she was tall, she weighed only 115 lbs. It was immediately apparent that she was suffering from a severe sexual biopathy. She had an anxious expression and suffered from anxiety dreams. Her husband had died eight years before and ever since that date she had lived in total abstinence. Even during her marriage her husband had been constantly sick and "too weak to pay attention to such things." The colostomy had intensified her nervous state. She believed she would faint when she passed intestinal gas without being able to control it. She suffered from insomnia, which had started long before her cancer appeared. During her attacks of anxiety, spasms occurred in her throat and anus; she "thought she would die."

This case had been diagnosed as cancer by several private physicians and also at the hospital.

Results of the tests were as follows: hemoglobin, 72%, autoclavation test, 99% T-reaction. Red blood corpuscles were pale, orgone margins narrow; degeneration was gradual, but with distinct T-spike formation. Culture from the intestinal excreta showed a strong T-reaction, numerous rot bacteria, formed cancer cells up to amoeboid forms.

Two days after the initiation of orgone irradiation, the hemoglobin content climbed to 82% and remained there. After about two weeks, the blood picture was vastly improved. The intestinal excreta now showed only a few fully formed cancer cells, but heaps of destroyed cancer cells and non-motile T-bodies. At the end of four weeks, the T-reaction of the blood on autoclavation was only 5%, or, in other words, a B-reaction of 95%.

Her pains had already decreased considerably after the fifth irradiation. The patient was able to get through the night with only *one* codeine tablet, which had never been possible before, and she was able to sleep. After the twelfth orgone irradiation, she stopped using the rectal suppositories, and during the following six weeks she needed to use them only twice. In addition, she no longer took codeine. Her appetite improved, but she did not put on any weight.

On May 29 examination of rectal excretions showed total absence of formed cancer cells and the presence only of cancer detritus, non-motile T-bodies, etc. The excretion was no longer gray but brownish, an indication of disintegrated blood from the tumor.

After the twelfth orgone irradiation, itching of the anus occurred. The patient perspired freely in the accumulator and her skin lost its pallor. She was free of pain, slept well, walked about, and enjoyed the company of friends, etc.

The patient continued the treatment with short interruptions until July 28, 1941. She was still free of pain and felt well. At the beginning of August she stopped coming for treatment. In the middle of September she told me over the telephone that she still had no pain and felt well, but that she could no longer come for treatment. On September 30 I wrote a letter to her relatives refusing to accept any responsibility for the future fate of the patient. I then discovered that it was her neurosis that prevented her from coming for treatment. Ever since puberty she had suffered from severe claustrophobia and for that reason was unable to use the subway to come to our laboratory. Her relationship to her close relatives was extraordinarily poor. Frequently I had the impression that their deep, unconscious hatred actually made them hope for her early death. They had no time for her and made the fact that she was a burden so clear that, in her quiet, resigned state, she no longer asked to be brought to the laboratory by car. I knew she was doomed, but I could do nothing. The family situation could not be overcome, and I did not feel free to give the patient an accumulator to use at home because her own physician was hostile, even though on May 24 he had admitted to her brother the improvement in her condition. When the patient had first begun the orgone treatment, this physician had threatened to report me to the police and refused to let me have the patient's case history. During the summer of 1942 I heard that the patient had died.

Her death was clearly due to the shrinking biopathy. Her condition had been greatly alleviated for a number of months by the orgone treatment, and her life prolonged by about one year. This case showed, however, that orgone therapy is not independent of social and family conditions.

2. OPEN QUESTIONS CONCERNING ORGONE THERAPY FOR CANCER

Orgone therapy will be capable of eliminating a series of cancerous afflictions or preventing their development, but it will never be able to master the cancer scourge by itself. Orgone therapy is only one of the sex-economic measures in the struggle against biopathies. Orgone energy can charge tissues and bring about expansion of the vital apparatus. But when the social milieu continually forces the organism into contraction, resignation, shrinking, etc., then the use of orgone energy is like trying to fill a bottomless barrel with water.

For classification let us separate the specific use of orgone energy from the more general social measures involved in the therapeutic process. The practicing physician will be interested only in the therapeutic application of orgone energy. But he must never lose sight of the general social causation of biopathies if he wishes to treat the human organism as a product of both biological *and* social influences.

Orgone therapy for cancer offers several advantages over the methods of radium and X-ray irradiation and surgery. It is true that irradiation with X-rays can halt the growth of a tumor temporarily. But this kind of treatment is accompanied by a general biological weakening of the organism. It reduces the appetite and causes nausea and vomiting. Its effects are local and have no beneficial influence on the shrinking biopathy. The results obtained by local radium irradiation are better, but they are still superficial and, like X-ray treatment, leave the biopathy untouched. Surgical extirpation of a tumor admittedly has a radical local effect, but does not, however, impede the development of metastases or in any way modify the general process.

By contrast, orgone therapy has the tremendous advantage of applying a body-own energy that can reach every part of the body by way of the bloodstream. The orgonotic charging of the erythrocytes fulfills two important tasks at one stroke: *the general expansion of the organism and the establishment of the organism's own defense forces against the T-intoxication.* Provided the disintegration in the organism is not too advanced, there is usually an increase of appetite, halt in weight loss and even an increase in weight, reduction of nausea and pains, and strengthening of the blood reactions. The tumor is not immediately destroyed. The first effect is shown in the invigoration of the blood. The attack of the blood upon the tumor and upon the systemic T-infection does not take place until the general biological invigoration has reached a certain level. Therefore, the excretion of liquefied tumor masses, in the form of a brownish red liquid, does not occur for some weeks, and the T-cultures from the blood do not become negative until after weeks of treatment. In many cases with biologically weakened blood and severe anemia, a fresh supply of young erythrocytes develops prior to the attack on the tumor; this process can be observed microscopically. Breast tumors have been known to disappear after about two to three weeks.

Our experience so far indicates that no matter where they are localized, the tumors always soften. As gratifying as this is, the fact remains that the cancer therapy becomes complicated precisely by the *destruction* of the tumors in cases where the detritus cannot be absorbed or eliminated. The process is familiar to us from our experiments on mice. Orgonotically strong blood flows into the tumor and the cancer tissue disintegrates. Large blood-filled cavities develop, which can even enlarge the tumor. A brown, non-putrid fluid composed of gigantic masses of inactive T-bodies collects in the cavities, exactly as in the case of orgone-treated mice. This can be observed microscopically by a study of the excreta. The outcome of the case now depends upon whether or not these enormous masses of waste materials of destroyed cancer tissue can be eliminated from the organism. A brain tumor in a woman was destroyed within two weeks. The intracranial pressure was reduced; the peripheral signs receded. But the tumor detritus clogged the lymph glands of the neck and the patient died, according to the report of her doctor, of *suffocation* from glottis edema.

Another woman, who had a stomach tumor the size of an apple, responded extremely well to our orgone therapy. The tumor, which was palpable, softened and became noticeably smaller. But, after eight weeks, the renal passages became clogged; her legs became edematous, the heart became affected, and the patient died of cardiac decompensation. In the case of this particular patient, the excretion of the waste products through the intestines was theoretically possible, but the patient suffered from chronic constipation. Consequently the intestines were unable to handle the elimination, and most of the waste products were absorbed into the blood-stream.

A third woman, who had an ovarian tumor, died of kidney complications after reacting to the orgone therapy with improvement of her general condition and with softening and recession of the tumor.

In the case of a five-year-old boy with an adrenal tumor and metastases in the spine, the X-ray pictures showed calcification of the bone defects after four weeks, and the primary tumor in the left adrenal gland was no longer palpable after two weeks of treatment. But the decomposed tumor pulp from the spine clogged the spinal canal and the boy developed a flaccid paralysis of the legs. He died later of hypertrophic degeneration of the liver, an apparent outcome of the failure of the process of elimination.

Enlargement of the liver with degeneration of the liver cells and clogging of the renal passages are the most frequent and typical results of the destruction of the tumor in cases where the destroyed tumorous tissue mass is not eliminated quickly and easily. We do not yet know any answer to this problem. It is correct but not very helpful to say that the tumor should not be allowed to grow beyond a certain size. Ways and means have to be found to deal with these secondary manifestations in cases that come for treatment so late. I would like to remind the reader that none of the cancer patients treated in the Orgone and Cancer Research Laboratory came to us immediately after discovery of the tumor. All had spent two or more years in other forms of treatment; all were terminal cases. We therefore do not know whether many tumors would not disappear without such secondary manifestations if the patients came to us *immediately after discovery of the tumor.* With smaller tumors, the mass of waste material would also be smaller and the danger of clogging the excretory passages therefore reduced.

It should be stressed here that the biological strength of the blood cannot be judged according to its hemoglobin content. We have encountered cases where the hemoglobin content was 80% and the T-reaction on autoclavation 100%. Since it is the T- and B-reactions of the blood that indicate its biological resistance, they must be regarded as essentially independent of the iron content of the blood.

In addition, I would like to consider briefly a few *sex-economic* problems in orgone therapy for cancer which have great practical importance. We are now aware that sexual resignation is active in the background of the carcinomatous shrinking biopathy. Patients come to us, therefore, with a pronounced *libido deficiency.* Orgone treatment brings about a reduction of the pains and an orgonotic charging of the blood system. These two effects lead in many cases to a reawakening of sexual excitation. If the repressions and armoring are very marked, the patient will not be aware of the sexual excitation. He will express it in a way understandable only to the sex-economist, namely in the appearance of acute anxiety, in genital spasms, in "heaviness" in the thigh and pelvic musculature, or simply by fleeing from the "weird" orgone radiation (which happened in two cases). In other cases, where the sexual life had not completely ceased and where the patient was still having sexual intercourse (though without orgastic potency, of course), the difficulties were more easily approached. Here the disturbance in the sexual life mostly takes the form of harmful practices and inhibitions as a consequence of ignorance. For instance, a man with cancer of the rectum developed pains in the testicles and spermatic ducts after his general condition had improved. He attributed the new pains to his disease, but I recognized their stasis character and was able to relieve them. His wife refused him sexual intercourse. He was too sick to look for gratification elsewhere and masturbation did not occur to him. During a consultation, attended also by his brother, who was very understanding, he realized that his pains were caused by genital stasis and that his only recourse was to masturbation. After a short time, the pains disappeared.

Another patient suffering from cancer of the urinary bladder sporadically developed violent pains in the pelvis, different from the pains caused by the tumor *before* the orgone treatment. I tried to obtain a clear picture of his sexual situation. For fifteen years the man had not had any sexual intercourse with his wife and for the past five years he had experienced no sexual gratification at all. I cannot say for sure whether this stasis had any direct influence upon the development of the bladder cancer, but it could be assumed that it did. I discussed the matter with him and he realized it was imperative to eliminate the genital stasis. His pains then disappeared so rapidly that there could be no doubt about the connection. All the more incomprehensible therefore is the medical attitude expressed in a review of the first issue of our journal: "One may reasonably object to the recommendation to practice masturbation in order to achieve relaxation of the genital apparatus." Why should there be such an objection? I do not believe there can be any rational argument against this measure. Moreover, I am of the opinion that much more attention should be paid to the pains and stasis conditions in the genital apparatus of cancer patients, as the two cases just mentioned so clearly reveal.

The greatest difficulty confronting orgone treatment of cancer is the general biopathic background of the disease. The shrinking of the entire autonomic system touches upon the very roots of the life functions. We, therefore, have to be prepared for great difficulties in any efforts to deal with this problem. The reader will no doubt have weighed the significance of the findings in the cancer case described in the chapter on "The Carcinomatous Shrinking Biopathy": *the organism shrank even after the local tumors had been eliminated.* This outcome shifted the whole emphasis of the cancer problem from the local tumor to the general shrinking. But, in this area, it is a question not only of biological problems but of social and sex-economic problems as well. It is as yet too early to say to what extent, if any, orgone therapy can counteract the tendency to general shrinking. It will probably depend on whether and to what degree the general sex-economic way of life of the patient can be improved. Additional practical experiences are needed before any conclusive observations can be made.

I have so far been reporting only the difficulties of orgone therapy and the problems impeding it. Let us now turn to its achievements, which are unequivocal and gratifying:

Case S. T., forty-two years old, came for orgone therapy on April 30, 1941. In February 1938 she had undergone a radical mastectomy of the left breast for cancer. Two months after leaving the hospital, tumors developed on each leg below the knees. The pains were severe and it was difficult for her to walk. She therefore stayed in bed most of the time. Even before the mastectomy, she had suffered from "rheumatic" pains in the legs. Her big toes had felt "numb." She had also suffered, for years, from "pulling" pains in the arms, fingertips, and in the neck. Headaches and dizzy spells had been a constant source of suffering long before the operation. She suffered also from obstipation. She had been through five premature deliveries and three miscarriages. Due to X-ray treatment, menstruation had ceased six months prior to her coming to us. The leg tumors were growing slowly but steadily. The pains always intensified when the weather was bad. Her arms were so weak that she often had to support one with the other when lifting something. Ever since her breast operation, her left arm had been swollen and painful.

Here before us was the typical disease history of a biopathy. Examination confirmed this picture. The entire neck musculature was severely hypertonic. The thorax was held high, expiration was almost completely inhibited, the neck was rigid and held in an attitude of defiance. The abdominal musculature was hard and could not be pressed in. The leg tumors were about the size of walnuts.

Blood test: Hemoglobin 80%; autoclavation test and Gram stain showed a 40% T-reaction. T-cultures were +++, with numerous rot bacteria. The erythrocytes were pale, with narrow orgone margin, but without T-spikes. Disintegration occurred within five minutes.

Vaginal secretion: T-bacilli, +++, with numerous rot bacteria and T-bacilli visible microscopically.

By May 4 she was able to walk better. The feeling of numbness in her arms and legs disappeared. The leg tumors were visibly smaller. On May 6 her physician confirmed the reduction in the size of the tumors and advised the patient to continue her treatment with us. She wrote to her son about the noticeable improvement in her condition. She was no longer bedridden, in fact, was able to walk around and do a little shopping. By May 7 the tumor below the left knee had disappeared and the tumor below the right knee was scarcely palpable. Her reactions in the accumulator intensified: she began to perspire warmly, indicating that a vagotonic response had been achieved. Her weight remained constant at about 173 lbs.

X-ray findings: Before coming to us, there were numerous shadowy areas in the bony structures, especially in the pelvic bones. On June 20, 1941, the X-rays showed considerable lightening of these dark areas, especially in the pelvis. *The knees were normal.*

The patient remained almost free of pain during the subsequent months, she no longer required morphine, lost no weight, and was able to do her housework without difficulty. She discontinued the orgone treatment in December 1941. In January 1943 she was still alive and well. It is not possible to predict if the cancerous process will set in again. It should be noted that the patient did not have an accumulator at home.

Case F. H., a forty-five-year-old man, came to our laboratory on April 19, 1941. One year before, a pulling pain which "choked him" had developed in the chest. Since then he had lost 25 lbs. He could no longer eat solid foods and could take fluids only by the teaspoonful, and with great difficulty at that. He suffered from a diaphragmatic tic ("hiccups") and insomnia, and he quickly became extremely tired when working. The *emotional* nature of this case was described in the chapter on "The Carcinomatous Shrinking Biopathy."

The diagnosis by the patient's physician was *inoperable cancer of the esophagus,* with almost total constriction of the lumen, confirmed by X-ray. The epigastrium was tense and the patient suffered from severe constipation. The thorax did not move with respiration. He weighed 144 lbs.

Blood Test: Hemoglobin, 70%, T-culture, +++, T-reactions, 95%. Erythrocytes with T-spikes showed immediate bionous disintegration, then transformed into small erythrocytes with homogenous cytoplasm.

The patient's reaction to the orgone accumulator was immediate and strong: warm perspiration, reddening of the skin, a feeling of fogginess after twenty minutes' exposure.

On April 28 the hemoglobin was 85% and remained at that level for the following months. Over the same period of time, the patient's weight increased by about 5 lbs. His fatigue was gone, and he was able to swallow soft solids (tenderized meat, noodle soup, etc.). *The T-reaction on May 9th was only 10%.* The choking feeling had disappeared; he slept well and was able to work without tiring. The skin became tanned. The patient was extremely happy and grateful. The orgone treatment lasted approximately twelve weeks. Two years later the patient was still alive and working. However, in this case, too, a relapse could occur.

Summary

Altogether, thirteen cases of cancer diagnosed at hospitals and given X-ray treatment and two cases I diagnosed were closely observed and treated with orgone irradiation. All cases, when accepted, were already in advanced stages of cachexia. In every case the cancer pains were alleviated and the use of morphine was considerably reduced, in some cases even eliminated. Recession of the tumors and improvement of the general condition of the blood and the weight factor were achieved in every case. Breast tumors were eliminated in all cases; reduction of size and softening occurred in all other tumors.

In four cases, X-rays showed calcification of the bone defects. In most cases, elimination of the destroyed tumor material was successful. In three cases, the orgone treatment did not improve life expectancy. In six cases, the orgone treatment delayed the process of death by five to twelve months and made the last few months of life considerably more bearable. In six cases, the process of shrinking was halted. In six cases, the capability for working was restored. Five out of fourteen cases diagnosed as inoperable and terminal were still living two years after the orgone treatment was completed, and were in tolerable to good condition. In one case, the orgone treatment had no effect in eliminating ascitic fluid in the abdominal cavity.

These results were encouraging even if far from satisfactory, and made us feel a responsibility toward continuation of the work. Compared with the condition of the patients before they began the orgone treatment, the results must be regarded as *surprisingly good*. However, the problem of the elimination of the destroyed tumor pulp remains unsolved.

The results confirmed the fundamental correctness of the bion research and, in addition, formed the juncture at which the T-mice experiments, the orgone blood tests, the tension-charge formula, and the findings to date in orgone biophysics proved to be correct and consequential.

3. FIVE YEARS' EXPERIENCE WITH PHYSICAL ORGONE THERAPY

It seems appropriate at this time to offer a brief summary of the results I obtained over a period of five years with the application of physical orgone therapy in diseases other than cancer. As astonishing as the therapeutic successes have been, equally great has been the mystical expectation that any new form of therapy tends to inspire in the general public. People expect to be freed of all misery, cured of every ailment, and even to be provided access immediately and effortlessly to some earthly paradise. Physical orgone therapy, i.e., the specific use of the orgone energy accumulator, is far removed from such views. It works with a new form of energy discovered only a few years ago and not yet sufficiently investigated and tested, namely cosmic orgone energy. Caution is therefore essential. Honest physicians, genuinely dedicated to their profession, are so disillusioned by the raucous propaganda of the pharmaceutical industry and so mistrustful of all kinds of "cures" that a genuine new therapy has difficulty gaining acceptance. Moreover, classical medicine is helpless in the face of biopathies, the diseases of the autonomic life apparatus which no drugs can affect. Orgone energy, on the other hand, has proven its effectiveness with precisely these diseases. For that reason, as the reader will understand, I took steps to keep orgone therapy outside the framework of everyday routine clinical practice, mainly to avoid certain temptations and mistakes:

1. In all my publications on the subject of the cancer biopathy, I emphasized the deep-rootedness of cancer and the failures of our treatment compared to isolated

astonishing successes. In traditional medicine the failures are not talked about.

2. The use of orgone accumulators was removed from all suspicion of profiteering by the creation of a foundation administered as a charitable organization.

3. Use of the usual propaganda methods for bringing the therapy before the public was avoided.

4. No cure was promised the users of the orgone accumulator. The decision about its effectiveness was left to the patient.

Physical orgone therapy is applied in the following ways:

IRRADIATION OF THE TOTAL ORGANISM IN THE ORGONE ACCUMULATOR

The patient sits in the orgone accumulator once or twice daily with or without clothes. According to the individual's receptivity, the duration of the irradiation will vary between fifteen and forty-five minutes. Some persons are strongly orgonotic and feel the effects after only five minutes or so. Others who suffer from anorgonia may need a full hour or more before they feel the sensations of heat and prickling. The full therapeutic effect is provided only with *regular, daily* use, and in the case of anorgonotic patients, not until after two to three weeks of regular use. People whose orgone energy field is restricted at first feel nothing at all. Sensations increase in relation to the extent to which the organism becomes charged.

Indications of a full reaction of the organism to orgone treatment are subjective sensations of warmth, sometimes intensifying to heat; warm perspiration; reddening of the skin, frequently in the face and neck but also elsewhere on the body; prickling and tingling sensations; objectively measurable rise in temperature; disappearance of tensions and pains.

To date, total irradiation of the organism has shown the following results when the accumulator was used regularly over a period of several months:

Anemias were eliminated within three to six weeks. This effect is one of the most definite findings. To the practiced medical eye, the disappearance of the anemia is accompanied by a clearly perceptible improvement of the blood circulation in the skin; the skin tans and no longer feels clammy or leathery. The tendency to contract colds is reduced in almost all cases. Colds that do occur are less frequent and less severe. Similarly, the disposition to "chills," which has little to do with viruses but does reveal a close connection with the atmospheric orgone conditions, is also reduced.

In a few cases, including my own, additional irradiations each day succeeded in nipping various diseases in the bud or in greatly reducing their effect. During the flu epidemic in New York in the winter of 1945–1946, for example, I suffered from the illness for only about twelve hours and my temperature never rose above 100° F. Other experimental subjects reported a similar brevity of the flu attack and mildness of symptoms. It is clear how significant this finding could be for the prevention of pneumonia as a consequence of severe flu.

A very gratifying and promising effect is the lowering of the blood pressure in vascular hypertension. This effect is explained by the vagotonic influence of orgone energy. It was observed in only four cases and requires detailed study.

Orgone radiation has proved beneficial in cases where an indefinable condition of weakness—referred to in orgone biophysics as an anorgonotic attack—impedes the life of the affected person. In cases where the anorgonia was accompanied by symptoms indicative of a tendency to cancerous tissue putrefaction, orgone therapy has almost always achieved successful results. The success is reflected particularly clearly in the improvement of the biological blood test reactions, in the change from a T-reaction to a B-reaction.

Several years ago, at the beginning of my experiments, I thought that while orgone energy might well exert a favorable influ-

ence upon the tissues, it could have no influence where structural
changes had already taken place. I therefore felt that the accumulator would not be effective in cases of arthritis where there are
marked contractures and joint changes. During the summer of 1944
I was called to examine an old, sick man in Rangeley, Maine. He
had been suffering for many years from severe arthritis, and for the
past few years had been totally bedridden. When I saw him my first
reaction was a disinclination to take on his case. His knees were
fixed in the bent position. He was unable to walk and could manage
only to shuffle along with stiff knees. He was emaciated, pale,
severely anemic, and close to death. His finger joints were rigid and
typically deformed. The family asked me to attempt to treat him
despite the apparent hopelessness of his condition. I made it clear to
them that I did not think anything could be done for him but that if
they wanted to try, they should. I sent an orgone accumulator to
their house, free of charge. For several months I heard nothing
more from them. Then, during the winter, I received news that the
patient was feeling better, stronger; his appetite had improved
considerably and, in addition, he was able occasionally to get out of
bed and walk around in his room. The next contact was in the
summer of 1945, when I was in Rangeley again and visited the
family. I scarcely dared to trust my own eyes and ears: I had the
feeling of having become one of those mystical faith healers. The
old man was no longer confined to bed, but was walking about the
house with almost no restrictions in his movements. His face had a
ruddy color, having completely lost its former pallor. I learned he
had really started to get around just a few weeks before, had taken
walks in the yard, no longer suffered from constipation, ate well,
and in general was in fine spirits. When he saw me, the man began
to cry. I must emphasize categorically that there can be no question
of suggestion or the like. In the first place, suggestion cannot influence advanced arthritis; in the second, I had spoken to the patient
only once and had told him expressly that I did *not* believe in the
possibility of a cure in his case; and in the third, I had not seen the
patient, nor spoken to him, for almost a year.

It was entirely the work of the orgone accumulator that was responsible for the changes in the patient's condition. A few weeks later the patient visited me at my laboratory, about ten miles from his home. He was deeply grateful and took a touching interest in our work.

I have treated only three cases of angina pectoris, one chronic, severe case and two milder ones. In all three cases, orgone therapy was successful in exerting an ameliorative effect. The patient with the chronic affliction had less frequent attacks and was able to stop taking drugs for a lengthy period, although he was not completely cured. In the other cases, all the symptoms disappeared after a few months of orgone irradiation.

I would like to reserve my account of the effect of orgone treatment in cases of schizophrenia for another context.*

I shall now relate the interesting case of a female patient who was able to avoid a dangerous operation as a result of orgone therapy. Physicians had found a growth in her descending colon and had diagnosed it as a probable cancer tumor and advised surgery. The patient had heard of my cancer experiments and wanted my opinion before undergoing the operation.

My examination by fluoroscope and palpation confirmed the presence of a hard tumor the size of a walnut in the middle of the descending colon. The tumor was movable. However, the orgone-physical blood tests yielded no trace of cancerous degeneration. I therefore advised the patient, who also suffered from obstipation, to postpone the operation until we had established the nature of the growth with the aid of orgone irradiation. I knew from experience that it could be a localized spastic knot, and that such spasms can often be relieved by orgone therapy.

The patient was provided with an accumulator in her home. Eight days later I saw her again; the tumor was no longer palpable. I had correctly surmised that the "tumor" was nothing more than a simple spasm. But since chronically spastic tissue can degenerate

---

* *Cf. Character Analysis,* "The Schizophrenic Split."

into cancer, I advised the patient to be careful and to use the accumulator regularly. She thus avoided the dreadful operation and was very grateful. Her obstipation was also mitigated and her total functioning improved. Such cases are gratifying and reassuring.

I would now like to add that children enjoy using the accumulator from a very early age. At the beginning of my experiments, I tended to advise pregnant women against the use of the accumulator, since I did not know what effects orgone irradiation might have upon the embryo and the functioning of the uterus. The first experiment with the orgone irradiation of a pregnant woman was conducted in my own home. I am grateful to my wife for having taken the risk. However, as a responsible co-worker in the laboratory, she said she was prepared to venture the experiment, true to the principle of our Institute that anything recommended to others must have been tried out first on one of us. The success of the orgone irradiation during pregnancy was marked. The mother felt strong and vigorous throughout her pregnancy. The child was lively, and the attending gynecologist stated that the fetal heartbeat was unusually strong. The child today clearly exhibits the biological effects of the orgone irradiation; he is tall for his age and enjoys extraordinary physical health.

ON THE LOCAL USE OF ATMOSPHERIC
ORGONE ENERGY

We can retain the principle of the orgone accumulator, while changing its form, by using a tube instead of a box. The most suitable material for this purpose is BX cable pipe used for the housing of electrical wiring. The tube should be covered on the outside with an organic substance, such as wool or insulating tape, and one end then inserted into an accumulator built as follows: a wooden frame with sides about 8 inches long covered on the outside with celotex and on the inside with thin sheet metal, with a mixture of steel wool and fiber glass or similar non-metallic material between the sheet metal and the celotex. The intermediate layer absorbs the atmospheric orgone energy readily and transmits it rapidly into the enclosed space of the interior. From there the concentrated orgone energy flows through the metal tube. A small metal funnel is attached to the free end of the tube and held close to the area requiring irradiation. Although further experience will no doubt suggest many adjustments, I tend daily to irradiate myself and other persons used as experimental subjects as follows: cardiac region, two to five minutes; root of the nose, about four minutes; mouth cavity, about five minutes; eyes with lids closed, from a half to a full minute; ear at the mastoid bone, one to two minutes; solar plexus region, three minutes.

The organism attracts orgone energy from the accumulator to itself and after a few minutes (the length of time differs from person to person) distinct sensations of warmth and prickling are felt at the place being irradiated.

The inside of the nose can be irradiated with thin glass tubes about 10 centimeters long filled with steel wool. The inside of the vagina can be irradiated in a similar way. Microscopic examination shows that rot bacteria are immobilized by the radiation after about one minute. Irradiation of the vagina is not tolerable for more than about thirty seconds; a strong burning sensation usually occurs.

Burns and wounds heal very quickly with local orgone irradiation, and in many cases it is possible to actually observe the healing process. Bedsores can also be treated successfully with orgone irradiation.

The powerful healing effect of orgone energy administered locally by means of a tube was fully tested for the first time in the case of a sixty-year-old man suffering from varicose ulcers. He had ulcers of various depths and an inflammatory reaction of the skin over both tibias. The condition had existed for several years and the man had been treated for months at a time in a number of hospitals without results. He was able to walk around only with pain and his ability to earn a living (he was a farmer) was considerably reduced. His life savings had amounted to $400, of which he had already spent $300 for medical treatment and hospital bills. He offered me his last $100 to try to help him. Naturally I refused to take his money and I did not promise him any "cure," but I placed at his disposal one of the small "orgone shooters." Actually I had no hope for his improvement. During the first four weeks there was no change despite orgone irradiations several times each day. Then, the ulcers began to heal. The skin became smoother and after six more weeks looked normal. Both legs healed. They showed a tendency to relapse, but the patient was able to halt every incipient tissue breakdown with additional, intensive irradiation. This poor farmer spread the story of "the miracle of his healing" all over the country-side. His gratitude and the restoration of his ability to earn his livelihood were very rewarding.

This particular success was talked about so much in Maine that during the summer of 1945 a young man came to see me from Augusta. He too was suffering from deep leg ulcers, which in this case were dry with necrotic margins and anemic surroundings and were about 2 cm. deep and 3 cm. wide. It seemed a hopeless case. The patient took a small orgone shooter home with him and was soon able to determine for himself the correct duration of irradiation sessions. After only two weeks, he made the 80-mile journey from his home to see me again. The ulcers had reddened, were separating from the surface, and showed considerable secretion. At the bottom and around the edges of the ulcers, regenerative tissue was clearly noticed.

Four months later he wrote me that one of the ulcers was healed and in the other the crater had disappeared, though without as yet having formed a new skin membrane.

Since varicose ulcers tend to defy every kind of therapy, this success with the use of the orgone accumulator was all the more astonishing. It is just as astonishing that the physicians who saw these results did nothing to make the orgone energy accumulator generally available. Every physician, it seems, waits for the others to "accept it officially." This attitude is incomprehensible and per-nicious.

In this particular case, I later learned that the patient had resisted use of the large accumulator, which I had prescribed in addition to the local "shooter." Furthermore, although I had warned against it, he continued to wear an elastic bandage on the leg that had not yet healed. I realized that without the general charging of the organism through the use of the large accumulator, the local healing would be limited.

Violent pains also disappear when the injured part is exposed to local orgone irradiation. A worker employed in building the laboratory at Orgonon* cut his ankle to the bone with an axe. The pain was so severe that the man was near fainting. I immediately irradiated the wound, and after two minutes the pain ceased. I then dressed the wound and he was driven to a physician in Rangeley for further treatment.

With burns, too, the pain is promptly alleviated. My concept of the nature of pain is that the autonomic nerves pull back from the damaged spot; in other words, they literally "pull" at the tissues. The disappearance of the pain seems to be ascribable to the fact that under the influence of orgone energy the nerves again stretch out, so that the "pulling" ceases. I am, of course, ready to accept any other interpretation if it explains the phenomenon better than mine does.

LOCAL ORGONE IRRADIATION BY MEANS OF EARTH BIONS

The old treatment that made use of mud packs was actually very well founded: mud is bionous earth and therefore rich in orgone energy. However, mud is not always easily available and its application is laborious and messy. A new way to administer the biological energy present in humus was discovered during Experiment XX.

---

* The name of the property in Rangeley, Maine, where Reich had his laboratories. [Ed.]

In this preparation, we obtain three simultaneous results. First, the orgone-rich water, which we use to further growth; second, the flakes produced by freezing the orgone water, which theoretically are of crucial importance for an understanding of primary biogenesis; and third, the *bionous earth* itself. We collect the earth bions that remain when the orgone water is filtered and preserve them in a dry condition. We then put them into thin linen bags of various sizes and sew them closed. Treatment consists of moistening one of these small packets of bionous earth and applying it to the painful or inflamed spot. The pain subsides rapidly and, since orgone energy is being administered from the outside, the organism is spared a certain amount of systemic effort in not having to expend its own energy in dealing with the inflammation at the affected spot. Experience so far suggests that an irradiation of thirty seconds to a minute is sufficient. Longer irradiation causes violent inflammation in some patients and should be avoided. This method of administering orgone energy seems also to relax local spasms; but before its efficacy can be properly judged, more experiences are needed.

Experiments with the fourth method of administering orgone energy, namely by the ingestion or injection of orgone water, are still in progress. There is no question, however, that it produces vagotonic effects and accelerates the growth of animals and plants.

To summarize, I think it is justifiable to claim that the discovery of orgone energy and its medical application by means of the orgone accumulator, the orgone shooter, bionous earth, and orgone water have opened up an abundance of new and, it appears, amazingly good prospects. Further investigations are of course necessary to establish the scope of the medical applications of this newly discovered biological energy.

Orgone therapy for cancer can claim today to have made the transition from an experiment to an essential tool for general practical application. Cancer prevention, however, is a much more complex problem, both technically and organizationally.

CHAPTER IX

Anorgonia in the Carcinomatous
Shrinking Biopathy

1. A CONTRIBUTION TO THE PROBLEM OF CANCER PREVENTION

The concept of *anorgonia* encompasses those biopathic conditions that share one common source, namely *a block in plasma motility.* This disturbance of plasmatic functioning is unknown in classical pathology but is quite familiar to the medical practitioner through everyday experience. Mechanistic pathology has not understood this disturbance because there are no structural changes in the tissues or lesions of the nerve tracts; rather, there is *a lowering of the total energy function* of the organism. There are various ways of referring to anorgonia in the popular idiom. Words and phrases intended to depict the emotional *expression* of an organism, such as "unalive," "dead," "stiff," "contactless," "unattractive," etc. (in contrast to "alive," "sparkling," "warm," "contactful," etc.), actually communicate the *impression* made upon us by another person. However, the concept of anorgonia, which is new and introduced here for the first time, denotes more than just "contactlessness"* or "unaliveness." It refers, in fact, to a well-defined, previously unknown, pathological condition of the organism which I have found to be especially pronounced in cancer patients and in persons with a disposition to cancer.

In order to describe anorgonia in the cancer biopathy, I must refer back to a well-known finding of clinical sex-economy. Its sig-

---

* *Cf. Character Analysis,* pp. 310–323.

nificance for health and disease can be much more profoundly understood today than it could before the discovery of orgone energy. I am speaking of the stability of plasmatic functioning in the healthy organism and of its opposite, the *biopathic falling anxiety.*

Let us briefly summarize what we have learned so far about the falling anxiety in biopathic diseases. Falling anxiety is always present in cases of character neurosis or somatic biopathy and manifests itself when the armoring is dissolved and orgastic sensations break through. "Orgonotic sensation" is actually the subjective perception of the objective process of "plasmatic excitation," which we have previously described, in a mechanistic way, as "vegetative current." To us, the appearance of the falling anxiety is a sure sign that plasmatic excitations and orgastic sensations are beginning to be felt throughout the entire organism. Falling anxiety can manifest itself in various ways, for example, as dizziness, "sinking" feelings, falling dreams, pressure or pain in the gastric region, nausea and vomiting. These and similar symptoms are all typical of the clinical pattern that characterizes the breakdown of the armoring, which is accompanied by orgonotic sensations, involuntary muscular spasms, cold shivers and hot flushes, prickling, itching, etc. The psychic manifestations of these biological symptoms appear as overall anxiety or insecurity. Roughly speaking, the essential states of the therapeutic process are loosening of the armor, orgonotic sensations, breakdown of the armor, clonisms, falling anxiety, intensified plasmatic excitation, and, finally, orgastic sensations in the genital apparatus.

If the armoring is dissolved correctly, unpleasurable organ sensations will gradually yield to pleasurable body experiences. We often hear patients who have just experienced clonic convulsions say that they "feel better than ever before." However, if the armoring is not dissolved correctly layer by layer, if rigid armor blocks remain or if the orgonotic currents are permitted to break through too abruptly, so that they strike too harshly against the still undissolved armor layers, the patient may easily react with complete withdrawal into the old armoring. Fear of the plasmatic excitations ("pleasure anxiety") intensifies his biopathic rigidity. As a consequence of the markedly increased quantities of flowing biological energy, the patient will feel overwhelmed by a sense of disorientation, to the point of sheer panic. This condition can intensify even further and produce suicidal impulses. So much for the known clinical phenomena.

The falling anxiety may predominate in either the somatic or the psychic realm. Most frequently it appears as a combination of both. In any case, the appearance of symptoms of falling anxiety indicate to us a *biopsychic crisis*, which is the first step toward health, in the sense of orgastic potency. If the orgone therapist is in control of the case, the presence of conspicuous symptoms of falling anxiety should not alarm him.

Falling anxiety is not dangerous in cases of pure character neuroses. However, my experiences with a succession of patients having cancer or a cancer disposition compel the conclusion that *falling anxiety can appear as a symptom of a deadly process. It is then indicative of a complete breakdown of the plasma function in the biological core of the organism.*

The crucial element is obviously the *depth* of the biopathic disturbance. The orgone therapist has to decide whether he is dealing with a superficial disorientation of the organism during the transition from rigid to free-moving functioning, as in pure character neurosis, or whether the entire plasma functioning is oscillating between *pulsation* and *non-pulsation,* as in the carcinomatous shrinking biopathy. These two conditions are not sharply delineated; the transitions are always fluid, and if the distinction between mild and severe falling anxiety syndrome is to be made, the therapist must develop a keen sensitivity for the fine transitions between the two. Actually, the carcinomatous shrinking biopathy is to be seen as nothing but a particularly severe form of character neurosis, if we are logically consistent and understand "character" to mean the *biophysical* mode of reaction of an organism. Thus, resignation can spread from the superficial to the deep layers of the biosystem and ultimately seize the cell plasma function itself.

We now want to investigate the biophysical mechanism of conspicuous falling anxiety in the cancer biopathy.

Whoever has attentively studied my earlier account of a case of the carcinomatous shrinking biopathy will have been struck by the crucial role played in it by the biopathic falling anxiety. The patient in that case might well have been able to maintain the health she had at first regained if only the appearance of sexual excitations had not evoked severe falling anxiety. She had actually collapsed in my office soon after becoming symptomatologically free of cancer. Her legs had suddenly failed her. From then on she was bedridden, developed a phobic anxiety against getting up, thereby preventing continuation of the orgone therapy, and she literally shrank to death within a few months. I had not really been able to understand her falling anxiety and knew only that sexual excitations had evoked it. The subsequent cancer cases that have come under my care for experimental treatment have all displayed this falling anxiety, with the same typical manifestations. I recognized these manifestations more readily in the later cases and was closer to understanding their biological basis, but I was still powerless to do much about treating the condition. Nevertheless, it was justifiable to expect that further research into the falling anxiety of the shrinking biopathy would probably result in the development of therapeutic measures. This expectation was in fact confirmed in two cases of cancer biopathy that were treated before having developed to a hopeless stage. In all, I have been able to thoroughly observe the falling anxiety in six cases of cancer and also, in its genesis, in an infant of four weeks. I am not including here cases of the falling anxiety in pure character neurosis. Of the six cancer cases, the two patients who came to me early recovered, while the other four, who came when their cancer had reached an advanced stage, died. I do not intend to present complete case histories but simply to excerpt those parts that are appropriate to the diagnosis of anorgonia and to falling anxiety. The key to the problem was provided by the case of falling anxiety observed in the infant.

2. FALLING ANXIETY AS THE EXPRESSION OF PLASMATIC IMMOBILITY: ANORGONOTIC PARALYSIS

I would like first to compile the findings that make it possible to understand the biopathic falling anxiety as an expression of plasmatic immobility. The observed cancer patients had in common the following symptoms of plasmatic immobility:

1. *General physical debility.* This condition manifested itself as a disinclination to move and as sluggishness in every movement. There was a strong tendency to want to remain lying down. It should be noted that *the disturbance of plasmatic motility had existed in each of these patients long before there were even the slightest signs of the subsequent cancer.* Three of the six cases had exhibited a retardation of speech and movements since early childhood.

The falling anxiety was clearly demonstrated to me for the first time in one particular case (first published in 1942). The patient reported that on a certain occasion when she thought she was being followed by a young man, *her legs suddenly failed and she had the feeling that she was going to collapse.* Later, in the terminal stage of her shrinking biopathy, her legs exhibited a marked atrophy, which had its basis in their previous weakness. All the motor and sensory reflexes were intact. Fear of breaking her spine was the reason the patient gave for constantly remaining in bed; but in my account of the case I was able to show that the real cause of her fear was not a mechanical pain in the vertebrae but the *falling anxiety.* The patient could be made to walk. During the period of her recuperation she had walked around a good deal, even though the deformation of the spine was irreversible. But later she was incapable of moving her legs and she feared that movement might cause some part of her body to break.

2. In all cases, the falling anxiety was accompanied by a *feeling of unsteadiness*. I witnessed the same disturbance in the case of the aforementioned infant while he was suffering from falling anxiety. If we look for the connection between the two phenomena, it is more probable that *the disturbed sense of equilibrium causes the falling anxiety*, and not vice versa. The falling anxiety is the rational expression of a biopathic disturbance of innervation, and not its cause. In a few cases it was a secondary threat to the life of the patient, since it caused the interruption of therapy, increased the atrophy of the muscles, and caused bedsores that accelerated the dying process.

One of the six cancer patients, who was suffering from cancer of the prostate, was free of local symptoms for some time as a consequence of orgone therapy (urine clear without cancer cells and T-bacilli, no local pain, etc.), but his leg muscles became atrophic and he developed a *functional abasia*. The motor reflexes also were normal in this case. During the summers of 1942 and 1943 I treated this patient daily for four months with the orgone accumulator and a simplified vegetotherapy. In this way I was able to study carefully the peculiarities of the paralysis. After the local prostatic tumor had been eliminated, the patient was able to walk around and seemed to regain his health; he had no pain, developed an excellent appetite, gained 7 lbs. in just a few weeks, was optimistic, and was even able to work. One day, in the middle of this progress, his knees buckled under him and he collapsed. All at once he had lost control of his legs and feet. "It's as if the life has suddenly gone out of my legs," he said. From that point on, he was unable to move his legs and had to stay in bed. A gradual, progressive shrinking of the muscle substance soon began in both legs. Two months later he lost control of defecation and urination. A sensation of numbness was felt in the legs and the perineal region and extended to the symphysis. His tactile sensations were unimpaired, but his sensitivity to pain stimuli was blunted. The urinary sphincter was spastic; the anal sphincter, on the other hand, was flaccidly paralyzed. He was unable to urinate and could not hold his feces. The localization of the sensory disturbance was not well defined; i.e., it did not correspond precisely to a specific spinal segment. The fact that the trouble was caused not by a central lesion of the spinal cord but by a *biopathic* paralysis of the plasma periphery was evident not only because the disturbance was irregular but also—and above all— because I had succeeded in first reducing and finally eliminating the paralysis. The biopathic character of the paralysis revealed itself only in the course of the orgone treatment of the immobility; i.e., the falling anxiety and the disturbance of equilibrium appeared only with the return of the patient's ability to sit up and move his legs.

Before discussing this further, I must eliminate a few objections. It is unlikely that the disturbance was of a mechanical nature. In the case of an organic lesion in the spinal cord, e.g., a tumor at the spot corresponding to the disturbance, the effects would have persisted and, with a growing tumor, would have increased. Diminution of the disturbance would have been impossible. The fact that there were pains similar to those experienced in neuritis might suggest a peripheral paralysis of the nerve. This is out of the question, however, since the pains were eliminated by purely orgone-therapeutic measures. Besides, neuritis itself would have to be explained as a symptom. With a mechanical lesion, peripheral or central, it would not have been possible to modify or eliminate the anal control disturbance. Yet this disturbance fluctuated with the general biopsychic condition of the patient. When he was relaxed and optimistic, he was able to move his legs much more easily and completely than during the periods when he felt hopeless.

The localization of the tumor in the prostate was directly caused by eight years of sexual abstinence. The subsequent spasm of the urinary sphincter and the paralysis of the anal musculature were sympatheticotonic in nature and according to our experience may be regarded as the *direct* cause of the carcinomatous degeneration of the tissue. Moving out from this center at the perineum, the biopathic paralysis spread in all directions and entirely affected both legs, including the toes. Thanks to the orgone accumulator, the patient did not develop any metastases. Torso and arms retained their mobility and strength to the end. Only the legs showed evidence of wasting. Thus, there must have been a specific reason for the localization of the paralysis in the legs.

During the summer of 1943 I treated the patient daily in order to restore mobility to the legs. First, I moved the ankle to gradually relax the spasms of the ankle musculature; then, day by day, I loosened up another small part of the leg. The procedure caused the patient great pain, but he was soon able to bend and stretch the toes, ankles, and knees. Then I treated the thigh musculature, and finally the hips. After about four weeks of orgone therapy he was able to move his knees and hip joints. Soon afterward he was able to sit up in bed, which gave him new courage and strengthened his readiness to fight his way to recovery.

I now suggested that he try sitting in an easy chair. His reaction was strange. He gave the impression of being enthusiastic but became evasive when the moment actually came for him to make the change, saying that perhaps he had better wait a while, etc. There could be no doubt of his fitness to sit up in an easy chair, since he could sit up in bed without any difficulty. It was clear he was afraid of moving from the bed to the chair, even though he knew he would be supported by two strong persons and that nothing could happen to him. To help him get used to the idea, I suggested that he sit on the edge of the bed. He was hesitant to do so. We helped him, holding him firmly. However, as soon as his legs were hanging free, he was overcome with intense anxiety. He became pale and broke out in a cold sweat. He was experiencing not pain but fear. After only half a minute he begged us to allow him to lie down again. (I had witnessed precisely the same behavior in my first cancer patient.)

I asked him to precisely describe the sensations that had caused him to abjectly beg to be allowed to lie down again. He told me that he felt very insecure. *His body felt numb from the hips down, as though it were not part of him, as though it might "break at any moment."* He was terrified that he might fall or be dropped and that his body would then break. He remembered a peculiar pathological condition that had afflicted him between the ages of six and eighteen. He used to have hard work to do in the woods and frequently *his knees and thighs would suddenly fail him and he either collapsed or had to sit down quickly.* No doctor had been able to diagnose this weakness, which would disappear only to come back several months later.

It is now clear to us that the later anorgonia of the lower part of the body was based on this childhood anorgonia. The anorgonia thus preceded the development of cancer by about sixty years. How such attacks of anorgonotic weakness occur is not known. I should add here that the patient's mother died shortly after his birth. He had been brought up without love by foster parents, who made him work hard even as a child.

The sensation of numbness in the lower part of the body had been dissolved by the orgone therapy, except for a spot the size of a small apple at the root of the penis. Reaction to stimuli was normal. He experienced no pain from movement of the joints; he was able, lying on his back in bed, to move all of them and even to perform dance-like leg movements. His panic at sitting up without support was therefore all the more baffling.

To get him used to the idea, I now had him sit on the edge of the bed every day for one or two minutes. This helped. After just eight more days his falling anxiety had diminished so much that we were finally able to sit him in a wheelchair and take him outside. The effects of lying in bed for several months and the atrophy of the legs had caused him *to lose the feeling of his own body and with it his feeling of equilibrium.* He had partially regained this, however, by the practice of sitting up, so that the falling anxiety disappeared.

Translated into the language of orgone biophysics, the process took place as follows: The biopathic shrinking process had almost destroyed orgonotic motility and with it organ sensation, which fact supports the conclusion that *organ sensation is a direct expression of the motility of the organ plasma.* When organ sensation is lost, what logically follow are a sense of alienation of the body and the fear of falling and "breaking." The feeling of numbness, when the sensory motor reactions are present, can be interpreted in only one way: *Organ numbness is the subjective perception of objective immobility of the orgone energy in the affected parts of the body.* The characteristic accompanying feeling is similar to that of an organ that has "gone to sleep" and has "pins and needles." The anorgonia of our patient differed from the condition of acute organ numbness only in its duration and its biopathic background. Otherwise it was the same.

We must now ask how anorgonia is to be explained. Is it *a loss of orgone content* in the tissues or an *immobility of tissue orgone energy, i.e., a restriction of orgonotic pulsation, without actual quantitative loss?* Let us postpone an answer.

For several months more the patient did well. He even regained control over defecation. Then bad weather set in and he experienced severe pains. To alleviate them, a physician, hurriedly summoned, injected snake venom. In a few days the patient was dead. It is possible he would have died anyway, since the carcinomatous shrinking had already penetrated deeply into the organism. Nevertheless, tissue that is weak orgonotically has an extremely low tolerance for poisonous substances. We have therefore made it a rule in the treatment of cancer biopathies never to use chemical agents if they have a sympatheticotonic effect on the vital apparatus or damage the tissue, even if they alleviate pain. They intensify the anorgonia instead of eliminating it.

I would now like to give a brief account of the case of a third cancer patient, who also died. The tumor (histologically diagnosed as a sarcoma) had developed in the right deltoid muscle. X-ray treatment had effected a recession of the tumor but had also caused a third-degree burn 6 to 8 inches square, a bad prognostic sign. The general biopathic condition of the patient was equally disquieting. The skin over the entire body was sallow and clammy. The legs were cold and showed a condition of the skin now identifiable as anorgonotic: livid coloration, cold and clammy, no perceptible orgone field. The patient was a very quiet, resigned person. He believed he had made a mess of his life and had attained nothing. He was especially concerned about his pelvis, which he felt was "numb" and "dead." He had actually wanted to come to me earlier, a full year before the emergence of the tumor, but had not done so because of the rumor spread by some psychoanalysts that I was insane. However, when the tumor appeared on his right upper arm, confirming his old fears, he decided to undergo the orgone therapy experiment. It is hard to say with certainty whether in this instance the babble of irresponsible colleagues cost a human life, but I am personally of the opinion that it did. Had the patient come to me a year earlier, he could perhaps have been saved.

The patient made good progress during the four months of continuous physical and psychiatric orgone therapy. He emerged gradually from his shell and on occasion even broke out in a rage, which he had never been able to do before. The X-ray burn healed quickly under the influence of orgone treatment, but the spot in the right deltoid remained unaffected. The patient gained weight, improved his neurotically complicated family situation, and made such rapid strides that the orgasm reflex was about to appear.

The reason for the localization of the tumor in the right deltoid was clear. For as long as he could remember, his right arm had been "weak"; he felt as if all impulses in that arm had been blocked. His right shoulder blade was more severely retracted than the left. During the twelfth treatment, violent beating impulses broke through in his right arm, but it was quite some time before he was able to let himself strike out freely with his fist. *Each time the beating impulse began to appear in his arm, the patient experienced a severe spasm of the glottis.* The constriction made the patient look as though he were *suffocating;* voice and breath were cut off and he produced a high-pitched whistling sound. His face assumed a dying expression. The eyeballs rolled upward, the skin became pale and livid, the respiration shallow, the pulse thin.

Orgone therapy had brought to the surface a syndrome that

had actually been present *for decades* in a milder form. The patient
himself traced a part of his resignation to the fact that as a small
boy he had never been able to defend himself successfully against
other boys. *As soon as the moment came for him to put up his fists
and start to fight, his throat constricted and he had to gasp for
breath.* This reaction made him helpless and cowardly. His self-
respect naturally suffered and he resigned very early in life. He
became cowardly, submissive, evasive, and he despised himself for it.

Let us carefully note this biopathic reaction of the patient's. We
shall meet it again at the end of his life and understand what
tremendous significance must be ascribed to the biophysical structure for the vicissitudes of life. It should be stressed that this patient
was not an exceptional case but a *typical* one.

The spasm of the glottis and the dying attitude of the patient
became his habitual reaction to any progress in the treatment. As he
put it, his pelvis was "dead" at the time he came to see me. The
orgasm reflex gradually began to emerge, but it was mechanical and
orgonotic sensations in the pelvis were absent. It improved when his
childhood masturbation inhibition was cleared up, but the anorgonia of the pelvis remained. Both of us had the impression that this
pelvis had never really "lived" and was "hopelessly dead." For many
years this deadness had been his greatest worry, and when he first
heard of orgone therapy, he knew immediately that it fitted his own
case.

After several weeks of strenuous efforts to revive the emotions
in the pelvis, finally and quite abruptly, a spontaneous contraction
forward, with intense orgonotic sensations, took place. This indicated that orgonotic motility was still alive in the depths of the
organism. But the patient's reaction to it was so violent that suddenly I understood the depth of the anorgonia.

Immediately after the pelvic contraction, he relapsed into the
"dying" attitude. This time the glottis spasm was so severe he could
scarcely breathe. A few days later isolated spots on the burned right
shoulder began to swell.

Spastic reactions to newly released plasma currents are well known to the orgone therapist. It cannot be expected that the orgasm reflex will develop without spasms. On the contrary, every new stage in the advance toward the establishment of plasma currents in the biological core provokes increasingly deep anxiety reactions, sympatheticotonic conditions at the place where the breakthrough occurs, the return of old, previously dissolved muscle spasms, etc. We encounter these factors in every case.

In the carcinomatous shrinking biopathy, the process is complicated by the fact that here, in contrast to other biopathies, the anorgonia is operative in the *core* and may well lead to a total block of pulsation. Experiences in clinical practice leave no doubt about this factor. The actual cessation of life functions is thus brought alarmingly close, so that the problem is whether, and how rapidly, the expansion function can be stimulated to counteract the anorgonia. The cases to be described will clarify this point.

To return to our case: Repeated blood tests showed that the patient's biological progress was maintained. When he first began treatment, his blood was extremely weak orgonotically: hemoglobin 70%, *T-reaction* 99%, disintegration of the erythrocytes *in seconds,* etc. After about six weeks of orgone treatment, the blood was normal: *almost 100% B-reaction,* duration of disintegration prolonged to about thirty minutes, wide orgone margin of the red cells, hemoglobin normal at 84%.

The complexity of the cancer biopathy was exhibited in this case by the fact that the surgical removal of the tumor and the restoration of full orgonity to the blood were not enough to halt the progress of the shrinking of the autonomic life apparatus. The subsequent death of our patient is clear proof of this. Nor could the prevention of cachexia by orgone-therapeutic means halt the process of dying. *The patient died with healthy blood and without cachexia.* This fact was confirmed with some astonishment by a specialist in the field of mechanistic cancer pathology shortly before the patient's death.

It should be clear now why I take great pains to stress repeatedly in my accounts of the experimental orgone therapy for the cancer biopathy that, although we are *on the way* to the elimination of the cancer scourge, there still remain basic pathological mechanisms to be understood and mastered. In view of the complexity of the disease, it seems strange that scarcely a week goes by without some announcement in the newspapers that this or that chemical will provide a cure for cancer. Radical cancer therapy will not be achieved so easily.

The attitude of traditional pathology is therefore all the more difficult to understand. Not only is its approach to cancer based on false premises; not only is it bogged down in the study of the local symptom and unable to proceed further; worse still, it also is so strangled by a sense of hopelessness that it seems unable to take cognizance of the fruitful efforts of orgone biophysics. I say *"seems* unable." The possibility cannot be excluded that its persistent silence on the subject of sex-economic cancer research is simply the outward manifestation of a "wait-and-see" attitude. At times in our work we have felt that we are speaking in a huge empty hall where "the walls have ears," but of course can say nothing. This situation should not discourage the friends of orgone biophysics. One day its potential will be recognized.

Let us survey the therapeutic situation of our patient: His anorgonia was pronounced; his characterological inclination to resignation was extreme. He had no tumors, but his plasmatic motility, which alone could save him, was still in the grip of anorgonia. It had just shown the first weak signs of recovery, to which the patient had reacted with severe orgasm anxiety and especially with spasm of the glottis.

The patient took lessons in non-specific vegetotherapeutic gymnastics in order to improve the motility of his body. One day he slightly strained the left gluteus muscle; three weeks later, a small tumor slowly started growing at that spot until, after three more weeks, it had reached the size of a small gourd. Although capable of walking, he once again took to his bed and never left it until his death. The tumor at the left hip stopped growing, but the small swelling on the right shoulder began to grow and spread.

One day the patient had difficulty urinating and—exactly as in the previously described cancer case—the perineum and the root of the penis became "numb." X-rays taken of the whole body showed that there were no metastases in the internal organs. This was remarkable for a lymphosarcoma. There was some glandular swelling in the right inguinal region and in the right and left axillae. The condition of the right deltoid became increasingly ominous. An edema appeared that spread over the entire right arm and up to the first rib. The glottis spasm occurred more frequently. The patient's voice became hoarse and the danger of death by suffocation from the glottis edema increased. The surgeons were powerless to help with the edema. A punch biopsy of the tumor at the hip yielded small malignant cells.

The numbness in the genital region could be alleviated repeatedly, and catheterization was unnecessary.

Then, one day, a persistent glottis spasm set in that resulted in death by suffocation.

Like the earlier cancer patients whose cases I have described, this patient did not die of a local tumor, or of weakness, heart failure, or cachexia. *The immediate cause of death was the glottis spasm that the patient had developed decades before the emergence of the tumor.* The localization of the tumor and the later edema in the right arm were plainly determined by a chronic biopathic inhibition of an impulse in the right shoulder.

We understand the *immediate* cause of death, namely the development of the glottis spasm in connection with the patients' orgasm anxiety. We also understand that his serious relapse was a reaction against the first stirrings of the plasmatic currents. *What we do not adequately understand is the biological mechanism at work in the tissues of the right shoulder* which eventually resulted in the appearance of the edema. The X-ray pictures showed the tumorous tissue at the right clavicle to be about the size of a small apple. The swelling of the arm and the shoulder could therefore not be ascribed to a substantial tumor growth. The "clogging of the lymph passages" may explain a part of the edema formation, but certainly not all of it. It can be assumed that the edema of the tissues blocked the drainage of the tissue fluids and that, conversely, a clogging of the lymph passages with tumor pulp produced the edema.

In place of the purely mechanical interpretation of the edema of cancer patients, I would like to suggest here a biophysical interpretation which I believe is more consistent with the cancer biopathy than are the simple mechanics of "the clogging of the passages." Since there are enough branch passages and secondary channels to permit drainage of the fluids from the tissues, there must be some other factor at work here.

That edema tends to appear in starvation is well known. There can be no question of "clogged lymph passages" in such cases, yet there is edema. Edema of the gums can accompany severe toothache. In this case, too, "clogged lymph passages" play no part, yet there is edema. Pregnant women often suffer from edema of the legs. If it were the pregnancy itself that caused a purely mechanical blockage of the elimination of the tissue fluids from the lower parts of the body, then *all* pregnant women would suffer from edema; but such is not the case. There is also the edema in burns and severe inflammations where there can be no question of a disturbance in drainage.

The following observations are reported by Hoff:[1]

> In all cases of paraplegia that have lasted any length of time, edema always occurs in the legs, due in all probability primarily to the disturbance of the blood circulation resulting from lack of movement. In two cases, however, Böwing observed, immediately after spinal injury, edematous swelling of the legs of such severity that it seemed explicable only by the assumption of trophic damage to the vessels. The same observation has been made by Marburg and Rance on patients with gunshot injuries of the spine. In a case of hemiplegia, we

[1] *Cf.* L. R. Müller, *Lebensnerven und Lebenstriebe* (3rd ed., 1931), pp. 753–754.

witnessed an edema of one side of the face accompanied by facial paralysis. These observations are an aid to understanding the angioneurotic edemas described most of all by Quincke. *It is not yet clear by what processes a disturbance of vegetative vascular innervation leads to edemas.* According to the investigations of Asher and his school it seems probable that the vegetative nerves can affect the permeability of the membranes and of the walls of the capillaries. . . . Unilateral edemas on the side of the head opposite the brain lesion are not rare, yet the impairment of movement alone is not a sufficient explanation. Böwing observed *the formation of vesicles on the skin, thinning of the skin with increased shininess, changes of the nails, and increased hair growth on the paralyzed side.* In cases of psychosis with organic brain changes, Reichardt frequently found trophic skin changes, particularly *ulcers,* which could not be traced to either emaciation or pressure damage. [Italics mine.]

Let us return to the edema in cancer. Observations in cancer patients, as well as the non-carcinomatous edemas just described by Hoff, permit the assumption of a *functional, biophysical* cause of the edema. The movement of fluids in the organism is not a purely mechanical function. It is highly improbable that the lymph glands and the lymph vessels are rigid and the motion of the lymph is purely passive and mechanical. In fact, we are compelled to assume that all organs, including the nerves, vessels, lymph passages, and tissue cells, are contractile, that they *pulsate,* although in different rhythms.

The life functions of the different organs are linked with their pulsation. We must be consistent in applying our functional viewpoint, according to which every organ forms a *living unit* independent of the total organism, fully equipped with sensory perception and the ability to react to stimuli. This finding has been unequivocally confirmed in experiments on extirpated organs, such as the heart, intestines, urinary bladder, etc. Therefore the assumption can justifiably be made that the individual organ reacts to injuries and disturbances of function in the same way that the total organism does. In all realms of life, the living reaction to disturbances of function is either an *intensification* of the specific function to destroy the disrupting stimulus or a *withdrawal* from the stimulus. Processes of regeneration and inflammation, increases of temperature of the blood, etc. are examples of the first type of reaction. The formation of PA bions and cancer cells as a defense against cancerous tissue disintegration also belongs in this category, as does destructive rage reaction.

Anorgonia belongs to the second type of reaction to disturbances of function. Whereas the first kind of reaction represents a struggle against damage to the organism, the second is comparable to a *resignation* or withdrawal; in other words, an isolation of the diseased part from the still-healthy organs. The isolation of diseased organs is known to pathology as sequestration. An example would be the expulsion of a diseased bone part. In the animal kingdom, a diseased limb is sometimes eliminated by simply biting it off. The counterpart to the physical isolation of diseased organs is inflammation with *regeneration*. In cases where regeneration, i.e., plasmatic growth reaction, is not possible, isolation occurs instead.

This isolation of the diseased organ can be observed very well in cancer patients. Its primary characteristics are the withdrawal of the autonomic nerves from the diseased spot and the cessation of their pulsation, which in turn result, in a simple and logical way, in a number of secondary disease symptoms: local anemia, sensory numbness, excess of carbon dioxide, and finally atrophy of the cell substance. In the case of carcinoma of the stomach or of the ovary, the appearance of severe ascites is usual, though there can be no question of a mechanical clogging of drainage passages. This accumulation of serous fluids causes general disturbances of function, such as intestinal paralysis, thus accelerating the dying process. The major factor in the stemming of the movement of body fluids in the region of the diseased organ is therefore the *anorgonotic blocking of motility* in the autonomic nerves. This provides a functional explanation of the edema. Edema and similar anorgonotic disorders are not mechanical, chemical, or physical functions but specific *orgonotic* life functions.

Can this orgone-physical concept be proved experimentally? The immediate reply is that anorgonotic conditions have been successfully eliminated or alleviated by physical and psychiatric orgone therapy. Since these two therapeutic methods both proceed from the assumption that the *autonomic system is contractile,* the practical results of the treatment confirm the correctness of the hypothesis.

Moreover, a large number of phenomena in classical physiology remain completely incomprehensible without knowledge of the orgone-physical functions. A particular example is the normal function of resorption in the intestines. The outcome of an edema caused by a local anorgonia depends on whether the edema fluid can be *resorbed.* This resorption in turn depends on the orgonotic potency and the pulsation of the affected tissues. Here mechanistic concepts fail completely. First, let us orient ourselves in the known processes of intestinal resorption.

The nature of the resorption ability of the organism forms an important and, according to physiologists, still completely unsolved problem of mechanistic physiology. *Does the resorbing membrane of the intestinal wall act like a dead membrane during the passage of foodstuffs or do the cells of the alimentary tract work actively during this process?* These are the questions the physiologists ask. The processes in the living tissue often contradict the purely physical-mechanical processes in semipermeable membranes. *The assimilation of fluidic foodstuff through the intestinal wall cannot be ascribed to osmosis.* Heidenheim[2] drew off blood from a dog, and after opening its abdomen, inserted *its own blood serum* into an empty intestinal loop, closed at both ends. *The dog resorbed its own serum.* In this experiment, there was *no difference of concentration between the intestinal content and the tissue fluid,* so that the purely mechanical processes of diffusion and osmosis have no part

[2] This information is from Höber's excellent *Lehrbuch der Physiologie des Menschen* (7th ed., 1934), p. 69 ff.

in the resorption. The physiologists subsequently tried to explain the fact of intestinal resorption as *the work of the intestinal muscles*. They assumed that the intestinal muscles, which can exert pressure on the intestinal contents from all sides, had pressed the serum *mechanically* into the blood, filtering it, as it were, through the intestinal mucous membrane. But experiments undertaken to clarify this problem showed that filtration as a result of mechanical pressure is impossible. Using pieces of small intestine extracted from a freshly killed rabbit as a diaphragm, Reid separated *two spaces filled with the same salt solution,* that is, *isotonic* spaces. These pieces of cut intestine were seen to transport the solution for a while from the mucosa side to the serosa side. Thus, according to Höber, who reports on this experiment in his textbook of physiology, *the intestinal wall itself does the work.* Höber sums up the process of intestinal resorption in these words: "It (the intestinal wall) presses or sucks the solution through itself." Then he adds:

> After a while it fails—when the intestinal wall dies, obviously, but also when it is chloroformed—which proves *it is determined by the viability of the cells.* How is this fact to be explained? One plausible hypothesis is that, first, the intestinal villi can be shortened by their smooth muscle fibers, and second, the lymph spaces of the subepithelial reticular connective tissue expand into a central chyle vessel which empties into the deeper, larger lymph vessels carrying chyle, i.e., intestinal lymph. Since periodic activity of the muscles causes the villi to alternately become erect and shorten, a sucking and pumping action is created: the villi do not thicken as they shorten, which makes the space of the central chylus vessel alternately small and large . . . If there really does exist such a functioning "villus pump," then the puzzling experiment conducted by Reid becomes understandable. It may be true that we have to give unqualified recognition to the part played by vital activities in the process of resorption, but the problem which then remains to be solved is no different from that confronting us in any muscle contraction. [Italics mine.]

It is clear that *the mechanistic interpretation of the function of resorption,* the movement of fluid through the intestinal wall, is deficient. The mechanical functions of osmosis and diffusion fail to explain the living phenomena. After he has tried in vain to defend the mechanistic position, Höber continues:

> However, observations also exist that are absolutely at variance with what is anticipated according to the laws of diffusion and osmosis. O. Cohnheim, for instance, demonstrated that when a cephalopod intestine is filled with sodium iodide and suspended in ocean water, all NaI disappears and is pushed out into the surrounding solution. It can be shown in dogs that under certain conditions the NaCl content of a solution in the intestines sinks *below* the NaCl content of the blood plasma during the process of resorption; that, in other words, *the NaCl wanders contrary to the concentration potential.* [The NaCl does not, therefore, wander from the higher to the lower concentration, as anticipated, but from the lower to the higher.] Here it is an accomplishment comparable to bringing a gas from a lower concentration or pressure to a higher one. It is an accomplishment like those carried out in a comparable way in other organs; for the work of concentration is typical of numerous glands. . . . This accomplishment provides new proof that the *living cells play an active role in the process of resorption.*

The statement actually makes no contribution to the solution of the problem, which has been formulated correctly by mechanistic physiology. However, the mechanistic formulation is of no help when it comes to understanding in what manner and according to what laws of energy the living cells accomplish their task, a task that contradicts the mechanistic laws of energy potential drop. The familiar laws of mechanics are not valid here.

Can orgone physics provide a better understanding? Its answer would be the following:

1. Since, according to the law of orgone physics, the stronger orgonotic system always attracts the weaker system, it is clear that

the intestinal wall can always absorb the intestinal contents, but the converse is not possible; i.e., the intestinal contents can never absorb the fluids of the intestinal wall. The movement of fluids in one direction only during the process of digestion is therefore to be ascribed to the law of orgonotic functioning. The bions of the food-stuffs in the intestine are extremely weak orgonotic systems in relation to the orgonity of the intestinal wall. This law of orgonotic functioning was determined on the basis of direct observation and was not invented for the sake of explaining biological phenomena. It was applied to biological processes secondarily, and successfully, after having been discovered in the orgone accumulator. The attraction of the weaker orgonotic system by the stronger is valid both in the living *and* in the non-living realm of functioning.

2. The circulation of the blood and the tissue fluids depends on the liveliness of the pulsation function in the organs. The more "alive," the more active an organism is and the stronger its orgonotic pulsation, the more rapid and complete will be the metabolism of its body fluids. Intensification and reduction of the metabolism are vegetative life functions that depend directly on the general pulsatory activity of the organs. The "decrease of vitality" can be understood in orgone biophysics as a *reduction of orgonotic motility,* sometimes to the point of complete anorgonia. From this perspective, the edema that develops with toothache, starvation, nerve injury or burns, poorly tolerated pregnancies, and locally confined cancer tumors has *one* essential cause: the pulsatory activity of the affected organ region is reduced and, consequently, the flow of body fluids is slowed down. An accumulation of fluids takes place in the part of the body where there is weakened pulsation: there is more fluid flowing into the diseased area than out of it.

The pulsatory activity of an organ depends primarily on the activity of the autonomic nerves. An immobilization of the autonomic nerves in any given part of the body must therefore result in a standstill of the movement of body fluids. The rapid formation of fluid-filled vesicles in burns can thus be easily understood, as can various other edemas.

To return to our cancer patient: From childhood he had suffered from inhibition of motility of the right arm and impairment of the speech organs. This inhibition of motility, with its attendant spasms and local anorgonia of the tissues, led to the local tumor in the right deltoid muscle. In the background of this local anorgonia, the general characterological resignation was active, centered particularly in the pelvis and the genitals. Corresponding to it was the local anorgonia of the genital apparatus which, shortly before death, led to a paralysis of the bladder function. Edemas developed at these two anorgonotic regions of the body as a consequence of the block in motility of the autonomic nerves. Death was caused by suffocation as a result of glottis spasm.

Let us now turn to another case that demonstrates the anorgonotic paralysis with particular clarity. As a child, this patient had suffered from an angina (inflammation of the throat), probably of diphtheritic origin, which was followed by a slight cardiac weakness. Her menstruation began at the age of twelve and in the beginning it was normal. But later she suffered on the first day from violent cramp-like pains in the region of the left ovary. Hot compresses did not help, and neither did drugs. From then on the lower abdominal region on the left side remained a "weak spot" where violent tearing pains were continually recurring. At sixteen the patient went to work in an X-ray laboratory. Three months after starting the job, she felt miserable, suffered attacks of nausea, palpitations, and loss of hair. A physician prescribed arsenic, but she tolerated it poorly. The cardiac complaints became worse. At seventeen, severe anemia, swelling of the breasts, and damage to the ovaries were diagnosed. The pains in the region of the left ovary grew continually worse. Different physicians arrived at different diagnoses, such as "spasm of the uterus," "inflammation of the ovary," etc. Medication did not help. Two years later her left leg began to tire easily and a phlebitis appeared. Two or three times each year the patient had "grippe," during which the weakness in the legs and the phlebitis regularly intensified. Soon thereafter she began to feel pains in the abdomen. The swelling in her left leg increased after the delivery of a child, and in addition she became hypersensitive over her whole body to pressure. She developed an anemia, with a hemoglobin of 56% and an erythrocyte count of 3.2 million. Various forms of therapy were tried, but nothing helped. The case history showed a great deal of conflicting medical opinion, with regard to both the diagnosis and the therapy. At various times the patient was treated with diathermy, liver injections, heat therapy, and evipan, all without success.

Blood findings: The orgone-physical examination of the blood yielded a pecular result; in fact, I had never before encountered such a blood picture. Hemoglobin content was 95%; the blood culture, however, was strongly positive. T-reaction on autoclavation and in Gram stain of the blood colloids was almost 100%. Microscopic examination revealed the following: the autoclavation test had indicated extreme orgone weakness in the erythrocytes, yet microscopically they showed no shrinking and *no premature bionous disintegration* (disintegration took twenty minutes); on the contrary, they exhibited *a broad, strongly radiating orgone margin.* One especially surprising factor was that some erythrocytes were far larger than normal. In every field there were numerous large cells with smooth plasm, similar to macrophages. The erythrocytes grouped themselves around these large cells, maintaining a distance that prevented contact of the membranes but, nevertheless, forming very strong orgone bridges. A few minutes' observation gave me the impression that the erythrocytes were enormously *overcharged.* This overcharge, which was manifested in the color and size of the erythrocytes, corresponded to the finding that the erythrocytes *disintegrated unusually slowly* in the physiological salt solution. Whereas the first bion vesicles normally appear in the blood corpuscles after about three to five minutes, in the case of this patient there was still no bionous disintegration even after fifteen minutes. By the time it finally started, the energy vesicles were extraordinarily large and radiating strongly.

I would like to summarize the particular character of this

patient's blood picture in such a way as to make my diagnosis of a *latent leukemia* intelligible.

A few years ago, when writing about my experimental orgone therapy for the cancer biopathy, I surmised that leukemia is not a disease of the white blood corpuscles but is rather a disease of the red corpuscle system. I conjectured that the erythrocytes are subject to a process of disintegration or putrefaction and that the white blood corpuscles proliferate in exactly the same way as when bacteria or other foreign bodies enter the bloodstream. *In leukemia this "foreign body" is the disintegrating erythrocyte itself.*

Our patient's blood picture contained the following contradiction: *microscopically,* the erythrocytes were overcharged, radiating too strongly; yet the autoclavation test showed internal putrefaction, i.e., *almost 100% T-disintegration.* It is difficult to reconcile the orgonotic over-radiation with the process of putrefaction that was occurring simultaneously in the erythrocytes. Still, many familiar processes in the organism involve exaggeration of the normal biological functions when the defense against pathological processes in the same organ makes it necessary. In my opinion, therefore, the patient was suffering from a chronic, latent tendency of the erythrocytes to putrefaction. *The organism reacted to this putrefaction of the erythrocytes with proliferation of the white blood corpuscles, development of large, macrophage-like white cells,*[3] *and a rise in temperature, i.e., with repeated lumination of the blood system to overcome the orgonotic weakness.*

In this case, as always, orgone therapy became the criterion for the accuracy of my hypothesis. If it was correct, then the supplying of orgone energy necessarily had to eliminate the tendency of the erythrocytes to putrefaction and all the corresponding symptoms.

---

[3] Diagnosis by stained smear preparation is not practicable in such cases. It is not the name or the structure of the different kinds of white blood corpuscles that is important but the living function of the grouping of white cells around red cells, and the orgonotic constitution of the live and the destroyed blood cells.

My expectation was borne out. One week after the beginning of orgone therapy the blood culture was negative. The erythrocytes were smaller than before and the number of white blood corpuscles in the field was reduced. Disintegration of the erythrocytes began after three to five minutes, and this time T-spikes also appeared.

In the third blood test, two weeks after beginning orgone therapy, there were no longer any large-celled, plasmatically smooth formations, and three weeks later both T-spikes and over-radiation had also disappeared. After three more weeks had passed, renewed examination of the blood revealed that the T-reaction after auto-clavation, which at the first examination had been almost 100% positive, was now only 10–20%. The blood picture was already almost normal. In the course of the following year, blood tests were undertaken about once a month. The culture reaction continued to be negative and there was no over-radiation of the red cells or proliferation of the white blood corpuscles. However, T-reaction on autoclavation, in the form of greenish discoloration of the colloid and T-disintegration, stayed constant at between 30% and 40%. Once, during this year, the culture reaction was positive; that occurred after the prescription of drugs by another physician.

The fever attacks, from which our patient had suffered for so long, were therefore to be understood as *reactions by the blood system to its own tendency to putrefaction.* The impression was that in this case the blood had reacted to its own orgonotic weakness as it would to a toxicosis. Proof of this interpretation is supplied by the fact that the fever attacks disappeared together with the hyporgonia and the T-reaction of the blood. It will have to be left to future research to decide if what we call "functional fever" is attributable regularly to *lumination* of the blood cell system, and therefore to a defense reaction against disturbances of vegetative functions. The blood system acted in this case exactly as it does in the face of bacterial infection.

The father of this patient had died of leukemia. For a while she herself had suffered from a suspicious leucocytosis. There were times during her functional fever when the number of leucocytes was as high as 14,000. Her physician had shared my suspicion of a kind of latent leukemia, even though the traditional methods of diagnosis could provide no tangible proof. Our blood tests left no doubt about the *cancerous* character of the blood picture. It is true that there were still no circumscribed malignant tumors, but there were numerous early signs, including tumors of the ovaries, putrefaction of the uterus, etc.

There is no doubt in my mind that the patient would have died of leukemia if the orgone therapy had not been successful.

Thus, a latent hyporgonia of the erythrocytes existed. The seriousness of this condition was disclosed later in the experimental orgone therapy, when we found that it could be eliminated only slowly, and had a strong tendency to recur. In other words, *the coherence of the plasma in the erythrocytes was weak and the tendency to putrefaction was therefore great.*

The attacks of weakness did *not* stop with the restoration of the normal blood reaction, but they occurred much less often, did not last long, and no longer prostrated the patient for months. Therefore the anorgonia could not be ascribed solely to the bio-energetic weakness of the blood system. Obviously anorgonia can affect specific organs and organ groups and in this way cause disturbance of the specific organ functions and produce local malignant growths. However, as this case demonstrated, anorgonia can be present *without* tissue disturbances; its effects can be purely functional.

Our patient was able to overcome every attack of weakness by using the orgone accumulator. But the tendency to anorgonia lasted for more than two years after the patient's recovery. Quite evidently we are dealing here with *a disturbance in the functioning of the total body orgone content,* existing *independent* of the mechanical or physiological organ disturbances that may be connected with anorgonia. The assumption of such an independent and total anorgonia is indispensable.

Anorgonia is not identical with the condition of plasmatic contraction that we encounter in vascular hypertension. While it can accompany or follow muscular and vascular hypertension, it can also appear *without* hypertension.

Nor is anorgonia identical with the carcinomatous shrinking process. Even if the shrinking invariably leads to anorgonia and death, anorgonia does not always lead to shrinking. I have seen anorgonotic conditions where there could have been no question of a shrinking of the autonomic system.

It is important to understand the hypertonia of the vital apparatus as a biophysical contraction that resists strong impulses from the biological core. The shrinking biopathy is accompanied by a *decrease* of the impulses from the core; there is a gradual *weakening* of the pulsatory impulse functions.

Anorgonia, on the other hand, is characterized by a *sudden* cessation of motility, as in shock paralysis, which probably represents *acute* anorgonia in its purest form. All the cases described until now have shown acute anorgonia together with the gradual shrinking process. Our first cancer patient collapsed in the laboratory only after she had started recovering and gaining weight. The same thing happened to our patient suffering from cancer of the prostate; he collapsed just when he was improving. Our third patient was also suddenly stricken by anorgonia at a time when his condition was visibly improving.

Fright paralysis and vegetative shock give us an indication of the phenomenon we are dealing with, namely *an abrupt standstill of the plasmatic functioning of the total organism*. If the acute anorgonia extends to the cardiovascular system, death occurs.

Our present patient's case revealed part of the mechanism underlying the cessation of plasmatic motility. She came to us for orgone therapy to eliminate the biopathic background of her latent leukemia. For several months she made considerable progress; the memory of her illness receded further and further. Then one day the old disease picture returned in its totality, as if nothing had happened in the meantime. The cause of this was the appearance of very strong genital sensations, which the patient stubbornly rejected. When these sensations of current in the vagina were felt, *orgasm anxiety* appeared, and with it, an anorgonotic state that lasted ten days and seemed to be seriously alarming. This time, however, I was not baffled and helpless. Previous experiences with cancer patients had prepared me for this development. In concentrated therapeutic efforts—the patient was treated every day—I tried to eliminate the acute anxiety reactions that made her shrink from experiencing genital sensations and thus from developing the orgasm reflex fully. A host of childhood experiences, which were now recalled, showed that the patient's mother had threatened to severely punish any activity that might induce genital excitation, e.g., dancing, and had discouraged such activity by calling it the behavior of a "whore."

I would like to emphasize this connection. It is the key to understanding not only biopathies in general, but the shock-like anorgonia in particular. What is important is not, of course, the word "whore," but rather all that the word implies—socially, psychically, structurally, and biophysically. For genital impulses *not* to be considered "whorish," either by compulsive social moralism or by the armored structure, they have to be mild, controllable at all times, and easy to repress. The vigorous natural impulse of uncontrollable welling-up (lumination) of the body plasma is officially designated, on the other hand, as immoral, criminal, or whorish, and is experienced subjectively as an indication of the "loss of self-control."

This fact has far-reaching social and biopsychiatric implications. The words "pleasure anxiety" and "orgasm anxiety" are too weak and too narrow to express the bio-energetic turbulences occurring within the organism when it experiences full orgastic excitation while still under the pressure of its armoring. This conflict between armoring and orgastic excitation has very serious consequences; far from being a harmless "clinical problem," it becomes a matter of life and death. I hope I succeed in communicating this fact.

Again and again, anorgonotic paralysis killed cancer patients under my care who were actually on the way to recovery. The first three patients whose cases I described died when the natural orgastic excitation collided with the plasma stasis. In the fourth case, I succeeded in preventing this outcome. The fifth case, which I shall now describe, will reveal the danger of anorgonia even more clearly.

The most salient features of the case history of this patient can be summarized as follows:

The initial signs of the disease developed between the ages of twelve and fourteen, that is, at the beginning of puberty. A pulling pain in the left hip, which was the first symptom, lasted, with interruptions, for several years. Not long afterward, the patient began to experience chest pains that recurred in frequent attacks over the next ten years. The diagnosis was "pleuritis." An X-ray picture of the lungs when she was twenty-two revealed "healed tuberculosis." At the age of about thirteen, general "rheumatic and neuritic pains" set in, lasting on and off for about fifteen years. At the age of twelve she underwent her first tonsillectomy, for "tonsillar infection." Inflammation of the salivary gland (parotitis) occurred during her fifteenth year, and at the same period she suffered from violent pains in her big toes, which often assumed a livid discoloration, caused presumably by angiospastic attacks. Since her early childhood, the patient had suffered from severe anxiety states which, by the time she had reached the age of nineteen, had intensified into attacks of acute palpitation. When she was fifteen she suffered an "infection" of the jaw and the roots of the teeth. A large part of the lower jaw, along with nine teeth, had to be resected. The diagnosis was "osteomyelitis." Between the ages of sixteen and twenty she was afflicted with various intestinal symptoms and diarrhea alternating with constipation. In addition, there were bouts of fever and, in particular, a general debility and fatigue that persisted right up to the time she started orgone therapy.

Intense pains in both inguinal regions occurred during her nineteenth year and surgery was performed again, this time for "appendicitis." After the operation, she suffered constantly for eight months from high temperatures accompanied by "diarrhea" and cold chills. The condition culminated in a "nervous breakdown."

She underwent a second tonsillectomy sometime between the ages of twenty-one and twenty-six, again for "tonsillar infection and inflammation." A diagnostic laparotomy was also performed on her during this same period, "for the purpose of finding the cause of the pains." On this occasion a few thread-like adhesions in the lower abdomen were cut through. The high temperatures persisted. The diagnoses were always "infection." In the period between the ages of twenty-four and twenty-seven, diagnoses of "anemia" and "enlarged liver" were made. For a while rectal bleeding occurred with every defecation. Two years later "amoebic dysentery" was diagnosed in a hospital, and she was operated on for hemorrhoids. At thirty she underwent a third tonsil operation, this time because of "suppuration." At thirty-one she began to suffer from a constant urge to urinate. Again she was operated on, this time for "multiple benign tumors" of the uterus; the body of the uterus and one cystic ovary were removed. Not long after this operation "stomach ulcers" were diagnosed. Two years before beginning orgone therapy a suppurating fistula appeared in the middle of the abdomen.

The gynecological findings were as follows:

> Two finger introitus. Urethra, Bartholin's and Skene's glands free. Cervix in axis. Uterine stump freely movable, no stump exudate. Left adnexa cannot be felt, had apparently been extirpated at the time of the supracervical hysterectomy. The right tube is normal. The right ovary extremely small. Speculum examination shows severe inflammatory changes due to trichomonas infection in an atrophic vaginal mucosa. Of other physical signs, I mention only the cystic mastitis.

The gynecologist diagnosed *dysfunction of the endocrine glands* as the cause of the plethora of infections.

Let us refrain from dwelling upon the tragicomic aspects of this patient's history of suffering. There are an infinite number of such people who, without being hypochondriacal neurasthenics, spend their entire lives going from one doctor to another with acute organic ailments. They not only receive varying diagnoses on the basis of their various symptoms, but are prescribed differing treatments from different physicians for one and the same symptom. It is characteristic of the calamity caused by the mechanistic viewpoint in internal medicine that medical understanding has been replaced by diagnostic catchwords, among which two are especially prominent: "infection" and "disturbance of glandular functioning." It makes no difference whether the attempt at a cure is based on the knife or on vitamins, the real problem is the reliance on mechanistic slogans and concepts. The "bacillus in the air" is nothing more than a makeshift term and "hormonal dysfunction" is a mere catchword. The scalpel has become the ultimate symbol of the mechanistic abuse of the organism. The question is never asked *why* the ligaments in the parametrium shorten, or *why* tumors develop in the uterus, or *why* "air bacilli" are able to affect all of the organs. Vaginal infection with protozoa is blandly assumed despite the fact that no such protozoa can be detected in the air.

In short, the great medical discoveries about infection, inner secretion, etc., have been reduced to a *deus ex machina,* a set pattern that not only founders any new questioning but also destroys countless human lives. Does it seem probable that this patient really was suffering from a dozen different diseases? It would be hard to believe. She was actually suffering from a single disturbance: the dysfunction of plasmatic pulsation. The individual diagnoses have no significance here. When the body plasma as a whole is not functioning in an orderly manner, biologically undercharged organs will be vulnerable to the invasion of bacteria, the glands of internal secretion will function poorly, ligaments will become pulled because of contraction of the muscles, the mucous membranes will atrophy, etc.

Imagine the following developments over the course of twenty years in a house built on sand: crevices in the chimney, cracks in the ceiling, warped floors, a child injured by a falling fixture, a broken water pipe, seepage of water through the walls. What is to be done with a builder who fails to recognize the reason for all this havoc? The obtuseness of the builder is exactly analogous to the mechanistic obtuseness in the diagnosis of somatic diseases. Words coined by mechanistics like "infection" or "grippe" simply disguise the fact that the disease stimuli are actually not known and not demonstrable. The orgone therapist who witnesses the emergence of catarrh or rheumatic or pleuritic pains as soon as the corresponding region of the body becomes contracted reasons that infections are possibly the result of biopathic disturbances of function. This entire area of research is still unexplored; everything remains to be done. During epidemics, such as cholera, typhus, poliomyelitis, etc., we will have to learn to ascribe at least as much significance to the orgonity of the organism as we do to the specific disease stimulus. Since it has now been established that specific micro-organisms can develop *autogenously, through the degeneration of body cells,* the "bacillus" can be regarded as a result of the systemic disease as well as its cause.

The tumors of our patient's genital apparatus, which necessitated total extirpation of the uterus, and the tendency toward tissue destruction by suppuration make this case similar to case 4. The fever attacks and the states of exhaustion indicate a severe disturbance in the equilibrium of the biological energy. It is true that with the exception of the genital tumors the precancerous symptoms were minimal, but they were sufficiently pronounced to justify the opinion that the patient would have died of cancer. Just as the psychiatric orgone therapist infers the development of a psychoneurosis from acute anxiety attacks even before its symptoms become visible, so in cancer pathology the development of a cancer biopathy can be inferred when its harbingers begin to appear. One of the tasks of cancer prevention will be the earliest possible recognition and elimination of these precursors of the disease. Physical and psychiatric orgone therapy is especially well equipped for this task.

Now to the patient's reactions in orgone therapy: Her thorax was typically immobile, her respiration shallow, the neck musculature tense, the spine lordotic, the pelvis "dead." Her facial expression was characterized by a stiff smile that seemed locked into the position of a twisted grimace. It was not difficult to perceive a deep depression and impulse to cry.

Elimination of the superficial respiratory inhibition at once evoked body impulses consisting of violent, jerky, pushing movements. This pushing reaction soon manifested itself as a defense against sexual attack, and was accompanied by a hateful facial expression. *The orgasm reflex served, paradoxically, to express hatred of sexual movements.* As a child, between the ages of six and sixteen, the patient had often been sexually abused by her older brothers, and had always been torn between excitation and repulsion. The excitation had compelled her again and again to permit the molestations; the repulsion had become somatically anchored in the "pushing away." Her orgasm reflex had thus taken on its special form.

I shall disregard the many details of her infantile history and limit myself to the anorgonia. It is not really important to know which early experiences determine the anorgonia, since there are no specific causes of the malady. Anorgonia is a purely biological reaction to a chronic block of the orgasm function. The one specific element of anorgonia is probably the contradiction between very powerful, natural, genital impulses and equally powerful disruptions in the orgasm reflex. I would surmise that children who do not develop an especially strong genital orgonity also tend to be less vulnerable to anorgonotic attacks. However, I must emphasize the tentative nature of this assumption.

To return to our patient: As long as the body contractions expressed hatred, the work proceeded along familiar lines. The change came when the contractions became softer, more yielding, and therefore pleasurable. At the same time that the expression of hate gave way to that of pleasure, the movement of the pelvis reversed its direction. Previously the pelvis had tended to move backward during contraction, "to push away"; now *forward* movements occurred in the pelvis. It was not long before the anticipated preorgastic sensations could be felt in the pelvic floor. At the same time, the inflammation of the vaginal mucosa receded and microscopic examination of the vaginal secretion showed a decrease in the number of trichomonal parasites, which were now preponderately immobile and even disintegrating. From then on I was able to observe, over a period of months, how genital frigidity was accompanied by intensified formation of protozoa and, conversely, how vaginal excitations were accompanied by a decrease in the formation of protozoa. This finding is in agreement with the orgone-biophysical assertion that protozoa form only when there is orgonotic weakness in the affected organs and they disappear when orgonity is strong. The fact that trichomonal protozoa develop from bionously disintegrating vaginal or cervical epithelium makes understandable their relationship to the orgonotic potency of the tissue.[4]

While the plasmatic currents in the vagina were still weak, the treatment of our patient in no way differed from that of other cases. But the situation changed when the patient experienced the first strong surge of sexual excitation. On one occasion she yielded much more than usual. An intense wave of excitation ran through the lower part of her body and she was unable to move. Her speech failed and she did not answer when spoken to. She could not get up. A flaccid paralysis of the extremities appeared. The general picture was alarming. The skin of the neck and the upper body was livid and blotchy, as in vegetative shock, and there was no reaction to such stimuli as pinching; yet the patient was not unconscious. When the anorgonotic attack had passed, she said that everything had gone "black" all around her; she had suddenly not been able to feel her body at all and had believed herself to be "dying."

The attack showed all the signs of acute anorgonia. The reflexes and tactile and pain perception were all present, but *motility had vanished.* The anorgonia lasted about forty minutes. I sat the patient up, but she sank back helplessly. After an hour she

[4] The organization of *Trichomonas vaginalis* from the epithelium of the vaginal mucosa has been demonstrated and recorded on film.

was able to sit up herself, but with effort. When she tried to stand, her legs buckled beneath her. Another hour of rest was necessary before she was finally in a condition to go home alone.

At the next session the armoring was again very strong, but once it had been successfully loosened, the anorgonia returned, this time lasting for a shorter period and taking a less intense form. The patient described the attack as a "fading out." From that point on I was able to induce the anorgonia at will. For instance, I could produce it by moving her head to one side or backward.

It is important to note that the attacks occurred without anxiety. Gradually the relation of the anorgonia to the orgonotic current became clear. The patient had always used superficial joking as a defense against serious emotions. She was also able "to go dead" when her emotions became too strong. The anorgonotic attack now supervened as a third mechanism.

The characterological shallowness and the affective dullness were superficial armorings. The anorgonia was and remained the real depth mechanism. It became perfectly clear during the subsequent months that evidence of the anorgonia had always been present. It was responsible for the patient's states of weakness and many of the suppurative processes. The anorgonia did not appear when the patient allowed herself to experience sexual excitation, but it did appear abruptly whenever excitation was not able to run its course, i.e., when it was checked while still mounting.

The anorgonia was accompanied by vertigo and falling anxiety. Its development could be "superficial" and prolonged over a number of days, or "deep," i.e., immediate and full. As was shown in case 4, the attack of weakness could often be overcome in the orgone accumulator. The release of the orgasm reflex also relieved it.

The mechanism of the anorgonia in this case corresponds fully to the cases described earlier: *The organism reacts to unfamiliar, strong plasmatic excitation with a block in motility* that manifests itself as "weakness," "collapsing," "fading out," disturbance of equilibrium, and falling anxiety. *It is as if the orgonotic expansion began*

*but was unable to run its course fully, as if the expansion impulse
suddenly died out.*

During the period she was in treatment the patient recalled
several childhood situations in which such attacks of weakness had
set in. For example, she had felt "paralyzed" whenever she had the
impulse to show affection to her father. A study of the details of
these incidents left no doubt that the paralysis was due to an ex-
ceedingly strong sexual excitation developing within her. Her father
was a hard, cold man. To feel the sensation of sexual current in his
presence was a horrendous experience. *Her paralysis expressed the
helplessness of a child who wanted to display affection but was
unable to tolerate the physical sensation that accompanies the
expression of affection.* The result was a block in motility and an
attack of weakness.

I succeeded in locating where the block occurred. As the
orgasm reflex intensified and spread from the thorax to the abdomen, the patient developed a strange reflex action. She literally
caved in from the umbilicus down; the legs jerked suddenly upward
and the trunk of her body thrust forward. She grabbed at her
abdomen with both hands as if she were in pain. Gradually, it
became clear—it was later confirmed by palpation of the abdomen—that the wave of orgonotic excitation going toward the genitals had been blocked by a spasm of the intestines precisely at the
place where the suppurating fistula had broken through the abdominal wall. (The fistula itself had in the meantime been healed
by orgone treatment.) It is evident that the abdominal organs
became spastic as soon as orgonotic waves of excitation pressed
toward the genitals. This caused the abdominal pains, the colics, the
diarrhea, and the constipation. What is not so clear is how such
spasms produce the histomorphology of uterine or intestinal tumors.
Yet there can be no doubt whatsoever about the development of
benign tumors of the genitals from spastic conditions of the abdominal organs.

Two weeks of intensive work were necessary to remove this
block in the abdomen. The orgasm reflex lost its harsh, jerky quality

and became instead a fluid movement. The pleasant "streaming" sensations of current soon appeared in the abdomen, and for the first time in her life the patient experienced, during the sexual act, the preorgastic sensations of current in the genitals. Once the block in motility was removed, the attacks of acute anorgonia ceased also. The superficial, prolonged states of weakness continued to recur until a few months later, when they also disappeared.

Thus, the concept of anorgonia was confirmed by the therapeutic process.

Symptomatically and dynamically, the condition of anorgonotic paralysis has now been satisfactorily defined. It includes those states that hitherto led a Cinderella existence in pathology as "functional paralyses." We now conceive of them as disturbances in the functioning of a concrete biological energy rather than as "hysterical" or mechanical lesions of the nerve tracts.

It is more difficult to differentiate the anorgonia that is the result of gradual plasmatic shrinking from the anorgonia that sets in acutely. The question is, *Is anorgonia produced by a loss of orgone content in the body, or is it merely the result of a block in the motility of the normal orgone content?* Moderate anorgonotic weakness can easily be distinguished from acute attacks of anorgonia. The mechanism is presumably the same in both cases. We have to assume that anorgonia of the type that manifests itself in acute attacks can develop into a chronic shrinking process and that, conversely, chronic anorgonia can culminate in acute functional paralysis. If the impulses to expand are blocked, the organism may resign and ultimately shrink. If the body is subject to a gradual loss of orgone energy, it may stop expanding. *What both conditions have in common, biophysically speaking, is the inhibition of expansion or, expressed psychologically, the inhibition of the pleasure experience.*

The next question is: How far back in the developmental history of the patient does this disturbance reach? In all five cases there were indications of mild and transitory anorgonotic attacks dating back to early childhood. But this fact does not answer the question. *The inception of anorgonia must occur very early, since the orgone functions of the body probably acquire their individuality during fetal development.* This does not signify "hereditary disposition," but *merely shifts the problem into the period before and immediately following birth.* It is important to bear in mind that the constitution of an organism is a formative process and not something that appears "ready-made." Its development undoubtedly continues beyond birth to approximately the end of the first year of life.

Just as the prevention of disease cannot begin early enough, so the research into the biophysical constitution must go back to the formation of the embryo. Thanks to our knowledge of many orgone functions, this is now possible.

The advance of science consists in the reduction of empirical data to primary causes and the progressive unification of these causes. Freudian psychopathology, through the discovery of the libidinal development in early childhood, considerably reduced the importance of that catch-all "heredity." The assertions of psychopathology are based on clinical observations of children two years of age and up. Orgone research goes further back. Orgone therapy for schizophrenics, for example, leaves no doubt that the central mechanisms of the disease are established during *the first few weeks of life.* The language of movement, the language of the organs, and the language of emotional expression utilized in orgone therapy are phylogenetically and ontogenetically older than the language of words and ideas, which is the instrument of depth psychology. The language of movement and body expression does not begin at a certain age and is not limited to the human animal, as is the language of word and idea. The language of bodily expression is a general function of the animal world, even if we have not yet learned to understand it. By utilizing it, orgone physics gains access to the living functions in man and animal *before the first year of life,* because emotion and expressive movement are connected to plasmatic pulsation.

I should like to report on the insights that are to be gained from experimental orgone therapy with schizophrenics at another time and conclude this account of anorgonia with the description of the expressive language of a newborn child. It will be shown that we can actually look for and find the early beginnings of anorgonia in the period before and just after birth.

3. FALLING ANXIETY IN A THREE-WEEK-OLD INFANT

I recently had the opportunity to observe the development of falling anxiety in an infant of three weeks. This observation filled a gap in the investigation of the cancer biopathy.

The infant in question was born into an environment in which the expressive language of the organism is professionally understood and used. It was therefore all the more disconcerting that the parents felt helpless when confronted with the infant's gesture language. They had the impression that *nothing at all is known about the emotional life of the newborn child.* The *emotional* needs of the infant are, of course, in no way satisfied by purely mechanical care. The infant has only *one* way to communicate his needs, namely by *crying.* This one form covers countless large and small needs, from the irritation of a diaper crease to colic. The infant's expressive language meets with no response from the environment.

I shall refrain from discussing here those damaging kinds of infant care that modern education has already eliminated from the world or is still combating: the rigid apportioning of food and inflexible adherence to feeding times a la Pirquet; forcible extension of the legs by tight swaddling in the manner of thirty years ago; denial of the breast during the first twenty-four hours, as still practiced in many hospitals; overheating of nurseries; the routine treatment of infants in large institutions; the practice of letting infants "cry themselves out," etc. Such compulsive measures express the parents' and physicians' inimical attitudes toward life. Their effect is immediate postnatal damage to the biological self-regulation of the organism, creating the basis for a later biopathy which is then misinterpreted as hereditary taint. All this is common knowledge today, even though it may not yet have had an impact on common practice in child care.

I would like to limit myself here to one specific damaging influence in the first weeks of life that has been neglected until now: *the lack of orgonotic contact, of a direct physical or of a psychological nature, between the infant and the person who takes care of it.* The capacity to understand the infant's language of emotional expression depends directly upon the closeness of this contact: the more complete the orgonotic contact, the better the understanding.

The most salient place of contact in the infant's body is the bioenergetically highly charged mouth and throat. This body organ reaches out immediately for gratification. *If the nipple of the mother reacts to the infant's sucking movements in a biophysically normal manner with sensations of pleasure, it will become strongly erect and the orgonotic excitation of the nipple will become one with that of the infant's mouth, just as in the orgastically gratifying sexual act, in which the male and female genitals luminate and fuse orgonotically.* There is nothing "abnormal" or "disgusting" in this. Every healthy mother experiences the sucking as pleasure and yields to it.

However, about 80 percent of all women suffer from vaginal anesthesia and frigidity. Their nipples are correspondingly anorgonotic, i.e., "dead." The mother may develop anxiety or loathing in response to what would naturally be a sensation of pleasure aroused in the breast by the infant's sucking. This is why so many mothers do not want to nurse their babies. Furthermore, an anorgonotic breast functions poorly physiologically; i.e., the milk production is disturbed. The excited mouth of the infant thus encounters either a "dead" nipple, so that it experiences no satisfaction, or the non-excitable rubber nipple of a bottle to which the mother, because of her phobia, has restricted the infant.

The impairment of plasmatic functioning in the mouth and the neck and shoulder regions that we find in biopathies leaves no doubt that severe damage to the infant's orgonity in the region of the head and neck is caused by these disturbances in the mother. Speech disturbances, lack of emotional expression, spasms of the neck muscles, eating disturbances, spastic hysterical vomiting, fear of kissing, depression, stuttering, mutism, etc., are consequences of poor orgonotic functioning of the mouth and neck organs. So much for the infant's first physiological contact with the world.

Let us now proceed to the emotional contact, which is determined directly by the orgonotic contact. The infant has no means of expression at his disposal other than various forms of movement (grimaces, movements of the arms, legs, and torso, expressions of the eyes) and crying. The mother grasps the expression of the infant's gestures at first through orgonotic contact (in psychological terms, through identification). If her own organism is free and emotionally expressive, she will understand the infant. But if she is armored, characterologically hard, timid, or otherwise inhibited, she will fail to understand the infant's language and therefore the emotional developent of the child will be exposed to a variety of damaging influences. The infant's needs can be satisfied only if its expressions are understood. But exactly what the infant wants is not always easy to know.

Every newborn child has its individuality, its *own emotional keynote,* which must be recognized if its individual emotional reactions are to be comprehended. The infant in this particular case of falling anxiety was characterized by an "earnest looking" expression. This "looking expression" was fully developed just a few minutes after birth; i.e., the newborn baby's eyes were wide open and gave the impression of "seeing." He took the breast immediately and vigorously. During the first week he did not cry very much. In the second week, however, he cried frequently, and none of the people looking after him were able to figure out what was causing him to cry. The pacifier did not always quiet him, and I often had the sense that the child wanted something *quite definite.* But *what?* It was two weeks before I understood that what he wanted was *body contact.* I will have to explain this point.

During the few hours the baby was awake, his eyes followed the red winding lines painted on the wall of his room. Red was clearly preferred over blue and green: the infant's gaze would stay much longer on the red, with a much more intense expression in his look.

At the age of two weeks, the infant experienced his first orgastic excitation of the mouth. It happened while he was sucking: the eyeballs turned upward and sideways, the mouth began to tremble, the tongue quivered. Then the contractions spread over the whole face. After about ten seconds they subsided and the musculature of the face relaxed. This excitation seemed perfectly natural to the parents, but we know from experience that many parents become alarmed when their child experiences oral orgasm. In the following four weeks, these convulsive movements occurred several times.

At the end of his third week of life, the infant experienced an attack of acute falling anxiety as he was being taken from his bath and placed upon a table on his back. It was not immediately apparent whether the movement of laying him down had been too fast or whether the cooling of the skin had brought about the falling anxiety. Whatever the cause, *the child began to cry violently, stretched his arms backward as though to gain support, tried to bring his head forward, showed sheer panic in his eyes, and could not be quieted.* He had to be picked up. As soon as the attempt was again made to lay him down, the falling anxiety reappeared just as violently. He could be calmed only by being held.

For the following few days the right shoulder blade and the right arm were pulled back and less mobile than the left arm. The contraction of the right shoulder musculature was quite distinct, and its connection with the falling anxiety was clear. *During the anxiety attack the child had drawn back both shoulders as if keeping himself from falling. This muscular attitude persisted; it failed to relax even during periods free of anxiety.*

I now believe that great significance attaches to this incident. The following explanations can be excluded, however:

It could not be a question of genital orgasm anxiety of the type that occurs after puberty. Nor could it be a rational fear, since a three-week-old infant has no concept of "falling" or of "height" or "depth." It also could not be a case of *psychoneurotic* falling anxiety, since there are no concepts before the development of word language and there can be no phobia without concepts. The psychoanalytic explanation of "instinct anxiety" usually offered in such cases is not satisfactory. For the question would then be: What kind of ego instinct was being warded off? There is no such thing as a moral ego at this age, and where there is no moral defense according to psychoanalytic theory, neither can there be instinct anxiety. There is no "ego" to "signal" an instinctual breakthrough with the anxiety attack.

Rationalistic as well as psychological explanations, therefore, provide no answer. *How is it possible for an acute anxiety attack to occur in a three-week-old infant who possesses neither consciousness of the danger of falling nor an instinctive defense signal of the ego against anxiety?* Recourse to the notion of an "archaic, inborn, instinct anxiety" would be plain laziness and prove nothing at all. *An anxiety attack is a functional disturbance and can be understood only in terms of the orgonotic body functions.*

Let us attempt a biophysical interpretation: If the fear of danger and the defense against an instinct are to be excluded, *what remains is the pleasure-anxiety mechanism of the orgonotic body system,* which functions with the very first stirring of the plasma. In "Psychischer Kontakt und vegetative Strömung" (1934) I had to make the assumption that *the sensation of falling is a purely biophysical occurrence brought about by a rapid withdrawal of the biological energy from the periphery to the vegetative center of the organism.* It is the same type of kinesthetic organ sensation that occurs in actual falling, in fright, and when orgastic expansion is suddenly inhibited. As I have shown clinically, falling anxiety is always at the root of orgasm anxiety. *The rapid and extreme pulsation of orgasm is experienced as falling if it cannot run its course unimpeded.* By contrast, the uninhibited orgastic contraction conveys the sensation of *floating* or *flying.*

The withdrawal of bio-energy from the body periphery repre-

sents an *anorgonia of the extremities; loss of the sense of equilibrium accompanies the anorgonia of the supporting organs.*

Falling anxiety is therefore not a "psychic formation" but the simple expression of sudden anorgonia in those organs that maintain the equilibrium of the body by *opposing* the pull of gravity. Whether falling anxiety and anorgonia are induced by the sudden onset of orgasm anxiety, by real falling, or by a fright contraction, the mechanism remains the same: *loss of peripheral plasma motility, accompanied by loss of the sense of equilibrium and of equilibrium itself.* The experience of anxiety is an immediate biophysical reaction to sudden contraction of the plasma system. The orgonotic contraction, however, is connected with *the loss of plasma motility at the periphery and, for this reason, manifests itself as the fear of falling.*

Whether the immobilization occurs as a result of a secondary pleasure block or because of a primary anxiety contraction is a matter of indifference. The effect is the same: *the falling sensation is the immediate inner perception of the immobilization of the body periphery and the loss of equilibrium.* The body's balance in the gravitational field is therefore a function of the full orgonotic pulsation at the periphery of the orgonotic system.

I must relate an incident that supports this interpretation. A boy I knew had caught a squirrel and was holding it in his hand. I was struck by the fact that the squirrel lay completely limp in his hand, without struggling, without biting, and without wriggling, indeed, without moving at all. It was completely *paralyzed with fright*, and was suffering an *acute anorgonotic attack.* After a few minutes the boy put the squirrel on the ground. At first it lay there as though dead, i.e., completely motionless. Then it tried to get up but fell down. In terms of physics, it could not overcome the pull of gravity. Its attempts to get back on its legs remained unsuccessful for about fifteen minutes. Yet it was not hurt, for later it ran and climbed very well. The disturbance of the sense of equilibrium and the continuous falling down produced increasing anxiety and caused more falling. For several minutes the squirrel convulsed in sudden contractions that were so strong it was thrown 10 to 20 cm. into the air. Finally the animal recovered from the attack and crawled into a bush where it rested for a long time before scampering away.

Let us now return to our infant. Is it possible to infer a *cause* of the anorgonotic attack? I think so. *For about the first two weeks the mother's orgonotic contact with the baby had been poor.* The child had obviously had strong impulses for body contact that had not been satisfied. Then the oral orgasm occurred, a completely natural discharge of the high-pitched excitation in the head and throat region. This increased the need for contact still further. The lack of contact led to a contraction, a withdrawal of biological energy as a consequence of vain efforts to establish the contact. If it were appropriate to use the terminology of psychology here, we would say that the child "resigned" (that it was "frustrated"). However, the "biological resignation" brought on the anorgonia, and the falling anxiety appeared. This calls to mind case 5, in which the same mechanism governed the biopathy.

I succeeded in my attempts to overcome the falling anxiety in the infant. Assuming that my conclusions were correct, I found the following three procedures necessary:

1. *The infant had to be picked up and held when he cried.* That helped, and the falling anxiety ceased to occur after about three weeks. Fear of strangers had appeared with the falling anxiety. *Before* the first attack, the child would happily go into the arms of every stranger; *after* the attack, he would begin to cry in fear. He had also reacted once with anxiety to the sudden appearance of a dog.

2. *The shoulders, fixed in a "backward" position, had to be gently moved forward, in order to eliminate this first onset of a characterological armoring in the shoulders.* I accomplished this playfully, laughing and making sounds the child loved. This was continued on a daily basis for about two months, always as if in play.

3. *The child actually had to be "allowed to fall" in order to let him get used to the sensation of falling.* He would be held under the armpits and gently raised and then lowered, at first slowly, then increasingly quickly. At first he reacted by crying, but in time began to enjoy the movements. Soon he developed a game out of this routine of being lifted up and then lowered. When he was able to hold himself upright he began to make "walking movements" with his legs. He leaned against my chest and looked up at my head. I understood. *He wanted to climb up on me.* Once he arrived at the top of my head, he squealed for joy. In the weeks that followed, the climbing and "falling" became a favorite game.

Fortunately, the first biopathic reaction was overcome. During the next six months we did not see any trace of the falling anxiety.

It is important to follow the development of this infant in an area that is directly connected with biopathic shrinking: *If the carcinomatous shrinking of the adult organism is rooted in chronic contraction and resignation acquired at an early age, it can be concluded that the prevention of the shrinking biopathy is dependent on the undisturbed development of the vital impulses in the first months of life.*

It would no doubt be simpler and more popular if a drug against the shrinking process in cancer could be developed, but since this is not possible, we have no alternative but to concentrate on *the sex-economic upbringing of the newborn infant.* So far as I can see, there is no other way, despite the serious social implications that this course of action involves.

We started with the adult's lack of understanding of the expressive language of newborn infants. This lack is far-reaching and quite general. The parents of the infant in this case believed themselves to be especially understanding when they allowed the newborn infant to decide for himself when his feeding times should be and how much nourishment he should take. But as early as the fourth week of the child's life, we noticed a distress that manifested itself in repeated crying. At first, we did not understand. Slowly the simple realization dawned on us that it is extremely dreary to lie all alone in a crib for hours at a time, day after day, with high walls on both sides and a cover over the top.

The aliveness of the newborn infant requires aliveness of its surroundings. The infant prefers vibrant colors to gray or dull tones, and moving objects to stationary ones. If the infant is set in his carriage so that the walls no longer obstruct his view, and if the top is removed, he can see everything around him without difficulty and will show a lively interest in the people passing by, in the trees, shrubs, posts, walls, and so on.

The concept of the "autism of the child," of his "being withdrawn into himself," is as erroneous as it is widespread. The autism of the infant is an *artifact* caused by the behavior of the adults. It is artificially generated by the strict isolation of the infant and by the characterological armoring of the adults responsible for his care and also of the theoreticians of child care. The infant will quite understandably not emerge from *himself*—or will do so only with the greatest difficulty—if only inflexible rules and ungenuine behavior are extended to him rather than living warmth.

It is perfectly true that today most newborn infants are quiet and withdrawn into themselves. But is lordosis or anxiety neurosis natural just because it is common? As long as parents, doctors, and educators approach infants with false, unbending behavior, inflexible opinions, condescension and officiousness, instead of with orgonotic contact, infants will continue to be quiet, withdrawn, apathetic, "autistic," "peculiar," and, later, "little wild animals," whom the cultivated feel they have to "tame."

This world will not change, despite all the political talk, as long as grownups fail to take the trouble to prevent their own deadness from exercising an influence on the still-unspoiled plasma system of the infant.

An infant does not respond with any expressive movement to honey-sweet "baby talk" or to the strict language of adults. *He responds only to the intonation and pitch of a voice, to a language that is related to his own.* In an infant just a few weeks old, it is possible to educe glowing pleasure and lively responses by talking to him in *his* guttural sounds, and making *his* movements, and above all, by maintaining a lively contact with him. False behavior on the part of the grownup inevitably forces the child back into himself. It cannot be emphasized enough that in this particular matter 90 percent of all adults are still completely unaware, and because of this, biopathic constitutions are being produced every day.

Deficiencies of inner secretion and of the highly interesting enzyme functions are the *results* and *symptoms, not* the causes, of later diseases of the biosystem. This must be correct if the mechanical-chemical viewpoint of biology is incorrect—*and it is incorrect.* The miserable state of health of the population of this planet is sufficient proof of this point.

The horrendous way Indians, Japanese, or any other kind of authoritarian Asiatics bring up small children should not be too great a surprise to us. We are not much better here in the "cultured" West. Only the methods of "taming the wild little animals" are different. The old-spinster spirit, intolerant of anything alive in its vicinity, is the same. In twenty or fifty years' time it will have become commonplace that persons who take care of children must experience love themselves and that their organism must know the orgastic sensation and convulsion before they can understand a small child. I am well aware how repugnant that must sound to some ears today, yet in everyday experience it remains true that the greatest danger to the development of the child is represented by orgastically impotent educators.

The so-called autism of the small child—his stillness, his pallor, his withdrawnness—is an artifact of upbringing, a product of our total social misery. Diarrhea, anemia, etc., will soon be placed in this category too—a statement that may sound far-fetched but is not. If the intestinal function is vegetative in nature, which it is, then the faulty emotional, i.e., orgone-biophysical, development of the child must play a crucial role also in diarrhea, pallor, anemia, and so on. To speak of "social misery" is meaningless, actually, for in the final analysis this social misery is itself the result of a world of stultified human animals, of a world in which there is always more than enough money for wars but never enough—not even a minimal fraction of what is spent on paying the costs of *one day* of war—to ensure the protection of life. This is true because stultified, stiffened human beings have no understanding of what is alive; in fact, they fear it. There is no kind of social misery to equal the misery of the infants of biopathic parents.

It is a widespread misconception that grasping, crawling, walking, and similar functions are one day simply there, that a child just starts in grasping at the age of *x* weeks, crawling at the age of *y* weeks, and walking at the age of *z* weeks. It is surprising that pediatricians have not worked out a schedule of how many steps an infant must take per day, just as they have determined the daily number of calories he should consume. A nipple that is erogenously alive, and warm contact with the mother, are much more effective than any chemical prescriptions in stimulating digestion and the total body functioning of the newborn. Once the contact is established between the infant and a warm, understanding environment, then—and only then—can natural processes be observed, rather than the artificial products of a pathological education. The educators themselves have to become sexually healthy before their scientific statements about children can be accurate. In my opinion, any statement should—and no doubt one day will—be judged *according to the character structure of the person making it,* just as a book is judged by its stylistic elegance or a surgeon is judged by the dexterity of his hands.

A framework for accurate observations must first be established. If orgonotic contact is present, it is possible to see the various functions manifest themselves in the infant long before they have a "purpose." The eye, for instance, follows a moving hand. The closing motion of the hand develops long before the infant actually takes hold of any object and has nothing to do with mechanical "grasping reflexes." *Purposeful grasping develops gradually through the merger of many functions, i.e., through the contactful coordination of movements of previously uncoordinated organs.* Purposeful seeing, for instance, is established when the eye comes into contact with a pleasure-inducing movement in the surroundings. Once the act of seeing is accomplished, then the function, already complicated, seeks *new* pleasurable subjects on which to fix the gaze. Unpleasurable stimuli produce contractions and do not develop an act of seeing. The excessive amount of anxiety and displeasure experienced by our infants later leads to "dull eyes," "myopia," restriction of movement of the lids and, with it, to the "dead" expression in the eyes.

In the face of these facts, what can be done with the mechanistic misconception that "seeing is the response of the retina to a light ray"? *Certainly* it is, but the reaction of the retina is only a vehicle, a means of seeing. *Is a child's dancing "only" the contact of feet and floor or "only" such and such a sequence of muscle contractions?* The emptiness of all the mechanistic interpretations of life is revealed here very clearly.

The child looks at you in one way when you smile at him and in another when you frown. *The crucial element therefore is the motor expression of the plasma,* not the individual stimuli, reactions, muscle contractions, etc. The light ray striking the retina always involves the same process of fixed wave lengths. Yet the infant's eye can be shining or dull depending upon the *tissue turgor,* which is increased by pleasure and inhibited by anxiety.

A person who has established good contact with the infant can encourage its functions. Whenever I came nearby, the infant I was observing made walking motions while lying down, to indicate to me his desire to "walk." When he was three and a half months old, he would become ecstatic as I held him under the arms and let him put his feet rhythmically on the floor and move along. He looked continuously at the walls or ceiling to convince himself that there really was movement, i.e., that the objects were moving past him.

Small children go through a phase of development characterized by vigorous activity of the voice musculature. The joy the infant derives from loud noises (crying, shrieking, and forming a variety of sounds) is regarded by many parents as pathological aggressiveness. The children are accordingly admonished not to scream, to be "still," etc. The impulses of the voice apparatus are inhibited, its musculature becomes chronically contracted, and the child becomes quiet, "well brought-up," and withdrawn. The effect of such mistreatment is soon manifested in eating disturbances, general apathy, pallor of the face, etc. Speech disturbances and retardation of speech development are presumably caused in this manner. In the adult we see the effects of such mistreatment in the form of spasms of the throat. The automatic constriction of the glottis and the deep throat musculature, with subsequent inhibition of the aggressive impulses of the head and neck, seems to be particularly characteristic. Clinical experience has taught us that small children must be allowed to "shout themselves out" when the shouting is inspired by pleasure. This might be disagreeable to some parents, but questions of education must be decided *exclusively in the interests of the child*, not in those of the adults.

I want to make it clear that I see the origin of the biopathic shrinking process *in the dependency of psychic and physical-chemical functions on the bio-emotional activity of the organism at the beginning of its development*. Here, *and only here*, will the means for the prevention of this process be found, not in drugs or cultural theories of sublimation.

I have stressed the dependence of psychosomatic functions on the bio-energetic functions of plasmatic pulsation. *Lively pulsatory activity from the first moment of birth is the only conceivable preventive against chronic contraction and premature shrinking.*

Bio-energetic pulsation is a function completely dependent on the stimulations from and contacts with the environment. The character structure of the parents forms a crucial part of this environment, particularly that of the mother, *who provides the environment from the moment the embryo is formed until the moment of birth.*

I should like now to discuss the few insights we possess into the *prenatal* development of the organism. They do not amount to a great deal and are not decisive. Much more will have to be learned before it is possible to open up the obscure problem of heredity. But the following notes—they are no more than that—are a beginning that can lead to further practical knowledge.

If the onset of a shrinking biopathy is to be placed at the embryonic stage of development, the next question will concern the influence of the mother's blood on the embryo, that is, the effect of the orgonity of her organism, especially the bio-energetic condition of the maternal genital organs, on the embryo.

The contractions of the chicken embryo, which have been demonstrated on film, confirm the clonic-pulsatory nature of embryonic growth. *The vitality of an embryo is manifested in these contractions.* The bladder-like form itself shows that the typical bio-energetic functions of *protoplasmic protrusion,* which can best be studied in flowing amoebae, are operative here. It is necessary to assume that a freely contractile uterus provides a much more favorable environment for the embryo than a spastic and anorgonotic uterus. In a uterus that is orgonotically vigorous, the circulation of blood and body fluids is more complete, making the energy metabolism more efficient. In addition, *the capacity for charge of the maternal tissue is transmitted to the embryo. This is, after all, a functional part of the uterine mucosa.*

It is therefore perfectly understandable why the children of orgastically potent women are so much livelier than the children of frigid, armored women—a contention that can easily be confirmed. So-called "heredity of temperament" is in large measure nothing more than the effect of the maternal tissue on the embryo. Seen in this way, a part of the problem of "heredity of character" can be grasped for the first time. Since emotional functions are determined by the orgonotic energy functions, it is understandable that character is initially only a question of the degree of energy activity. In other words, *temperament is an expression of the quantity of the pulsatory activity of the orgonotic body system.*

The "heredity factor" would thus be tangible in principle as a quantitative energy factor. It is only logical that a system rich in energy resigns less easily than an energy-impoverished system. A legitimate conclusion is that the energy level of an embryo is determined by the energy level of the maternal genital organs. Quantitatively energy deficiency can be understood as a decrease of orgonity, and it can be understood functionally as reduced pulsatory activity of the plasma. It is quite likely that the reduction of plasmatic pulsation in the embryo can secondarily cause an anorgonia. Thus, we cannot automatically assume that the embryo itself was initially anorgonotic, even though the mother may have suffered from decreased orgone energy metabolism. Two possibilities have to be considered: the internal anorgonia of the embryo, and the anorgonia resulting from anorgonia of the maternal genital apparatus.

Let us pursue this train of thought a little further. Naturally, concrete observations will correct or amplify what is obscure here.

During the sexual act of the parents, the embryo participates in the orgastic contraction of the uterus. It cannot be otherwise because of the physiological-anatomical situation. Prior to birth there are also *developmental contractions* that cannot be distinguished bio-energetically from the contractions stimulated by the mother's orgasm. If, in addition, the female organism has possessed high orgonity before pregnancy, then the bio-energetic conditions for the orgonity of the embryo are favorable. These conditions are later qualified by the genital character structure of the parents, which continues in the realm of psychic development what the bio-energetic function established in the embryo. After birth, the new-born infant experiences independent orgastic contractions in the head and neck.

Since high orgonity leads to strong, expansive, instinctual activity, anorgonia is prevented. The *anlage* of a carcinomatous shrinking biopathy or an anorgonia has thus become unlikely, though not entirely impossible. Destructive influences in later life can force even the most vigorous organism into resignation and shrinking.

But let us return to our newborn infant: From the fifth month of pregnancy on, the movements of the child were extraordinarily vigorous; so vigorous in fact that the mother often experienced pain.

The obstetrician noticed that the child's heartbeat also was unusually strong. The delivery was a difficult one—a first pregnancy with premature rupture of the membranes and twenty hours labor. Nevertheless, there was no asphyxia at birth. The mother's blood remained orgonotically strong and free of T-bacilli throughout the entire pregnancy.

To recapitulate: *The biosocial prerequisites for strong orgonity of the child in utero are high orgonity and orgastic potency in the parents, absence of anorgonia in the uterus, and an absence of T-bacilli and no excess of CO_2 in the maternal blood.*

Conversely, low orgonity and orgastic impotence in the parents, anorgonia of the uterus, disturbances of inner tissue respiration, T-bacilli in the maternal blood, hyporgonia of the blood, and muscular armoring together create the disturbances of functioning now recognized as the possible cause of a later anorgonia in the child.

The mechanistic-mystical theory of heredity has thus lost more ground to *functional* pathology. The problem is no longer one of uncontrollable "inherited embryonic damage" "predisposing" the child to "hereditary cancer"; instead, we are dealing with changeable life functions, with energy quantities and disturbances of pulsation. These disturbances do indeed create a tendency toward anorgonia, but the tendency does not have to develop if favorable living circumstances eradicate the initial damage. The living organism is very adaptable to both the bad and the good conditions of life.

The time from the formation of the embryo to about the end of the first year of life is considered in orgone biophysics to be the critical period in which the "constitution of the orgonotic system of functioning" is established. This constitution, measured in terms of orgonity and the pulsatory capability of the tissues, determines the degree of plasmatic impulse activity.

Embryonic development should be thought of as terminating not at birth but at the time—roughly at the age of ten to twelve months—when all the biological functions become fused into a unified, coordinated *biosystem*. This critical span of life is decisive for later bio-energetic functioning. The critical period for psychic development lies approximately in the third to fifth year of life. Its outcome is profoundly influenced by the progress of the critical, earlier *biophysical* period. It is this earlier period that holds the solution to the puzzling fact that after treatment, even when all the pathological mechanisms have been worked through, an intangible *something* always remains: an undeviating hopelessness in the life activity, a stillness in the organism, an irritability—in brief, what classical psychiatry usually calls "inborn disposition."

Much remains obscure about falling anxiety and anorgonia. Neither anxiety nor anger is a pathological manifestation of the life system. It is natural for a child to feel fear when it falls or is attacked by a dog and it is natural for a newborn infant to express anger when its needs are not gratified.

But falling anxiety is more than a fear of danger. It can appear long before there is any consciousness of danger. It is connected with rapid contractions of the vital apparatus, and, in fact, is produced by such contractions. Just as actual falling causes biological contraction, so contraction causes the sensation of falling. It is therefore understandable why a *contraction* that occurs in the process of orgastic *expansion* precipitates falling anxiety. And it is equally understandable why falling anxiety appears when the muscular armoring is pierced and the first plasmatic currents are felt. *A contraction occurring in the middle of plasmatic expansion disturbs the sense of equilibrium.* But still there is something that remains unexplained. Let us try to pinpoint it even if we are unable to explain it.

A basic function of the living orgonotic system is that it opposes and overcomes the earth's gravitational pull. The *dead* stalk of a leaf is completely subject to the force of gravity; the *living* stalk grows in a direction *opposite* to the force of gravity. (This phenomenon cannot, of course, be due simply to the processes of mechanical tension, since a dead stalk remains lying on the ground and does not raise itself even if filled with water.) The flight of birds depends on the overcoming of the force of gravity. The upright stance of man requires a vast amount of balance *against* the pull of gravity. We know that this balance fails when the unity of the body motor functions is somehow disturbed. This motor disturbance can be purely mechanical, such as a leg injury or tabes, but it can also be *functional.* Anorgonia of the entire body or of essential body organs signifies a disturbance of capacity for balance, hence a tendency to fall and the corresponding falling anxiety. The process is clear so far. But the manifestation of falling anxiety in a three-week-old infant (which we now know was precipitated by the cooling of the skin after a bath) remains mysterious. It is true that the function of rapid vascular contraction already exists, but the *experience* of falling does not. Where then does the *expression* of falling anxiety originate? Turning to a "phylogenetic experience" would explain nothing, because a phylogenetic experience is relevant only when anchored in actuality. Memory function does not exist without an actual mechanism.

At this point we must give up trying to completely understand anorgonia and the falling anxiety and be content with understanding the connection between the block of orgonotic pulsation and the loss of organ sensation and equilibrium. The relation of orgonity and anorgonia to the force of gravity is clear. In the anorgonotic state the limbs are "heavy," and movement can be accomplished only with great effort. In the state of high orgonity, on the other hand, one feels "light," "floating." Let us take such figures of speech literally and seriously. *In anorgonia, less biological energy is free and active. The inert mass of the organism becomes greater and thus heavier in relation to the active energy that has to move the body. In high orgonity, more bio-energy is free and active and the mass of the organism becomes lighter in relation to it.* What we are dealing with is a genuine, *alterable* relationship between mass and energy in the biosystem.

It is not possible to go any further at the present time without invoking the metaphysical construct that supposedly thinks, feels, acts, and reacts in the background of living functions. This would lead nowhere. We therefore prefer to wait for a more favorable opportunity to finally solve what remains unexplained. For the present it is enough to understand how early and in what orgonotic functions the carcinomatous shrinking process and its anorgonia set in.

CHAPTER X

The Cancer Biopathy
as a Problem
of Sexual Sociology

Many years of clinical experience will be required before we completely understand the devastations to the life system caused by the emotional plague. This is all the more distressing because the shattered sex-economy of cancer patients, which is essentially due to the emotional plague, is consistently overlooked even though it is perfectly obvious: Deprived of the natural sexual function, potential cancer patients develop a general characterological resignation.

First, there appear local, harmless "disturbances" such as stomach ulcers or perhaps only gastric hyperacidity, hemorrhoids, a spasm of the throat, genital numbness, menstrual problems, stiffness of the chest musculature, etc. The chronic disturbance of the biological functioning increasingly undermines the respiration and pulsation of the tissues, which slowly begin to disintegrate and putrefy. T-bacilli appear and accelerate the process, which extends over a number of years. Finally, protozoa develop and proliferate until the tumor becomes palpable and visible.

Clearly, even the earliest diagnosis of the local cancer tumor is *too late,* because the biopathy has already completed its devastation of the organism. The task of cancer therapy therefore must be to influence *the general disturbance of function in the biosystem,* to foster the B-reaction of the organism. Reduced to a single thought, this means that *as long as education continues to produce characterological resignation and muscular armoring on a mass scale, eradication of the cancer scourge will be out of the question.* Of course, it will be possible to eliminate a few tumors and save a few lives. But it is a dangerous illusion to think that cancer can ever be overcome with any single treatment, whether it be drugs, the knife, or orgone energy.

I once had such illusions myself. When I first saw the effects of orgone irradiation on cancer tumors in mice, I breathed a sigh of relief. At last, I told myself, the way to a cancer therapy is opened; now we can start to cure cancer and perhaps even learn to prevent it. I felt a secret delight at the prospect of finally getting away from the "cursed sex problem" and escaping safely into the "pure," sex-free atmosphere of organic pathology. But I was deceiving myself. The facts were there; justice had to be done to them. They soon robbed me of the convenient illusion of having found an easy way out. Great problems cannot be solved easily. The difficulty of the path is merely a reflection of the difficulty of the problem. I did not get away from the "cursed" sex-economy, and for this I have to thank the incontrovertibility of the facts.

My cancer patients made me acutely aware of what I had been seeing for the past twenty-four years, *the devastation of sexual disturbances*. There was no getting away from it, no matter how I tried: *Cancer is a putrefaction of the tissues, occurring while the body is still alive and caused by pleasure starvation of the organism.* It was not simply inadequate research methods or therapeutic errors in biology that had been responsible for the overlooking of this extremely simple fact. I had stumbled upon it only because I had to remain consistent as a sex-economist; I had to follow the consequences of sexual disturbances wherever they led. What is really responsible for this oversight is our whole way of viewing life: our moralism, the sexual crippling of our children and youth, the moralistic prejudices in medicine and education, in short, our fear of life and our blindness to it, attitudes that we have handed down from generation to generation for thousands of years. We have outlawed the most important life function; we have stamped it sinful, even criminal, and denied it any social protection. In addition to that, we have added an unpardonable deed: we have tolerated and still tolerate the presence of those things that hinder natural love-life—pornography, sexual gossip and defamation, sexual compulsion, and medieval sex laws. Filthy fantasies, whether hypocritically moralistic or openly sadistic and pornographic, still determine how our children are brought up and whom we should embrace. We have lost our trust in the natural laws of life and now we are beginning to notice the consequences.

The vitality and resilience of the human organism is to be wondered at. Considering the devastations to which it is continually subjected by mechanistics and mysticism, it is amazing that the human organism does not perish more rapidly. Our hope lies precisely in this resilience. If a mistreated organism can survive for decades before developing local growths, then our present terror of cancer can be ended, but only if we approach the problem without illusions, above all refusing to accept the neurotic ideas of a plague-infested humanity.

The *World Almanac* for 1942 contains a statistical summary for the state of New York of the frequency of the diseases we call *biopathies.* I quote the figures as they were presented in an article written by a colleague.[1] While the percentage of diseases of a non-biopathic nature (pneumonia, diphtheria, etc.) sank considerably in the years between 1921 and 1940, the percentage figures for *biopathic* diseases (mental illnesses, cardiovascular hypertension, cancer, suicide, criminality, etc.) show an extraordinary increase over the same period:

DEATHS, CHIEF CAUSES, NEW YORK STATE
(rates per 100,000 population)

NON-BIOPATHIC DISEASES

| | PULMONARY TUBERCULOSIS | | PNEUMONIA | | DIPHTHERIA | |
	Deaths	*Rate*	*Deaths*	*Rate*	*Deaths*	*Rate*
1921	9,503	88.6	10,645	99.3	1,702	15.9
1925	9,162	78.9	13,571	116.8	1,001	8.6
1930	8,146	64.6	12,908	102.4	656	5.3
1935	6,847	52.4	11,018	84.4	102	0.8
1940	5,793	42.9	6,143	45.5	15	.01

[1] *Cf.* W. F. Thorburn, "Mechanistic Medicine and the Biopathies," *International Journal of Sex-Economy and Orgone Research,"* Vol. I, No. 3 (1942).

DEATHS, CHIEF CAUSES, NEW YORK STATE (*continued*)

BIOPATHIC DISEASES

	CARDIOVASCULAR		CANCER	
	Deaths	*Rate*	*Deaths*	*Rate*
1921	36,594	341.4	11,163	104.1
1925	43,370	373.3	13,201	113.6
1930	48,487	384.5	15,144	121.8
1935	55,109	422.1	18,600	142.5
1940	64,987	481.3	21,384	158.4

INSANE IN NEW YORK STATE
(rates per 100,000 population)

	Males	*Females*	*Total*	*Rate*
1920	19,515	21,265	40,780	390.0
1925	22,667	23,858	46,525	413.6
1930	28,674	27,737	56,411	444.0
1935	36,124	33,943	70,067	493.0
1941	45,870	43,393	89,263	664.2

CONVICTIONS FOR CRIME IN NEW YORK STATE

	Total
1920	40,691
1925	77,202
1930	175,530
1935	363,743
1940	1,155,986

SUICIDES IN NEW YORK STATE
(rates per 100,000 population)

	Total	*Rate*
1920	1,442	13.5
1925	1,664	14.3
1930	2,135	17.2
1935	2,180	16.7
1941	2,188	16.2

These figures not only show that biopathies are fundamentally different from the non-biopathic diseases, but also indicate that they are not understood. Mechanistic medicine, which is not sex-economically oriented, has no access to them. *Biopathies are diseases that result from disturbances of the biological pulsation of the autonomic life apparatus, thereby reducing orgonotic potency.* They are socially determined and result from *sexual stasis.* The number of biopathies is steadily increasing. The situation is extremely serious and calls for an investigation and, hopefully, a solution.

Sex-economy and orgone physics offer medicine and pedagogy a few important insights that could be of help, although not in the way one might think. We have not discovered any chemical cure-all that, if applied on a mass scale, would be capable of suddenly doing away with the scourge of biopathic diseases. It is not so simple. The struggle against biopathies will be one of the most difficult tasks ever faced by human society. I would even venture that no human effort, not even the conquest of the plagues in the Middle Ages, can compare with this task in magnitude, depth, and danger. Its resolution will in all probability require the greatest revolution in thought and action that man has ever had to accomplish. It will be an achievement not of individuals but of society as a whole.

Biopathies are an endemic disease of the earth's population. The fact that the number of mentally ill people doubled in New York State over a period of twenty years (a figure valid for every state or country) is a statistic that speaks for itself in unequivocal terms. It is impossible to expect that biopathies will be eliminated rapidly, easily, and without danger; the necessary knowledge is not there, or if it is there, it is not well enough organized, and there are still too many erroneous fundamental doctrines. We are only at the very beginning of the first insight into the colossal disaster from which the human race has been suffering for thousands of years and by which it seems about to be engulfed. This disaster cannot be understood or overcome by little medicinal remedies, ideologies, political slogans, or prayers. These methods will all only serve to deepen it. The first priorities must be the preservation of insight that has been gained, the *furtherance and protection of truth under all circumstances,* the courage to comprehend the enormity of the social disaster, and a trust in the natural life function. An essential feature of this biopathic misery is the fact that the natural life function is ignored, feared, and everywhere repressed. Yet it is, and will remain, the only hope. *It is and will remain bound to the natural sexual function of the animal species "man."* There is no getting away from this conclusion, and it is a good thing, too.

Dr. Friedrich Lönne, chief physician at the Theresienhospital in Düsseldorf, wrote in his treatise *Wirksame Krebsbekämpfung* (1937): "We have to reckon with the fact that every year in Germany about 15,000 women die of cancer of the uterus and the vagina and about 3,500 to 4,000 die of breast cancer. Of the 15,000 that die of cancer of the vagina and uterus, more than 12,000 have a cancer of the cervix . . ."

Cancer of the genital organs and cancer of the breast are far more common than cancer of any other organ. The *sex*-biopathic nature of cancer emerges unmistakably from this fact. If considered in conjunction with the prevalence of sexual frigidity in women, this finding is merely an expression in cancer statistics of the disturbances of the sexual functions, which were known to us for a long time from our sex-economic clinical practice. It is precisely this relation between sexual pathology and cancer statistics that leads to an important conclusion: *The local cancerous process is a manifestation resulting from the damaged sex-economy of the organism. Consequently, the elimination of cancer requires a radical change in the entire sexual hygiene of the population.* In the face of this conclusion, the statements of many cancer specialists do not sound very logical. Because of their impotence in the battle against cancer, they hold to the old, erroneous theories. Instead of drawing the same conclusions that we did, based on the predilection of the cancer tumor for *sexual* organs, they write this sort of thing:

> Scientific cancer research today is of the opinion that besides the local causes for the development of cancer, a second,

systemic factor must be assumed, namely weakness of the anti-blastic system. [The *antiblastic system*, not understood until now, is in reality nothing other than our "B-reaction," that is, the "orgonotic potency" of the organism.] In the *practical* treatment of cancer we have, for clinical reasons, to keep to the theory of the *local* origin of cancer. For, if we had to overcome a systemic disease already present *before* the appearance of the local cancer tumor, then even the best operation or the best form of irradiation would be only a partial and rather questionable solution. Physician and patient would both lose their confidence in the curability of cancer, for a method of treating a *systemic* disease, if it really exists, is not known to us [from *Krebskrankheiten* (Leipzig, 1937)].

In other words, if we do not know a way to cure the cancer *biopathy,* then it simply does not exist and we must stay with the theory of the *local* origin of the cancer *tumor,* otherwise both patient and doctor will lose confidence! *What confidence? Confidence in what?* Confidence in an illusion, an illusion blocking the way to an understanding and elimination of the carcinomatous biopathy. Lönne's argument is similar to that of many psychiatrists: they deny the social origin of sexual repression and the sexual-biopathic nature of neuroses and psychoses because, if they were to establish such connections, they would come into sharp conflict with many social institutions and would be *forced* to publicly defend unpopular *facts.* Such tactics have nothing to do with either medicine or science in general. They are motivated strictly by business interests and a concern for one's livelihood.

The reader will now better understand why the first cancer case I chose to describe was a carcinomatous shrinking biopathy with no diagnosable malignant tumors, and why, throughout this account of the cancer disease, the *biopathic background rather than the local tumor* is emphasized.

It is asserted in the literature on cancer statistics that the increase in cancer deaths over the past decades is to be ascribed to more accurate diagnosis, both on the living organism and post-mortem; in other words, that the increase is an artifact. In order to uphold the "pure hereditary nature of cancer," it is denied that primitive peoples, who still lead a natural sexual life, are relatively free of cancer and that the increase in the statistical record of cancer deaths corresponds to a real growth of the disease.

Following is a table giving the statistics on cancer deaths in Norway between 1853 and 1925 (according to Gade):

	Cancer Deaths per 100,000 Inhabitants	Number of Physicians in the Country	Percentage of Cancer Death Certificates Made Out By Physicians
1853	7	295	20.4
1860	12	330	28.8
1870	27	410	38.5
1880	42	551	50.0
1890	58	658	55.4
1900	91	1066	82.7
1910	93	1177	88.3
1920	105	1281	92.4
1925	118	1496	98.5

The interpretation of such statistics by the theorists of heredity is understandable in the following way: the heredity mystique does not admit that the social environment influences hereditary factors. Even though it is correct, the doctrine of the heredity of acquired characteristics has not to this day won practical acceptance. We have every reason to doubt the rational scientific character of the heredity doctrine. However, there can be no doubt at all that an emotional factor plays a completely uncontrolled role in all considerations of heredity. And it is precisely this emotional factor in the mystical theory of heredity that excludes the influence of the social environment and eternalizes the inherited characteristics. According to this theory, inherited diseases are already present in the "hereditary basis" and are therefore inaccessible from the standpoint of prophylaxis. Consequently, changing the social environment is considered to be misleading and superfluous. Indeed, since cancer is found in plants and animals, in other words, quite generally throughout nature, there is no difference, from this point of view, between primitive peoples who live in close relation to nature and mechanized man. Accordingly, the cancer tumor corresponds to an "embryonic malformation" and is treated in hereditarian textbooks in conjunction with teratism. It follows from this hereditarian approach that there can be no genuine increase in cancer deaths, only an artificial one, explained by the idea that better techniques of diagnosis and a greater number of physicians have resulted in a rise in the number of cancer tumors that are diagnosed.

The secret purpose of all these hereditary arguments is to try to save the erroneous theory of the unalterable hereditary basis from being supplanted by the living, functional concept of the interaction of plasma and environment. Not one single productive thought on the subject of medical influencing of so-called hereditary diseases emerges from the mechanistic, metaphysical theory of heredity. Thinking of this kind leads straight to the mystical idea of the hereditary superman and inferior man, that is, to the ideas of the emotional plague. We should not be surprised, however, because this kind of thinking represents the conservative function of the theory of heredity, on which the works of Darwin, De Vries, Freud, and others have barely had an impact. The theory of heredity is not a science but an ethical alibi.

For the reasons I have outlined, it is difficult to make any comment on sham statistics such as those just given. The number of physicians in Norway rose considerably after 1853, making an evaluation of the figures in that case extremely difficult. However, it cannot be convincingly maintained that the increase in cancer deaths in New York State between 1921 and 1940 is attributable simply to better methods of diagnosis. Little has been learned about cancer diagnosis since 1921, and there was not a marked increase in the number of physicians. Yet, over the course of twenty years, the death rate from cancer increased in New York from 104.1 to 158.4 per 100,000 of population.

The argument that the increase in cancer mortality is an artificial statistic or that it can be explained by the increase in average life expectancy becomes invalid if one does not *isolate the cancer biopathy from the other sexual biopathies* but instead considers it alongside the parallel rise in deaths from cardiovascular biopathy and the growing number of cases of schizophrenia, criminality, and suicide. Once this connection is made and the common sex-economic and social background of all the sexual biopathies is understood, then such empty talk is silenced. We will be confronted at that time with the naked fact of the murderous effect of the emotional plague and of the ignorance of physicians and educators in questions concerning the natural sexual life of children and adolescents. No other negligence committed by medicine can compare with this inexcusable general indifference to sex-starvation diseases. It was not the fault of medicine and pedagogy that hundreds of thousands died of the bubonic plague, nor that countless women died of puerperal fever. The agents causing these diseases were unknown. But in the final analysis murderous biopathies are socially produced by the irrational reactions of sexually pathological people. The avoidance of sexual problems or the compulsively moralistic judging of them is an automatic reaction on the part of physicians and educators. The opposition of these social groups to the struggle against sexual biopathies is proof of this statement.

Nevertheless, a powerful hope confronts these distressing truths. Once it is understood that there are biopathic diseases of the vital apparatus that can be simultaneously *the cause and the result of social ills,* the picture, at first troubling and complicated, simplifies. It is true that there is no human being capable of functioning alone as a saviour: there can be no redeemer, no matter how much the mass of people hope for one. But the constant deepening of the social misery will bring about what no individual could ever achieve: *the human masses, who suffer so much, both biopathically and socially, will be compelled to think rationally and to regain contact with their basic biological being.* This revolution will probably be one of the most significant results of the emotional plague of the twentieth century. There are already many positive signs of its development.

Ten or twenty years ago, a concern with the sexuality of the child and the adolescent was taboo, almost as much for the scientist as for the layman. Today that is no longer the case, and it is becoming less and less so. Sexual suffering has become too obvious and too widespread. The attempts—still predominantly unofficial—to get at the misery are becoming more numerous and more insistent. They are not yet included in any political program, but for the first time in human history, political programs themselves are being examined very carefully with regard to their usefulness and rationality. We already hear the question being asked as to whether politics itself is not a social sickness. The consciousness of the natural demands of life is coming more and more to the fore, not as a challenge or dream of individuals but as an achievement of human society.

The reader will ask what these general social questions have to do with cancer. The answer is, a great deal, in fact everything! The main purpose of this book is to demonstrate convincingly that cancer, as a special form of biopathy, is *inseparably* connected with the problem of sexuality and with the social structure of our society. Moreover, cancer has remained an unsolved problem up to the present day because neither its sexual nor social causation has been taken into consideration. What does organic pathology have to do with sociology? is a question that we often hear. But what the sexual life of the masses has to do with politics and sociology is no longer wondered about, as it was a few years ago in Europe. On this subject, sex-economy has succeeded in breaking down the wall of traditional thinking. Today there is no longer any "non-political" sexology, as there still was at the Third World Congress of the World League for Sexual Reform in Vienna, in 1930. Today it is well known in the realm of biopsychiatry that sexuality and sociology can be treated only in relation to each other. It will not be long before *organic pathology, in evaluating a tissue lesion, will investigate its social and sexual causations.* Human beings are *biosexual* and *social* organisms that develop disturbances in the tissue functions just as they do in their emotional lives.

Those who are familiar with the figures on the increase of the cancer biopathy will have asked themselves *why* this particular disease has spread the way it has. Several years ago psychiatrists found themselves confronted with the same question when they were forced to recognize that psychic diseases were not limited to those showing hysterical and compulsive symptoms and that *character neuroses* were increasing steadily and affecting more and more people. The answer then was that before the turn of the century, sexual repression and armoring were total. Breakthroughs of neurotic symptoms were, therefore, correspondingly restricted to manifestations such as hysteria, etc. The totally armored individual was the "normal person." Since then, sexual demands have broken through with increasing intensity, requiring recognition and gratification. The circumscribed symptom neurosis gave way more and more to the general character neurosis: *heightened life demands collided with old, rigid forms of living, irrational dogmata, and inner neurotic inhibitions.*

Human beings who become conscious of their sexual needs because of changing mores but who simultaneously lack the ways and means of naturally discharging their sexual energy and experiencing full gratification are necessarily torn apart. They become biopathically ill, asocial, and criminal. There is no way back to yesterday! We are dealing with *progress,* even if it is a *painful* and momentarily dangerous process. Attempting to stem it simply increases the misery that already exists.

To the reactionary and the mystic this will confirm the dangers of "immorality" and make them demand a return to the old, resigned way of living. (Actually, they make this demand constantly, but have nothing constructive to say that might alleviate human suffering.) However, there is no turning back biosocial development. There is only the possibility of allowing the development to occur in less painful and less dangerous ways.

What applies to the growing incidence of the cancer biopathy is applicable to biopathies in general. The entire development of society has begun to replace the old ways of sexual living with new ones. At the turn of the century, a woman of thirty-five was a matron. Today, she is a young woman full of *joie de vivre.* The same applies to a man of forty or fifty. But education and medicine have not kept in step with this social development. *The structural capacity of people to live fully has remained far behind their knowledge and their demands. The stasis of biological energy in human organisms is therefore much greater* than it was twenty or forty years ago. Around 1900, a frigid woman, sitting at home with no job and no outside contact with men, was much less likely to have experienced conscious sexual conflict than she is today, when she takes an increasingly more active part in social life. Industrial development and the present war are the main causes of this situation. We can probably expect even more revolutionary changes in the life of women. No one except the fascists will demand that she "return to the hearth," and we find that even fascism has been powerless in this matter. It now follows that if the human organism is exposed to *an increasing discrepancy between what it wants from life and its capacity for gratification, then, clearly, the stasis of biological energy will increase proportionately.* And the greater the sexual stasis, the greater the physiological and emotional damage to the organism. Cancer is the most significant somatic expression of the biophysiological effect of sexual stasis; schizophrenia is the most significant expression in the emotional realm. It is no coincidence, in fact, it is logical, that the state of Massachusetts, which has stringent laws against contraception even in the middle of the twentieth century, also has one of the highest cancer death rates in the United States.[2] The finding that cancer is a disease caused by sexual starvation will have to be taken seriously.

[2] *"What are the public health aspects of cancer?* Cancer is responsible for more deaths than any other disease with the exception of heart disease. Approximately one out of every eight deaths in Massachusetts is due to this disease. Massachusetts has one of the highest death rates of any state from this disease." *Whats and Whys of Cancer,* Massachusetts Department of Public Health (1939).

The enormous increase in biopathies is therefore a simple expression of the discrepancy between the desire for a sexual life and the incapacity for a sexual life. The desire for life has grown enormously but the increase of the capacity for living (sexual potency, capacity for responsibility, self-regulation, etc.) has not been corresponding. The conclusion is not that the will to live should be reduced but that *in the human organism a structural capacity for living that keeps pace with the demands of life should be established.* It is essentially an educational and social task, and not a medical one. Clearly, the establishment of the full capacity for life and pleasure will require the elimination of restricting institutions and laws, some of which date back a hundred, some a thousand, years. If, therefore, adolescents of either sex enter into *satisfying, natural* love relationships *before* reaching the "legal" age, and are then exposed to reform school, an antisocial environment, because of some age-old laws, it is the old laws that should be done away with, not the natural sexuality of the young people. From this one example the reader can easily figure out for himself which reactionary forces such a social experiment will have to contend with, and how intense the conflict will be. Obviously the struggle for a "new world order," such as is longed for everywhere, will not be merely theoretical but will have to deal practically with specific life problems. It is precisely these life problems that have led our troubled world into chaos, and the need for profound and revolutionary solutions has prevented those who are calling for a new world order from speaking concretely and frankly. The change in society will be brought about not by political plans and phrases but by *the actual solution of individual problems.*

THE "ORGONON" PLAN: ON THE POSSIBILITY OF CANCER PREVENTION

Until the summer of 1942 I had not allowed patients to keep orgone accumulators in their own homes. A number of friends had suggested it, but I refused for several reasons. From a purely legal point of view it was unclear in what form the orgone accumulators should be released for public use. Not being particularly fond of business matters, I had no desire to become an entrepreneur. Yet, to have left the manufacture and distribution of the orgone accumulator to businessmen would have meant surrendering orgone research to the money-making practices of today's pharmaceutical industry. I was deterred also by the thought of the ugly competition that inevitably would have broken out. I had neither the time nor the inclination for that sort of thing. I applied for a patent on the accumulator, but with the explicit notification to the Patent Office and to all my colleagues that I was patenting it for the sole purpose of protecting it from unscrupulous exploitation and profiteering. Like water and air, orgone energy can be obtained for nothing and is available in unending quantities. The purpose of collecting it in the accumulator (a process similar to filling a wash basin with water) is to supply it in *concentrated* form. It is important to provide a means of access to concentrated orgone energy for even the poorest people.

It will be asked why I did not simply present my discovery to the world, as is customary. Even though I have no interest in gaining any financial rewards from the discovery, I could very easily have basked in the fame that would have resulted from making my findings public. But I had to bear in mind the future of orgone research. No social institution had deemed it necessary to offer our Institute the economic support that any below-average experimental work in the chemical field could obtain easily. I was also influenced by the fact that in Scandinavia orgone researchers had to cope with the pettiness and irrationality of conventional officials in science. These officials had tried to completely destroy the work because they sensed that orgone physics was a dangerous opponent and competitor to the mechanism and mysticism that dominate natural science. My opponents had vigorously attacked me in Norway in 1937–1938; it was a crucial warning. I had to rid myself of any naïveté. It is dangerous to expect help from social institutions that owe their existence to the *lack* of knowledge. What if Edison had had to look to the manufacturers of gas lamps for material support in the construction of his electrical incandescent lamps? Atmospheric orgone energy is to chemical drugs what the electrical bulb was to the gas lamp.

I always recall that Madame Curie did not have enough money to buy radium for her research and had to rely on gifts while at the same time the money barons were making millions from radium. Having seen the business ethic in practice, and knowing how routine science depends on it, I learned caution and circumspection.

Since I would not sell, donate, or personally exploit the patent, there seemed to be no way to make orgone energy generally available for practical use. But as so often happens in such situations the natural course of events led spontaneously to a solution, which I will now describe.

For many years I had enjoyed the friendship of a seventy-year-old trapper and fisherman in Maine, where I have a cabin. I had set up a laboratory there for the study of atmospheric orgone energy. The high relative humidity during the summer months in New York made work in the city impossible, and the research in orgone physics was then transferred to Maine.

In February 1942 I learned from this man's family that he had fallen ill with cancer of the prostate and was in the hospital for X-ray treatment. The tumor had been discovered a few months earlier and in November 1941 his doctors had given him only six to twelve months to live.

The news affected me deeply. We had become close friends years before, when I had told him about the nature of bions. This simple man revealed a natural understanding of the living process far more acute than academic biology or physics could have provided. I had my large microscope with me and I asked the man if he would like to see the life energy in bions. To my complete astonishment, my friend correctly described bions even before looking into the microscope. For many decades he had been observing, with the keen instinct of a human being intimately attuned to nature, the growth of seeds and the character of earth humus. He had formed the following picture: Everywhere, he told me, there are very small, very delicate "bubbles" (vesicles); they represent "life," and from them everything that is "life" develops; they are so small that they cannot be seen with the naked eye; but the moss on the rocks develops from them, and the rock, exposed permanently to rain, "softens" on the surface and forms these "life bubbles." He had often tried to talk with academic visitors about them, but their response was always a strange smile. Yet he knew he was right. I knew he was right also, for how could moss "seeds" "strike root" in the rock?

When this man saw, now magnified to 4000x, the vesicles whose existence he had already surmised, he experienced what he described as "the deepest shock of my life." He had never believed that one day he would actually see those "bubbles," which he thought of each time he tried to conceive of the greenness, the growth, the flowering, and the fertility of the soil around him.

I had not told him anything about atmospheric orgone energy during the first summers, because I was afraid it might spoil our friendship. It later turned out that he too, from the same fear, had said nothing to me about his ideas.

When I returned to the orgone-physical work in Maine in the summer of 1942, I found my friend in a cachectic state. He had lost a great deal of weight, was stooped, was scarcely able to work, tired very quickly, had no appetite, and was losing hope. He knew he did not have long to live; a physician had told him so. He told me that he could not accept his fate. He was, in fact, resisting it vigorously. He did not want to die; this world of woods, mountains, and lakes, in which he had spent almost seventy years of his life, was too beautiful, too much a part of him. It was impossible for him to conceive of not being able to see and enjoy it. He loved the solitude of his woods, in which for decades he had earned his livelihood with hard work.

The X-ray treatment had partially alleviated his severe pains for a short time; now they were returning. He had no money, having been a poor businessman all his life. His family was in despair. The physicians had given no hope at all; death was expected within a very short time. The man did not want to go back to the hospital. He had felt miserable there and had rebelled against everything and everyone. He was not only a bad businessman but a bad patient as well. As a person close to nature, he did not adapt easily to the "values" of culture and civilization.

He knew too much about nature, love, and life to possess the highly respected characteristic of "resignation to fate." He was deeply religious in the *good* sense, but he despised the church business. Hence, the people in the area considered him an apostate, although they had great respect for him. I always felt that, with the appropriate financial conditions, he could have become an outstanding natural scientist. How many great talents are lost because the necessary material means are lacking.

When I asked him one day whether he believed in God he replied: "Of course, he is everywhere, in me and all around us. Just look over there." He pointed to the blue color in front of the distant mountains. "I call it life, but people laugh at me, so I don't like to speak about it." Thus, he too was aware of the existence of orgone energy in the atmosphere.

For weeks I had been discussing with his family the possibility of getting him to use an orgone accumulator. He mistrusted all medicine and was stubborn too. It was therefore not going to be easy to persuade him; his daughter was hesitant about trying.

When he confided his impressions to me and called the blue in the atmosphere "life," I told him about my own findings. I told him that he was completely right and that what he called "life" was in fact the biological energy that I had discovered and named "orgone." I told him it could be concentrated, and could be seen flashing like lightning. The Northern Lights, I told him, were a manifestation of a special state of orgone energy. One evening I showed him the orgone radiation in the orgonoscope. He immediately understood the nature of this radiation, without any of the compulsive doubts that our mechanistic and mystical academicians develop in such cases in order to preserve their scholarly dignity. We prevailed upon him to build an orgone accumulator for his own use. Cautiously and suspiciously he went to work. We were anxious to have him finish it, because he was declining rapidly. When the accumulator was finally built, and he had sat in it for the first time, he told us with a beaming smile that he had felt a prickling sensation in his hands. In spite of this, he could not be persuaded to use the accumulator regularly. I eventually found out that he was resisting the very idea that he was ill. A friendly talk was of little help. Then stormy weather caused severe pains to set in and he could no longer move; he had burning pains in the urethra and was on the verge of giving in to his disease.

After a great deal of work on my part, and with the help of his strong will to live, I persuaded him to sit in the accumulator twice a day, for an hour each time. The pains stopped in a few days. Microscopic examination of the urine showed disintegrating cancer cells; the T-bacilli were immobile, even though they were present in large numbers. He was able to get up again, eat well, and walk around. I made him promise me that he would take good care of himself for at least a year and give his organism a chance to recover. I also told him not to feel ashamed of being ill.

The effects of the accumulator, combined with my psychotherapeutic efforts, were successful. I followed the improvement of his condition for several weeks. He came to visit me in my cabin, four miles from his home, and asked about the properties of the energy that he called "life." He intuitively understood everything that I had worked out experimentally. When the summer was over I departed, convinced that he would soon stop using the accumulator regularly. But I was wrong. He came to like the accumulator and acknowledged that for the time being it had saved his life. He wrote that he was feeling much better. The pains had gone, he was gaining weight, and felt, as he put it, "young again." In the space of two months he put on 7 lbs. For a time he excreted a brown fluid, i.e., the tumor detritus.

Here was a man who was supposed to have died a long time

ago. Yet at the time this report was written he was still alive and lively, with almost no pain and no need to use drugs. Whatever his future fate might be, he was enjoying, at the end of his life, the power of what he called "God" and "life."

This man was Herman O. Templeton. He became the first manager of the Orgone Institute Laboratories, which we established under the name "Orgonon" in Franklin County, Maine.*

What I am now going to describe is *only a plan* for the Orgone Institute. Its realization does not depend on the Institute alone. We do not know how long it will take for social administrators to recognize the danger to human existence that results from sexual biopathies. Nor do we know how long this war will last and impede the fostering of human development. But the Orgone Institute has, nevertheless, undertaken a few decisive steps toward the prevention of biopathies. I now leave it to the readers to judge whether our efforts deserve the support of the public; I am talking not merely of recognition and praise, but of *tangible* economic and social support.**

Templeton was the first cancer patient to have an orgone accumulator in his own home. The benefit of being able to treat oneself at home cannot be overestimated. If my friend developed pains, he did not need to wait for an appointment with a doctor, or travel 50 miles to see one, as he would otherwise have had to do. He could utilize the orgone irradiation immediately, and as often as he needed to. He had the leisure to become familiar with the radiation—to become friendly with it, as it were. The accumulator was not some medical apparatus in a clinical laboratory. The patient could show it to his acquaintances and let them sit in it. They could

---

* Mr. Templeton subsequently died from an anorgonotic attack. [Ed.]

** While much progress was made toward the implementation of the plan described by Reich in the following pages (written in 1943), the circumstances that eventually led to his death gradually brought the actual functioning of Orgonon to a halt. Today, as a part of the Wilhelm Reich Infant Trust Fund, Reich's estate, Orgonon awaits a renewal of support, which will enable it to again become the research center of orgonomy. The unprecedented interest in this young science gives us hope that the support will be forthcoming. [Ed.]

discuss the phenomena with him and confirm his experiences. He was not the passive object of a course of treatment, but took an active role. He was learning to think about and control the energy that helped him so much. He was becoming a new type of social worker, acquainting those in his own social sphere with this subject, independent of his doctor. He was also saving a great deal of money that would otherwise have had to be spent on travel, the doctor, drugs, etc.

These medical and social effects, produced by having the *orgone accumulator in the home,* are the basis of the Orgonon plan. Our recuperating cancer patient volunteered to take over the construction of the accumulators. Later, his daughter succeeded him in this task. In time, if everything went as planned, the demand for accumulators would increase. A piece of land was therefore needed where we could set up workshops. But in order to buy the land and build the workshops we needed money. Orgone research requires large amounts of money, which those of us working at the Institute cannot provide and which no one else will provide. For that reason, the small sums charged for the use of the orgone accumulators will eventually have to cover not only the costs of their manufacture but also the entire research work. As people become increasingly familiar with the nature of orgone energy, they will voluntarily contribute to orgone research. Their reward will be the health-providing effect of the orgone accumulator.

So rather than selling or exploiting the orgone accumulator, we would put it to work for orgone research. This could be done only in the form of a non-profit, public institution.*

The Institute bought a 150-acre farm in Maine for $4000. The money was made available as an interest-free loan by a schoolteacher who was a student at the Institute; repayment was to take place at any time during the course of the following years. There were a few old buildings on the land from which enough material

---

* The Wilhelm Reich Foundation was established in 1949 for this purpose. It no longer functions. [Ed.]

could be obtained to construct the essential workshops. Herman Templeton took over the administration of the building projects.

The National Research Council in Washington was advised of the plan.

Orgonon is situated at an altitude of 1600 feet, and has a dry, sunny climate. It is thus eminently suited for experimental orgone research. In time, all of the biophysical work can be transferred to Orgonon. The difficulty of working in a small New York laboratory overcrowded with instruments and apparatus would at last be overcome. Orgonon could become the home of orgone-physical life-research, which has been wandering from country to country now for fifteen years. It deserves some stability and peace.

The orgone accumulators built at Orgonon remain the property of the Institute. Just as one rents a telephone, one acquires an orgone accumulator for the desired period of time, in return for a monthly contribution to the "Orgone Research Fund." The income for this fund comes from contributions by students and associates and others, payments for experimental tests in the laboratory, and the monthly rentals for the use of the accumulators. The fund is our only source of money for the running costs of the project, the salaries of the workers, and the costs of expanding the orgone biophysical research.

Because the orgone accumulator produces a vagotonic excitation of the organism and charges the blood orgonotically, thereby increasing the resistance of the organism to disease, it will become an indispensable instrument in the fight against those diseases that consist of a reduction in the biological defense reactions of the organism and a contraction of the vital apparatus. I have no doubt that the initial hesitant reaction to the novelty and simplicity of the apparatus will be overcome and that the officials will eventually authorize the distribution of orgone accumulators. I have relinquished any idea of material gain, not out of magnanimity but simply in order to eliminate any suspicion that I might be trying to compete economically with the powerful pharmaceutical industry.

I would like to emphasize that my research with the orgone energy accumulator is *not directed exclusively to cancer, even though orgone energy has proved its efficacy primarily with this disease; it is directed toward the bio-energetic charging of the organism.* I maintain that *cancer prevention depends on our being able to increase the orgonotic potency in the organism long before T-bacilli or even cancer cells develop. It is important that we prevent the shrinking of the vital apparatus and the ensuing putrefaction.* This task falls into two parts, a biophysical aspect and a broader social-medical one.

The biophysical task consists in the direct administration of orgone energy by means of the accumulator. The broader, social task is to educate people to understand and prevent the sexual biopathies of children and adolescents, which lead not only to the carcinomatous shrinking biopathy but to *every* kind of biopathy. Of the two, the former task is much the easier, though at first, it will have to be carried out on a limited, experimental scale, in one of two ways:

1. As the number of users grows, we will keep an exact record of how many of them develop cancer or other diseases after three to five years. This will give us a picture of the possibilities of cancer prevention. (The emotional factor, the shrinking of the life apparatus as a result of resignation, is, of course, incalculable. In all probability, it can be prevented only by the fulfillment of the social task.) Let us assume that, from a given time, 5000 accumulators are in use. If the 5000 users were to develop cancer at a lesser rate than the general populace this part of the task would be accomplished. The principle could then be applied nationally or internationally.

2. With the help of public organizations this task also could be solved in the following manner: a district of a state or city with approximately 10,000 inhabitants would be provided with "an accumulator in every home." Social workers would keep exact records of the number of cancer cases occurring in this district. These would be compared with the records of other districts where the orgone

accumulator was not being used. In two to five years it would be possible to draw valid conclusions about the possibilities for general cancer prophylaxis.

This plan may appear fantastic to many readers, but I would say to them that if it is possible to mobilize the populations of an entire planet for purposes of war then it must be possible to mobilize a district of 10,000 inhabitants for the purpose of a crucial experiment. I am well aware of all the circumstances that will create difficulties, but the execution of this plan *is* possible. It must not be left undone.

Appendix

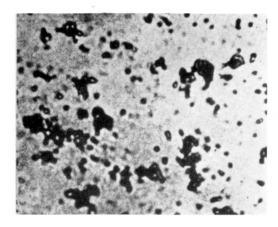

FIGURE 25. Coal bions, produced from incandescent coal dust subjected to swelling in solution of bouillon and potassium chloride

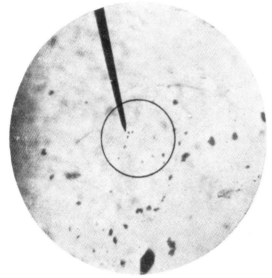

FIGURE 26. Three T-bacilli (*pointer*). Gram stain (red). Photo taken *immediately* after a blood charcoal preparation was made. Magnified about 5000x; actual size less than 0.25 micron. The large black spots are fine coal dust

FIGURE 27. Cast-iron filing, dry. Approx. 300x

FIGURE 28. Iron filing after fifteen minutes in a solution of bouillon and potassium chloride. The vesicles, originally non-motile, separate and order themselves in lines which correspond to a magnetic field. Approx. 500x

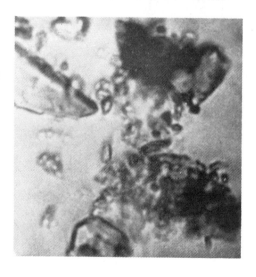

FIGURE 29. Energy vesicles in earth particles and humus

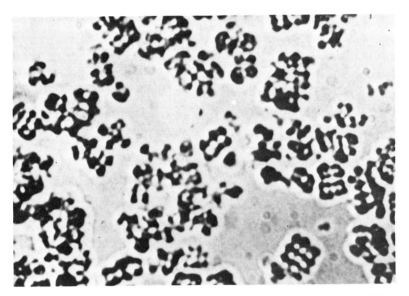

FIGURE 30. PA bion culture. Approx. 3000x

FIGURE 31. Blue PA bions from autoclaved human blood in the living preparation. Approx. 2000x ("B-reaction")

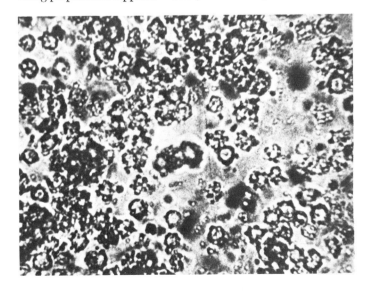

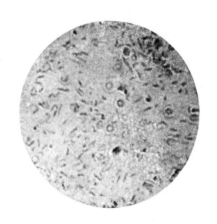

FIGURE 32. T-bacilli obtained
from sarcomatous tissue. Approx.
5400x

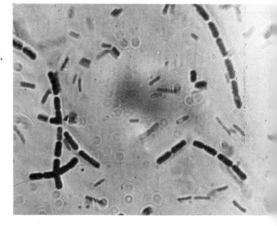

FIGURE 33. Bacilli obtained
through air infection. Approx.
1000x. Compare with Fig. 32

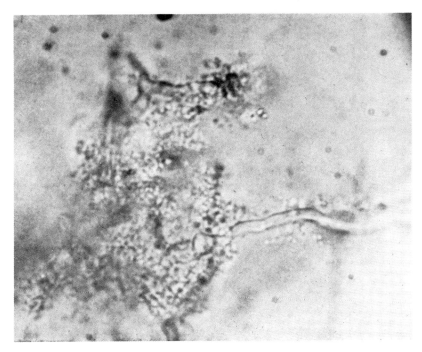

FIGURE 34. Vesicular (bionous) disintegration in a grass infusion. Approx. 700x

FIGURE 35. Bionous vesicles showing an intense blue glimmer in a blade of grass. Approx. 1500x

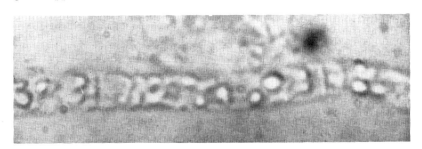

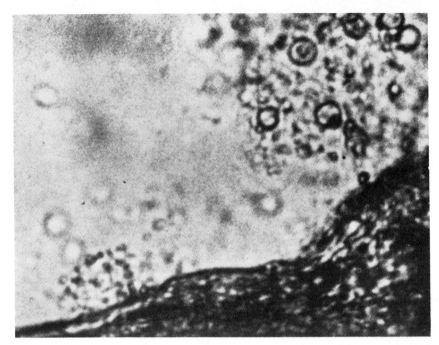

FIGURE 36. An early phase in the development of amoeba limax. Spherical forms at the upper right resulting from grass which has undergone swelling; developing into amoebae. At lower left a protozoan forming. Approx. 1000x. Time-lapse photography was used to observe the process

FIGURE 37. Same preparation as Fig. 36 in a more advanced phase. The large spherical forms at the left in the process of developing into flowing amoebae. Approx. 1000x

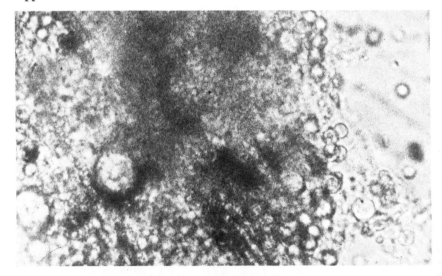

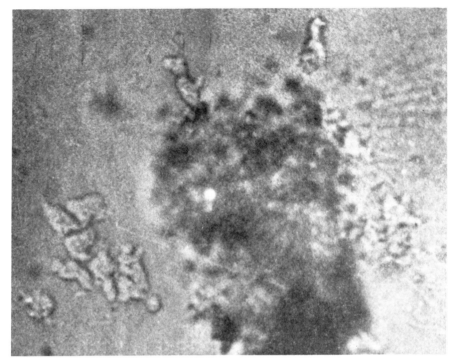

FIGURE 38. Protozoal germs dissolving (along the right margin of disintegrated grass). At the left and top, amoebae in the process of separation

FIGURE 39. Heap of bion vesicles in advanced phase of organization

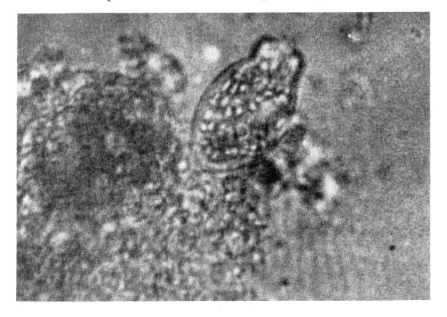

FIGURE 40.   Protozoan developing from
moss.   Approx. 3500x

FIGURE 41a.   Beginning protozoal
formation at margin of bionously disintegrating grass. Approx. 700x

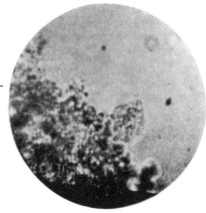

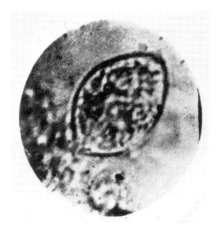

FIGURE 41b. Bion vesicles in an organized heap. Approx. 1500x

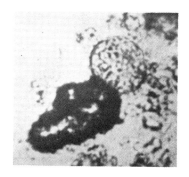

FIGURE 41c. Protozoal germ (bionous vesicle) developing at right margin of disintegrating grass

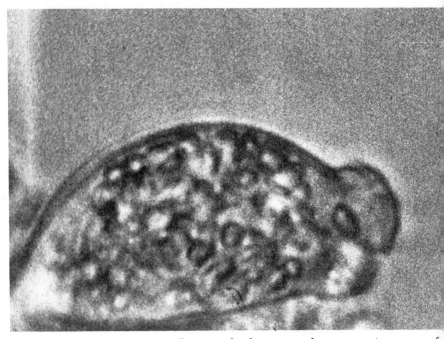

FIGURE 42. "Org-protozoan." A completely organized protozoan in a state of expansion, although not yet detached from the grass blade. Observe vesicular structure of the protoplasm. Approx. 3000x

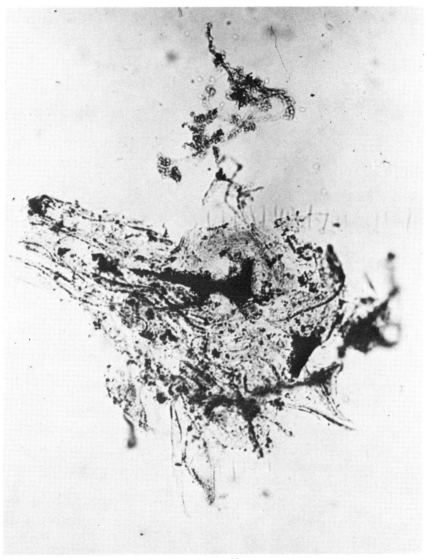

FIGURE 43.

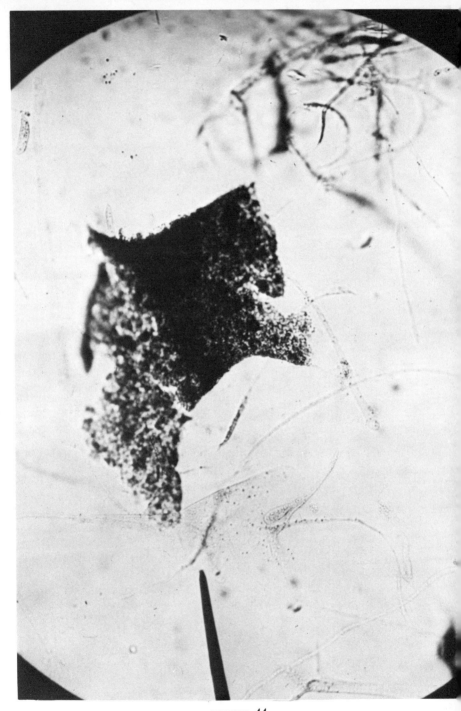

FIGURE 44.

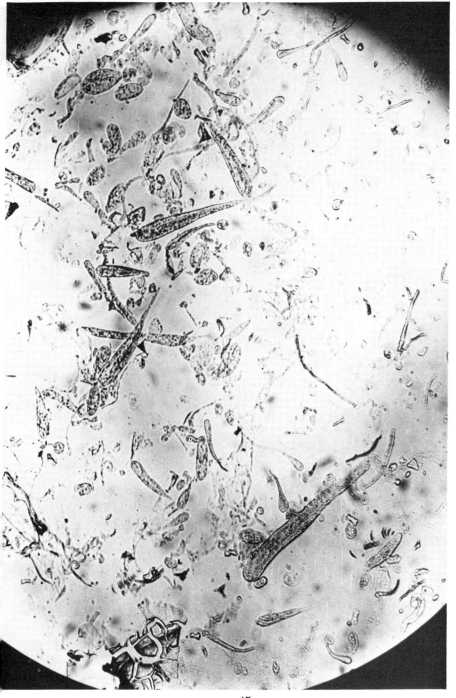

FIGURE 45.

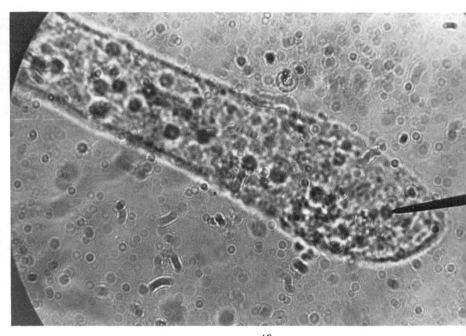

FIGURE 46.

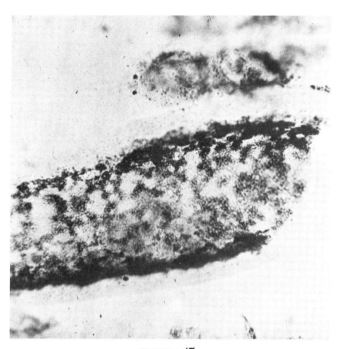

FIGURE 47.

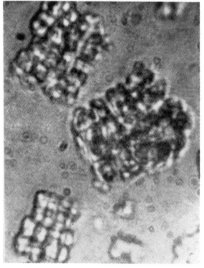

FIGURES 48a and b. The bion culture (SAPA) which disclosed the existence of biological orgone energy, 1939

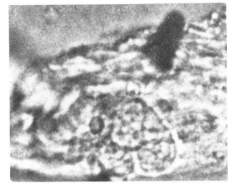

FIGURE 49. Cancer of the bone (fibula) in which the tissue shows vesicular structure with a heap of cancer cells in an advanced stage of organization. Approx. 1000x

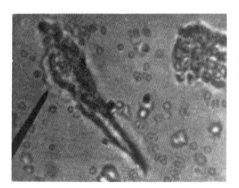

FIGURE 50a. Precancerous spindle-shaped cell formation (*pointer*) and SAPA bion (*upper right*) from vaginal secretion

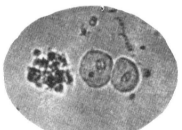

FIGURE 50b. Contraction to spherical shape and immobilization of two amoeboid, oblong, mobile cancer cells due to the effect of a SAPA bion

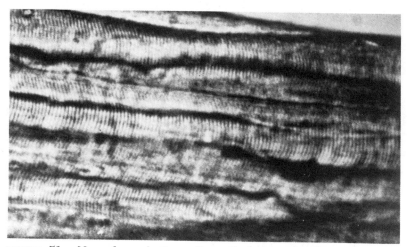

FIGURE 51.   Normal muscle tissue (human) showing striated, non-vesicular structure. Observed in the living state in physiological salt solution. Approx. 1000x

FIGURE 52.   Cancerous muscle tissue from human uterus, showing bionous structure. Protozoal organization appears at right margin. Observed in physiological salt solution. Approx. 1000x

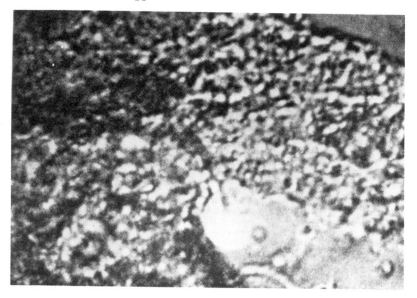

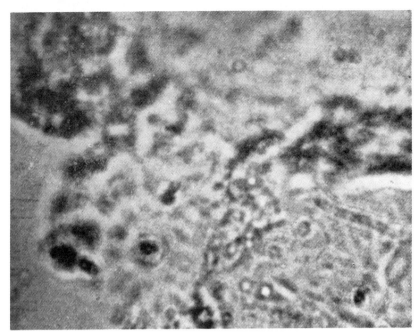

FIGURE 53. Epithelial cells from breast cancer. Observed in an unstained, live state in normal NaCl solution, one hour post-mastectomy. At upper and lower right, healthy epithelial cells showing no structure. Bionously disintegrated epithelium toward the center, extending downward. At left margin, heaps of cancer cells are seen in the process of formation. Approx. 1000x

FIGURE 54. Three typically club-shaped cancer cells from human tumor. Approx. 2300x, enlarged

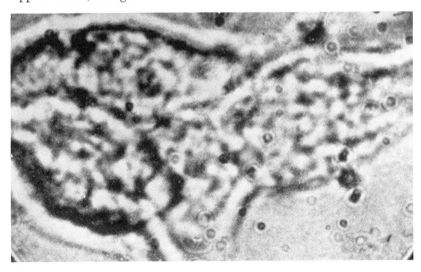

FIGURE 55a. Epithelial cells in KCl solution; from a wart on the cheek, showing precancerous changes (X)

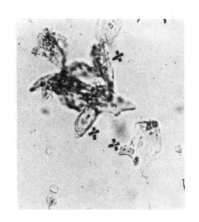

FIGURE 55b. Proliferation (X) from epithelial cell of same wart

FIGURE 56a. Precancerous epithelial cells from cervix, showing T-bodies and strongly luminating vesicles

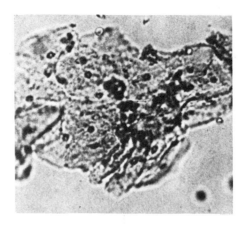

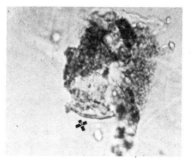

FIGURE 56b. Cancerous cervical epithelium showing spindle formation (X)

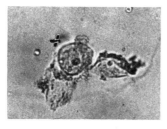

FIGURES 56c and d. Cancerous cervical epithelium showing developing cancer cells (X)

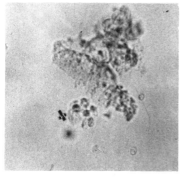

FIGURE 56e. Single spindle-shaped cancer cell from vaginal secretion (CA III)

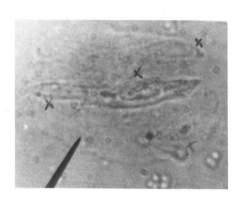

FIGURE 57. Formation of strongly chromatic spindle forms (X) inside an epithelial cell (*pointer*) obtained from vaginal secretion of a woman suspected of having cancer (CA III)

FIGURE 58a. Healthy epithelium, gastric glands of mouse

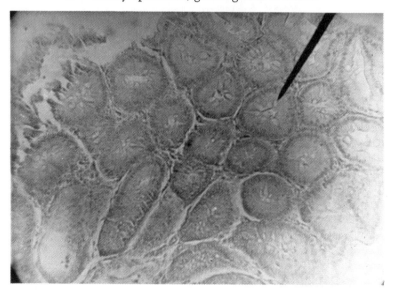

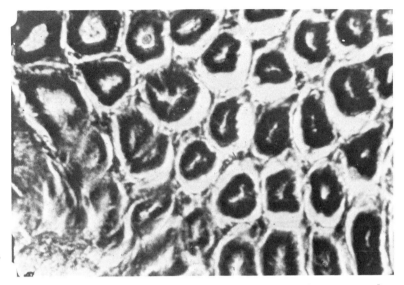

FIGURE 58b. Beginning carcinomatous degeneration of gastric epithelium in T-mouse, CA II and III. Cross section

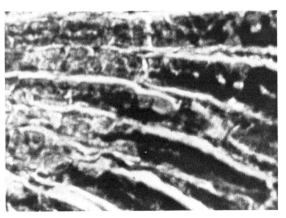

FIGURE 58c. Carcinomatous changes in intestinal gland cells of T-mouse (darkly stained with hematoxylin-eosin), corresponding to club-shaped forms in the living preparation. Phases CA II and III. Longitudinal section

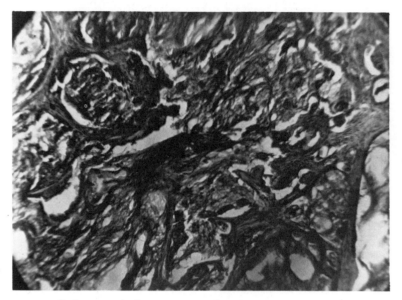

FIGURE 58d. Putrid disintegration of cancerous gastric mucosa of T-mouse (CA V)

FIGURE 59. Metastases in subcutaneous tissue of the neck, taken from T-mouse (CA III)

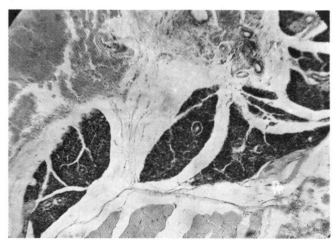

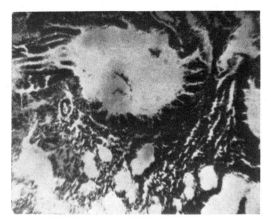

FIGURE 60a. Section of lung of a T-mouse stained with hematoxylin-eosin, showing cancer cell metastases. Approx. 300x

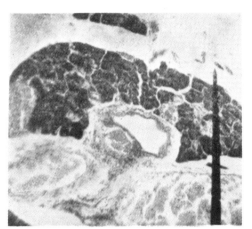

FIGURE 60b. Subcutaneous tissue of T-mouse showing cancer cell metastases, stained with hematoxylin-eosin. Arrow points to individual spindle cells. Approx. 300x

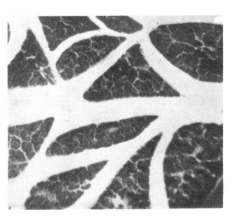

FIGURE 60c. Same metastatic cells taken from peritoneal cavity of a T-mouse. Stained with hematoxylin-eosin. Approx. 300x

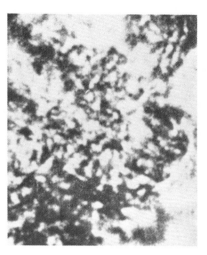

FIGURE 61a. Cancer cell model experiment Nr. 14. Coal bions shown penetrating substance of egg medium. Approx. 300x

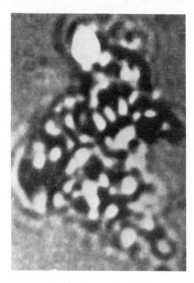

FIGURE 61b. Same as 61a, at approx. 2000x

FIGURE 61c. Bion cells in the living state

FIGURE 61d. Same, Gram-stained

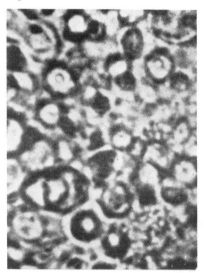

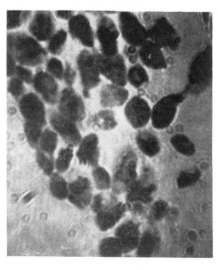

FIGURE 61e. Tumor produced in a healthy mouse by injection of T-bacilli

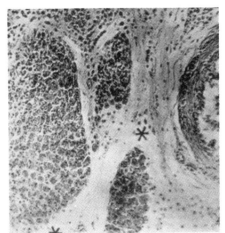

FIGURE 61f. T-bacilli seen in peritoneum of same mouse. Stained

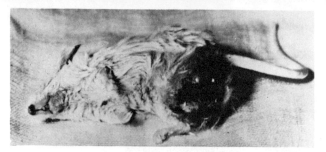

FIGURE 62a. Cancerous tumor in gluteal region in mouse, following injection of T-bacilli obtained from blood taken from a healthy human and allowed to disintegrate (10 Ge T)

FIGURE 62b. Same tumor excised from gluteal muscle

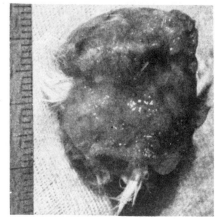

FIGURE 62c. Section of same tumor, stained, at the boundary between healthy and chronically inflamed tissue. Arrows indicate individual, large, deeply stained cancer cells

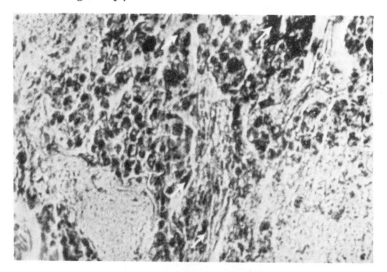

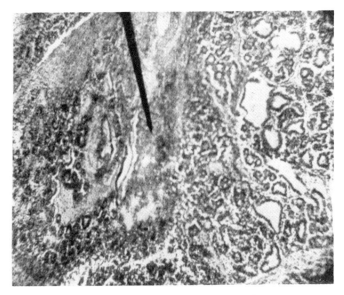

FIGURE 62d. Cyst formation in section of same tumor. Pointer directed to area showing chronic inflammation between healthy musculature and adenocarcinoma

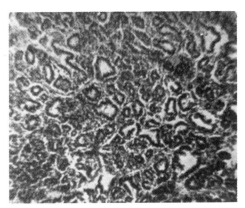

FIGURE 62e Another section showing complete adenocarcinomatous change in the muscle

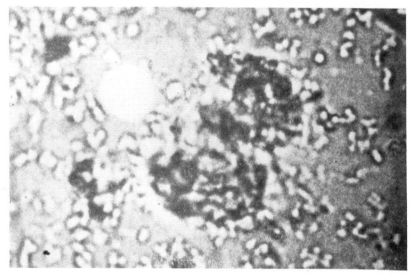

FIGURE 63. Blue PA bions penetrating into and destroying masses of cancer cells. Shown in living preparation. Reproduced from motion-picture film

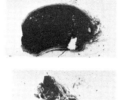

FIGURES 64a and b. Compact, hard breast cancer tumors from two untreated mice

FIGURE 64c. Sections from stomach and duodenum in which artificial cancer was produced (T-mouse). Atrophic gastric mucosa; polypous cancerous growths; masses of cancer cells in the peritoneum

FIGURE 64d. Mouse tumor showing putrid disintegration

FIGURE 64e. Tumor taken from mouse treated with orgone energy. Large cavities, previously blood-filled. Detritus (*left*) containing dead T-bacilli. Replacement by connective tissue (*center*). Residual cancer masses (*middle* and *right*)

FIGURE 64f. Tumor from a mouse treated with orgone energy. Large, previously blood-filled cavities now contain cancer tissue and detritus consisting of T-bacilli

FIGURE 64g. Tumor from mouse cured with orgone energy. Small amount of distintegrated cancer tissue present. Detritus, in center, sterile. Replacement connective tissue in lower part

Index

abasia, orgonomic explanation and treatment of, 348–52

Adam and Auler, 251

agglutination of bacteria and orgone energy withdrawal, 42

air germs, theory of, x, xix, 50, 238, 240–1, 243; absurdities of, 74–81; refutation of, 77–80

"algae," and bions, 51

amoebae, and cancer cells, 37; flowing (amoeba limax), 55; and the living process, 154; in sputum of a cancer patient, 215–16; destructivity of, 274; locomotor function of, 58

anemia, secondary, cause of in cancer, 41; effect of orgone accumulator on, 335

angina pectoris, orgone accumulator in the treatment of, 337

anorgonia, in cancer, 343–400; and shrinking, 370; degree of orgonity and susceptibility to, 376; functional paralysis and, 380

anxiety neurosis, and local tumor formation, 231

Asher, 359

autism, infantile, 390–2

autoclavation of red blood cells, *see* blood tests

autocurative mechanism in cancer, 298–300

autoinfection due to tissue disintegration, 219

autonomic nervous system, xix; traditional and orgonomic view of, 154; the amoeba and, 167; and the pleasure function, 168; and cancer pain, 167–8; and the falling sensation, 182; and cell nucleus, 224

bedsores and burns, local orgone treatment of, 339

Bergson, Henri, 8

Bierisch, R., 269

biogenesis, xix, 50; and the origin of cancer cells, 239, 241, 242, 246

biological energy, stagnation of, x, xi; properties of, 12–13

biological functioning, diagram of, 38, 165

biological pulsation, 58–9; and sexual stasis, 153; and the life process, 154

biological vigor, 37; and hemoglobin, 327

bions, discovery and definition of, 14–15; degeneration of, 14–15; and protozoal organization, 15; composition of, 15; experimental production of from coal, 17; development of carbon bion, 16; microscopic examination of, 16–17; biological stain reaction of, 19; sources of, 20–1; forms of movement of, 22, 52; iron, 25;